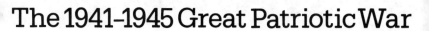

The 1941–1945 Great Patriotic War

The 1941–1945 Great Patriotic War

Password 'VICTORY'

RECOLLECTIONS STORIES REPORTS

IN TWO VOLUMES

Volume II

Raduga Publishers

Moscow

Compiled by *Vladimir Sevruk*
Designed by *V. Chistyakov*

ПАРОЛЬ: ПОБЕДА!

/Рассказы и очерки о Великой Отечественной войне/

В 2-х тт., т. 2

Составитель Владимир Севрук

На английском языке

Printed in the Union of Soviet Socialist Republics

П $\frac{4702010200-090}{031(05)-85}$ 014—85

ISBN 5-05-000019-X
ISBN 5-05-000021-1

CONTENTS

1943–1944

1945

The 1941–1945 Great Patriotic War

1943–1944

After the defeat of Hitler's troops on the Volga, the Red Army began offensive operations from the foothills of the Caucasus to Leningrad. The first was an offensive of the Transcaucasian Front in January 1943. The fighting at Novorossiisk, where Soviet marines were landed, was particularly fierce. During the seven months Soviet soldiers beat off hundreds of enemy attacks, holding out on a small beachhead called Little Land.

A close-knit group of Communists of the 18th Army led by Leonid Brezhnev, who headed the Army's Political Department, was the life and soul of the heroic defence of the Little Land. It is from there that the liberation of the Crimea later began.

Liberation... This word was the motto of 1943 and 1944. The tank battle on the Kursk Bulge, the breakthrough of the Leningrad blockade, the enormous operation codenamed Bagration to liberate Byelorussia, and the driving out of the invaders from the Ukraine, Moldavia, Lithuania, Latvia and Estonia — only a few pages from this heroic chronicle have been included in this edition.

The partisan movement assumed tremendous proportions. In Byelorussia alone eleven thousand trains, including armoured ones, were derailed and 1,500 tanks and armoured cars were put out of action.

A selection from Ananyev's novel, Attacked by Tanks, published in this section, describes the battle on the Kursk Bulge. Violent fighting on the ground and in the air went on for fifty days. The enemy set up an unparalleled concentration of weaponry, having deployed ten thousand artillery pieces, three thousand tanks and self-propelled mounts, and more than two thousand aircraft, or three quarters of the entire air force engaged at the Soviet-German front.

After the defeat of the Nazi troops on the Kursk Bulge, it became clear to everyone that, despite the absence of the Second Front in Europe, Nazi Germany was faced with military catastrophe.

Marshal Rokossovsky, writers Alexei Tolstoy, Vladimir Bogomolov, Vitaly Zakrutkin and others tell about the inflexible will and the strength of spirit of the Soviet people, who bore the brunt of the war against fascism.

Leonid Brezhnev
(1906-1982)

Leonid Brezhnev was born into a worker's family. He himself started his career as a worker, and took part in the renovation of the countryside along socialist lines. Upon graduating from an institute, he became a metallurgical engineer. Later, he was promoted to Party work. Brezhnev held various Party posts from secretary of a regional Party committee to the General Secretary of the Communist Party Central Committee. He was at the front from the first to the last days of the war. When the war ended he was the head of the 4th Ukrainian Front Political Department. Brezhnev was four times Hero of the Soviet Union and held the rank of Marshal.

Prominent politician and statesman, Brezhnev was the author of interesting memoirs which have been translated into many foreign languages. "Little Land", a chapter from his memoirs, is presented in this edition.

Little Land*

1

I didn't keep a diary during the war but the 1,418 days and nights of that ordeal by fire are not forgotten. There were many incidents, meetings and battles; there were moments which I, like every front-line soldier, will never forget.

Today I'd like to talk about a comparatively small sector of the front which our soldiers and sailors dubbed *Malaya Zemlya* (Little Land). It was indeed "little"—less than thirty square kilometres. And it was great, for even an inch of ground may become great when soaked with the blood of heroes devoted to their cause. To give the reader some idea of the situation, I may say that on the days of landing operations everyone who managed to cross the bay and set foot on Little Land was decorated. I don't remember a single crossing during which the fascists did not kill or drown hundreds of our men. Yet there were always from 12 to 15 thousand Soviet fighting men on this beachhead which we had seized from the enemy.

On April 17, 1943, I again had to get to Little Land. I remember the date well and I don't think anyone who was there will ever forget it: on that day the Nazis began Operation *Neptune*. The very name indicated their plan—they wanted to drive us into the sea. We learned this from intelligence reports. We knew they were planning not just another offensive but a decisive all-out attack.

It was my duty to be there in the front line, in the suburbs of Novorossiisk which jutted out into Tsemesskaya Bay, on the narrow beachhead of Little Land.

It was in April that I was appointed head of the political department of the Eighteenth Army. In view of the battles that lay ahead, the Eighteenth Army was reorganised into an assault army, and reinforced with two infantry corps, two divisions, several regiments and a tank brigade; the Novorossiisk naval base of the Black Sea Fleet was put under its operational command.

In war no one chooses where he will fight, but I must admit my new appointment pleased me. The Eighteenth Army was always being sent to trouble spots, it needed special attention and I was with it, you might say, all round the clock. I got on well with the Army Commander K. N. Leselidze and Military Council member

*English translation © APN Publishers 1978

S. E. Kolonin. So my transfer to this Army from the front political department was just a formal recognition of the actual state of affairs.

One crossed over to Little Land only at night. When I arrived at Gelendzhik city wharf, or *Osvodovskaya*, as it was also called, there was not one free place at the moorings; boats of every kind filled every inch of space and men and cargo were already on board. I boarded the seine-boat *Ritsa*. It was an old tub reeking of fish. Her companion-ways creaked, her sides and bulwark-rails were grazed and scarred and shell splinters and bullets had riddled the deck. She had obviously seen a good deal of wear before the war and was having a rough time of it now.

A fresh sea breeze was blowing and it was chilly. Cold is always harder to endure in the south than in the north. I don't know why it should be so but it is. The seine-boat was being taken over by our men before my very eyes. They were mounting machine-guns and antitank rifles at various points and levels. Everyone was looking for a more or less comfortable spot, sheltered from the sea if only by a thin board partition. A military pilot soon appeared on board and things started moving.

It was a rather strange sight, as if all the ships were crowding to the roadstead, but that was only a first impression. Each boat knew its precise place. The *Ritsa* led the procession with Nos 7 and 9 motor boats chugging behind. Our seine-boat took them in tow on a line. The other boats were strung out in a convoy at intervals of 400-500 metres and we headed for Little Land escorted by submarine chasers.

During the three-hour journey I intended talking with the reinforcements, I wanted to know more about them. But I couldn't address all of them at once. The landing parties had already settled down on deck and I didn't feel like making them get up. I decided to go from group to group, a question here, a word there, sometimes sitting down for a longer talk. I found most of the troops were battle-hardened men in good spirit. I knew very well I had to talk with the soldiers, but I also knew that sometimes it is more important for soldiers to be aware that the political worker, the political leader is with them, sharing the hardships and risks. And the tougher the battle situation the more important this is.

Ahead of us the sky over Novorossiisk was aglow. The thunder of artillery reached our ears but we were already used to it. A naval battle was raging far over to our left. As I learned later, German torpedo boats had clashed head-on with ours. I was standing by the pilot on the starboard side of the open bridge; his name, I seem to remember, was Sokolov.

"The soldiers do this landing once," he said, "but the seamen do it every night. And every night there's a battle. They got used to it. We pilots feel a particular responsibility for everybody. Actually, we often have to sort of grope our way along when piloting the boats. On land sappers locate a mine field, clear lanes through it and then boldly lead the men through. But on our sea route the Germans are laying new mines all the time—from planes and from ships. Where we got through safely yesterday we may hit a mine today."

As we approached Tsemesskaya Bay the roar of battle grew louder. The beachhead was not usually bombed heavily at night but now waves of enemy planes were coming in from the sea; the thunder of explosions drowned the drone of their engines and the planes seemed to steal up noiselessly. They would swoop down and, banking steeply, immediately fly away. Our men braced themselves, their faces became grimmer and soon we found ourselves lit up by flares.

The darkness of the night during crossings was rather a relative notion. German shore searchlights swept the water and "lanterns" —parachute flares—dropped by planes would almost continuously be floating overhead. Two enemy torpedo boats suddenly shot out from somewhere to starboard and our submarine chasers met them with heavy fire. Fascist planes were also bombing the approaches to the shore.

Bombs kept falling—some far away, some nearby, throwing up great masses of water which in the light of the searchlights and the tracer bullets glittered with every colour of the rainbow. We expected to be hit any minute and yet the blow, when it came, took us by surprise. I didn't even realise straightaway what had happened. There was a loud crash up front, a column of fire shot up and it seemed as if the seine-boat had blown up. That was in fact what had happened: our boat had hit a mine. The pilot and I were standing side by side and the blast hurled us into the air together.

I felt no pain, and the thought of death never crossed my mind— I'm quite sure of that. The sight of death in all its aspects was already nothing new to me, and though no normal person can ever get used to it war makes him continually aware death may come to him. In such a moment it is sometimes said a person remembers his loved ones, his whole life flashes before him, he even manages to grasp something very important about himself. This may happen sometimes, but the only thought that flashed through my mind then was that I must not fall back on to the deck.

Fortunately I landed in the water some way from the seine-boat. Surfacing, I saw she was already sinking. Some of the men had been thrown off by the blast like myself and others had jumped overboard. I had been a good swimmer ever since boyhood, for I grew up by the Dnieper, and I felt quite sure of myself in the water. I got my breath, looked round and saw both motor boats had cast off their towlines and were slowly approaching us.

I found myself near No. 9 boat and pilot Sokolov also swam up to her. Gripping the fender, we helped the men weighed down with arms and ammunition and hardly able to stay afloat to get on board and they were pulled up by those in the boat. I think not a single man had let go of his weapons.

The enemy searchlights had already found us and there was no escaping them. The German guns opened fire on us from the Shirokaya ravine west of Myskhako. Their fire was inaccurate but the boat was thrown from side to side by the blasts. Then suddenly, though the thunder was as loud as ever, shells stopped bursting around us. Our guns had probably opened fire at the enemy batteries. At that moment I suddenly heard an angry shout:

"Are you deaf or something? Give us your hand! "

As I learned later, it was Petty Officer 2nd Class Zimoda shouting at me, holding his hand out. He couldn't see my shoulder-tabs in the water, and it really made no difference at such a moment. Landing craft have a shallow draught and sit low in the water. Grasping the guard rail I hoisted myself up and strong arms lifted me on board.

Only then did I start to shiver: even in the Black Sea April is not the best time for a swim. The seine-boat had already gone down. The men were wringing out their clothing and cursing the enemy under their breath. "Damn them, the bloody Huns! " Gradually everyone calmed down, settling behind boxes and bundles. Some were curled up, others lying flat, as if that were safer. But our main job lay ahead. The main thing was the battle we were about to join.

And in this tragic setting lit by explosions and tracer bullets a song suddenly welled up. One of the sailors, a very tall fellow, I recall, struck up a song. It was a song born on Little Land and was about the iron will and strength of just such fighting men as were on board the boat at that moment. I knew the song but it now seems it was only then I really heard it for the first time. One line is engraved in my memory: "In those wooden cockleshells men of iron sail."

Heads rose slowly. Those lying sat up and those who were sitting rose to their feet, then someone else took up the tune. I'll never forget that moment: the song squared the men's shoulders. Despite what they had just come through, everyone felt more confident and ready for battle.

The boat soon scraped bottom and we started to jump ashore. Sharp commands rang out. Men began unloading the boxes of ammunition and others ran shouldering them to the shelters—we didn't have to urge them on, the steady fire did that. Dropping one load, they immediately ran back for another all the time under fire, to the unceasing accompaniment of bombing. Meanwhile the wounded ready for evacuation were already being carried from the shore on stretches: these were the men our reinforcements were to replace.

Beyond the pebbly beach there rose a steep slope where there were recesses. The first thing to do was to try and reach these recesses and take cover from the fire; then after scaling another dozen metres or so, one had to jump into the trench that led to the heart of Little Land. Once there the men felt calm although, I repeat, the main job still lay ahead. From there passing along communicating trenches one could reach every unit and maybe even every detachment fighting on the beachhead.

Crossing over was always dangerous, the voyage itself was risky, and then there was the unloading, the rush to take cover and scaling the steep slope; but every time I came to Little Land I couldn't help thinking what it must have been like for our men who landed there when German machine-guns had been mounted where there were now life-saving shelters and when the Nazis armed with submachine-guns and grenades and out of sight of our assault force were running along the communicating trenches. Everyone who realised how much harder it had been for those pioneers must have gained strength from the very thought.

Despite everything the fact remains that we managed to hold on to Little Land for just as long as the plans of the Soviet Command required—namely, for 225 days. How we lived through those days is what I want to relate.

2

We certainly did not want war. But when it began the great Soviet people courageously joined mortal combat with the aggressor.

I remember the Dnepropetrovsk regional committee of the Party calling a conference of lecturers in 1940. I was then thinking hard about political education fostering in people a patriotic spirit and a readiness to defend their homeland. And we were discussing just that. As everyone knows, a non-aggression pact had been signed with Germany. The papers had photographs of Molotov meeting Hitler and Ribbentrop meeting Stalin. The pact was giving us a needed breathing-space, time to strengthen our country's defence capacity: but not everybody appreciated this. I remember as if it were today one of the people at the conference, a good lecturer by the name of Sakhno, getting up to ask:

"Comrade Brezhnev, we have to explain the non-aggression pact: that it's in earnest and anyone who distrusts it is engaging in provocative talk. But people don't seem to have much faith in it. So what are we to do? Should we explain or shouldn't we?"

It was a rather awkward moment: four hundred people were sitting in the hall awaiting my reply and there just wasn't time to ponder the matter.

"Yes, we must explain it," I said. "And we'll go on explaining, comrades, until fascist Germany is razed to the ground! "

At that time I was secretary of the Dnepropetrovsk regional committee of the Party with responsibility for the defence industry. And though maybe some people could indulge in complacency, I had to keep my mind every day on what lay ahead of us. I had to attend to quite a few important and urgent matters connected with organising and coordinating a powerful defence complex such as the south of the Ukraine was at that time and, in particular, the area along the Dnieper.

Plants producing purely peacetime goods were switching over to war production; our metallurgists were learning to make special grades of steel; I had to keep in touch with several ministries, to fly to Moscow and to travel endlessly all over the region. There were no such things as days off and I was rarely home with my family; I remember that in the early hours of June 22, 1941, I was working late at the regional committee offices and then drove out to an army airfield being built near Dnepropetrovsk. This strategically important project was under Central Committee supervision and work went on day and night; it was about dawn before I could leave the site.

On my return I saw K. S. Grushevoi's car parked outside the building—he was then deputising for the regional committee first secretary. I gathered at once that something had happened. There was a light in his window and that looked odd in the dawn glow. He looked out of the window and beckoned me to come up. As I was going up the stairs I sensed something was wrong but all the same I was startled when I heard him say: "It's war! " That very moment I firmly and irrevocably decided what I had to do as a Communist. I addressed a request to the Central Committee that I be sent to the front—and my request was granted that same day: I was assigned to the Headquarters of the Southern Front.

I am grateful to the Central Committee of our Party for backing my wish to be with the army in the field from the very beginning of the war. I am grateful that in 1943, when part of our country had been liberated, the Party heeded my request not to be recalled along with other frontline Party workers to do administrative work in the rear. I am also grateful that in 1944 the Party complied with my request not to promote me to a higher post which would have taken me away from combat operations, and that it allowed me to stay with the Eighteenth Assault Army till the end of the war. I had only one desire—to defend our country, to fight the enemy wherever he might be, to see the war through to final victory. There was no other way to bring peace to the world again.

My life at the front was bound up with the Eighteenth Army and it became forever near and dear to me. With the Eighteenth Army I fought in the Caucasian Mountains when the fate of our country was being decided there, I fought in the Ukrainian plains, crossed the Carpathian Mountains and joined in liberating Poland, Romania, Hungary and Czechoslovakia. I was also with this army on Little Land, which played an important part in liberating Novorossiisk and the whole of the Taman Peninsula.

You can find yourself in a situation in which you see, learn and feel more in one year than you could otherwise grasp in a whole lifetime. Events on that beachhead were so concentrated and the fighting so fierce and continuous that it seemed to have been going on not for 225 days, but an eternity. And we came through it all.

You will not find *Malaya Zemlya*—Little Land—in geography books. To understand what follows, you must clearly picture to yourself this rocky plot of land hugging the water. This plot of land just six by four and a half kilometres across had to be held at all costs.

How did it become a beachhead? Novorossiisk lies on the shores of Tsemesskaya Bay which cuts deeply into the mountains. It has two cement plants—the Proletary and Oktyabr. We were on one side of the bay, the Germans on the other. By the beginning of 1943 the whole of the left bank was in enemy hands. From high ground he commanded our fleet movements and we had to rob him of this advantage. So the idea arose of sending in a landing party to seize a suburb of Novorossiisk. This would not only be a surer way to stop the enemy entering the waters of the bay but would also make all our subsequent operations easier.

The Nazis were well aware of this. I'll try not to give too many figures but one figure I must now give: when we established the beachhead the fascists bombed and shelled it continuously raining vast quantities of shells and bombs on us, not to mention submachine and machine-gun fire. An estimated 1,250 kilograms of death-dealing metal for each defender of Little Land.

Nearly two-thirds of the Eighteenth Assault Army fought on this beachhead and since I spent most of my time on Little Land some of those kilograms of death-dealing metal were meant for me.

The landing on Little Land and the battles fought there are, to my mind, a brilliant example of the art of war. We chose the men carefully and they had special training. Assault groups were trained at Cape Tonkiy in Gelendzhik; they were taught jumping into the water with machine guns, scaling rocks and throwing grenades from awkward positions. They learned to handle every kind of enemy weapon, to throw knives, to strike blows with rifle butts, to bandage wounds and arrest bleeding. They memorised agreed signals, learned to load submachine-gun magazines blindfold and to tell by ear where the fire was coming from. Without such thorough training a daring landing and especially the initial night assault was quite out of the question, for everything had to be done in the dark by touch.

Only volunteers—and then only men who had fought bravely in previous engagements—were allowed to join the first group which was called the special task force. Major T. L. Kunikov was put in charge of landing operations. This intelligent and forceful officer had already come to my notice in previous engagements where he commanded a marine battalion. Sen. Lieut. N. V. Starshinov was deputy commander for political affairs and Major F. E. Kotanov was chief of staff. They had also shown their mettle in combat. All three were awarded the title of Hero of the Soviet Union—Kunikov posthumously (he was mortally wounded on February 12, 1943) and Starshinov and Kotanov for battles fought later, after Little Land.

They were given the right to recruit men for their landing force from any unit at the Novorossiisk naval base. This was an exceptional privilege, of course, but one dictated by necessity. We realised that in a landing force like this literally every man had a very great part to play. In this way five assault groups were formed to make a combined force of 250 men. They would have to endure the hardest trials and they really did fulfil their duty.

At the Novorossiisk museum in 1974 my attention was drawn to a notable document. It was a dispatch by Sen. Lieut. V. A. Botylyov, who had landed on the beachhead on the same night as Kunikov. He wrote: "I report first assault group casualties: one dead, seven wounded. Of whom CPSU(B) candidate members: one dead, four wounded; Komsomol members: two wounded; non-Party people:

one wounded. First combat task set by Command is fulfilled. Political and moral spirit of the group is high."

At this point it may not be inappropriate to recall that three million Communists met a hero's death at the front in the Great Patriotic War and five million Soviet patriots joined the Party's ranks in the war years. "I want to go into battle as a Communist! " Before almost every battle I heard this phrase which became legendary and the harder the fighting the more often was it heard. What privileges could anyone expect, what rights could the Party grant him on the eve of a fierce engagement? Only one privilege, one right, one duty— to be the first up and into attack, the first to dash forward in the face of withering fire.

Before the landing operation the task force took a vow. Communist Kunikov lined up all the men in a small open space, once again reminded them it would be a deadly dangerous operation and said anyone who felt unequal to the task need not participate in the operation. Kunikov did not order men who might have changed their minds to take three steps forward. Sparing their pride he said:

"In exactly ten minutes' time I want you to form up again. Any of you who are unsure of yourself need not fall in. You will be returned to your units as having completed a training course."

When the force reformed only two men were absent.

Even now, many years later, one cannot read without deep emotion the solemn vow they took before setting out to sea. "Going into battle," they said, "we vow to our homeland to act swiftly and boldly, without thought for our own lives, for the sake of victory over the enemy. We shall give our courage, strength and last drop of blood for the happiness of our people, for you, our beloved homeland... To go forward and forward only—this is and shall be the law guiding us."

Whenever I cast my thoughts back to those stormy days and recall that solemn vow, I feel deep emotion and pride. Many individual cases of heroism are known in history, but only the people of our great country, Soviet people, led by our great Party, proved capable of mass heroism.

3

And so the night of the landing came. I very well remember the prevailing mood at the pier. I saw no gloomy faces. If anything they were cheerful and showed impatience. Sailors were lugging crates at the double and shouting "Polundra! " I remember asking a sailor: "What's 'polundra'?" and was told that it meant "Watch out! " That was how I learned the meaning of the word.

It was a very dark night on February 3, 1943. The motor boats with the task force on board left Gelendzhik quietly for Tsemesskaya Bay. Deploying there, they headed for the shore as signal flares rose in the air. Simultaneously our artillery bombarded the shoreline that was already in our sights. Into the rolling thunder of explosions burst blazing volleys from a "Katyusha"—it was the first time in military practice that a multiple rocket launcher had ever been mounted on a trawler, the *Skumbriya.* Two torpedo boats going full out cut across the bows of the assault craft laying a smoke screen in their wake to shield the craft from shore-based enemy fire. A patrol boat opened fire on the area of the bombardment. The moment Kunikov's men rushed ashore our batteries lifted their barrage.

In war not everything goes according to plan. An engagement often takes a course not quite, and sometimes not at all, as mapped out at headquarters. And that is when the courage, dedication and initiative of every commander and political officer and of every soldier and sailor are indeed beyond price. The historians of the war know that an attempt had been made to establish a beachhead elsewhere, at a place thirty kilometres away, near Yuzhnaya Ozereika. That is in fact where the main landing should have been, but a storm blew up delaying the departure of the landing craft; the ground forces were also late arriving at the starting point. Meanwhile the breakthrough by Kunikov's men, which the enemy had not expected, proved very successful, so we immediately exploited our advantage.

The landing that was intended as a show of force became a secondary attack and then the main landing. With it began the epic of Little Land. Forcing their way through a curtain of fire our task force managed to seize a tiny but very important sector of the shore in Stanichka just outside Novorossiisk. About a thousand fascists were killed, four guns were seized and immediately turned to fire on the enemy. An hour and a half later the second group of the task force landed here and then the third. There were now 800 men on the shore.

The enemy brought up fresh units to the landing site, the fascist air force bombed it, heavy guns began pounding the beachhead and a rapid succession of desperate counter-attacks followed. But it was too late: our troops had managed to get a firm hold. They captured several street blocks in Stanichka and three kilometres of railway line. And they did not retreat an inch though their losses were heavy.

The soldiers and sailors were true to their vow and they knew they had to stand firm until the main forces arrived. They were still in high spirits over the success of the landing and that's how I remember them.

Over a period of several nights two marine brigades, an infantry brigade, an anti-tank regiment and several other units were landed on the beachhead. Hundreds of tons of ammunition and food supplies were put ashore. Five days later there were already 17,000 fighting men in and around Stanichka and Myskhako equipped with sub-machine-guns, mortars, cannon and anti-tank weapons. Then five partisan detachments—Za Rodinu (For Our Motherland), Groza (Storm), Nord-Ost (North-East), Novy (New), and Yastrebok (Little Hawk)—were landed on Little Land.

I take this opportunity to say a word in praise of the partisans. If anyone thinks of them as isolated groups of some sort in the enemy rear, he is wrong. Many detachments did spring up spontaneously, but they had a central headquarters under Party guidance and from time to time carried out large-scale operations coordinated with the plans of the regular army command. This was so on Little Land, where all five detachments were in charge of P. I. Vasev, secretary of the Novorossiisk city committee of the Party, who worked closely with our headquarters.

I would like to say again that the landing on Little Land may be considered a brilliant example of the art of war. The successful landing by the first task force, the swift build-up of forces, the advance of regiments and corps along a well-fortified and mined shore, all called for efficient co-operation between infantry, engineers, sailors and gunners. The gunners (the "gods of war", we call them) could not afford to make the slightest error: at many points our units were within a grenade's throw of the enemy. Our pilots had an even tougher task. I remember our men spreading their vests on the breastwork of the trenches to mark our forward lines every time our air force went into action.

It should be noted that we occupied an extremely unfavourable geographical position. We were holding a narrow strip of shore—long, bare and flat, while the Germans held all the high ground and the forest. You may ask: how did our people manage to survive when hundreds of tons of deadly metal were raining down upon them, when the enemy forces greatly outnumbered ours and the enemy had a clear view of Little Land from the surrounding hills? All these disadvantages were counter-balanced by experience, composure, careful judgement and hard work every day.

It was then I came to realise that apart from everything else war spelled titanic labour, the labour of yesterday's steel workers, fitters, miners, farmers, harvester operators, stablemen, builders and carpenters. The labour of people who had donned soldier's uniform. Not only devotion and courage but also great tenacity, perseverance, know-how and skill were manifested in war.

The whole of Little Land had become what was in fact an underground fortress: 230 well-concealed observation posts became its eyes, 500 gun emplacements—its mailed fists; scores of kilometres of communicating trenches, thousands of foxholes, fire points and slit trenches were dug in the ground. We had to hew shafts through rock and to build ammunition stores, hospitals and even an electric power station underground. Of necessity everybody moved about only in the trenches. It wasn't easy but you were finished if you stuck your head up a bit. You had to remain sitting for long periods, and when the fascists were at last driven back some of our men suffered from what we called "sitting sickness."

The engineers displayed amazing resourcefulness. The sappers connected shellholes, some of which were more like craters, with trenches and turned them into dug-outs. Three lines of defence with one-kilometre gaps between them were built on this narrow strip called Little Land. Minefields were laid along each one. Underground lines of communication functioned reliably. The command post of the landing force, cut six and a half metres deep into a cliff, could secretly move troops along the communicating trenches to wherever the situation gave cause for alarm.

There was virtually no no-man's-land zone in the Stanichka area: enemy positions were only fifteen to twenty metres away from our own. But whenever I went there I saw that that part of the front line—the line of constant alert and danger—was also heavily mined and strewn with obstacles and barbed-wire entanglements. The sappers putting them up had had at times to engage in hand-to-hand combat.

This fortified beachhead became a kind of fortress-city. Even streets came into being—Gospitalnaya (Hospital Street), Sapyornaya (Sapper Street), Pekhotnaya (Infantry Street) and Matrosskaya (Sailor Street). No one house stood on any of these streets. No one knew who thought up the names, but they were very appropriate. Sapper Street was a ravine well sheltered from enemy fire, while Hospital Street was a stretch of hilly terrain exposed to fire and men there often landed straight in hospital. All the fortifications had to be built under enemy fire. There was no machinery and no building materials, but our capable fellows burrowed cleverly into the ground where they meant to stay. You could say that every man who helped build that fortress was a hero.

I have particularly fond memories of the older sappers. They were not sent to lay minefields in full view of the enemy; these "old hands" had what seemed a peaceful task: they were felling timber a few kilometres from Gelendzhik, near Dzhankoi, lashing the logs into rafts and floating them down to Little Land at night. But what a job it was! I have already said we never had a dark night in Tsemesskaya Bay. And the enemy artillery would pound away at the unarmed rafts. The sappers could neither return the fire nor manoeuvre their unwieldy craft. They would slip into the chilly water and continue to the shore gripping the logs. Whenever a shell hit a raft they would reassemble it on the spot, in the water, so as not to lose a single precious log. If the tug was sunk they would fire a code signal flare and wait for some other motor boat to arrive. That's what those "old hands" were like.

The reader may have the impression the life of the thousands of men on the beachhead consisted of nothing but attacks, air raids and hand-to-hand fighting; but it was not so. During the long period of time the beachhead existed a way of life grew up there which allowed for all kinds of ordinary human pursuits. We published and read newspapers, held Party meetings, celebrated holidays and attended lectures. Even organised a chess tournament. The army and navy troupes of singers and dancers gave performances, artists B. Prorokov, V. Tsigal and P. Kirpichev were working there and they produced a portrait gallery of heroes of the defence.

I remember a group of comrades from the Central Committee arriving once. They had never been in a situation like ours and they asked me to introduce them to the defenders of Little Land. We set out in a torpedo boat and the moment we started our men fired a flare to identify ourselves. The Germans fired continuously as we approached the landing point. They had high-angle guns, so it was very important for us to hug the shore and pass along its very edge. Again shells burst very close to us. If you had not known they were aiming at you, you could have appreciated the extraordinary beauty of the scene. A long-range marine battery, reminiscent of the Tsar Bell in the Kremlin, was sited on the beachhead, and it had been turned into a command post. It was to this post we had to make our way under fire. I was already used to such things but I think our guests were very impressed. I remember a marine suddenly appearing out of the darkness carrying a heavy load.

"Give us a hand, brother! " he said. "We must have this! "

When today, a third of a century later, I recall what fell to the lot of our soldiers, commanders and political officers, I find it at times almost impossible to believe all this really happened and that they managed to stand up to it all. But they did, they withstood it all, came through it all, routed the fascists and won victory.

That day, perhaps because I was showing people fresh from Moscow round Little Land, I seemed to see in a different light all I was used to and familiar with. I had seen it all before but now my eyes were really opened to the constant deadly peril, the unbearable difficulties and the boundless, dedicated heroism of our fighting men.

Things were very tough indeed at times. We were cut off from the mainland, we were short of salt and sometimes we ran out of bread. Whole units were sent into the forest to gather wild garlic. It was also very damp in our catacombs, men froze at night and the political department officers had to see to the provision of heating, to order iron stoves and gather firewood. But despite everything Little Land remained Soviet land and the people there remained people—they made plans, joked, laughed and even held birthday parties. For instance, on February 15, that is, eleven days after the first landing, a member of the task force, a certain Shalva Tatarashvili, turned 23. His best friend, Pyotr Vereshchagin, gave him as a birthday present 23 rounds of ammunition from his own submachine-gun magazine. It was a very precious gift: ammunition was short and we were expecting another enemy attack.

Much in that life which continued next door to death seemed at first glance quite incompatible with war. The head of the political department of the 255th Marine Brigade, I. Dorofeyev, once made a check and found we had fifteen deputies to city, district and rural Soviets in our brigade so we decided to call a meeting of our local councillors. What problems could they tackle? The same as in peacetime: the people's needs, public services. The first decision they took was to build a bathhouse. And it was built! An excellent Russian steam bath was built "out of working hours", I suppose one could say. I was invited to sample it. The room though small contained the steam well.

Resourcefulness, ingenuity and wit were very much appreciated on Little Land. Quite a few people had such gifts. I remember an enterprising fellow, sent on some business to Gelendzhik, finding a stray cow in the hills. He decided to bring it to Little Land. He brought his cow to the pier and asked the motor-boat commander to let him take it on board. Everyone around had a good laugh but backed the idea because it meant milk for the wounded. The cow was safely put ashore, securely sheltered and gave a regular supply of milk to the hospital housed in the cellar of a state farm that used to make wine.

But the important thing was not the milk. The cow was a source of great joy, especially for men who came from the countryside. After every air raid or bombardment they would come running to see whether their Daisy Bell was safe, to make sure she hadn't been wounded and to pat and fondle her. There is no simple explanation for this, but the appearance of this utterly peaceful beast in our midst in this highly tense atmosphere helped people to preserve a certain mental balance. It was a reminder that all life's joys would return and that life would go on if only you could defend it.

The men of our Little Land received a splendid present on May Day, 1943. As day dawned everyone gasped and smiled with pleasure. During the night several men had put up red flags at various points of the brigade's positions. In the morning everyone saw them, including the Germans, of course.

I remember the striking impression the appearance of a red flag on the screen in *The Battleship Potemkin* made in the days of black-and-white cinema. And on Little Land, every inch of which was torn up by bombs and shells, littered with shrapnel, fire-scorched and bloodstained, and ringed by enemies, these fluttering flags were simply overwhelming. Exultant shouts resounded over the lacerated earth. Everyone felt something deep and personal had happened to him. After the first flush of excitement a mood of unrestrained gaiety gripped us all. People laughed for joy and with a new awareness of their strength: "Look at that, you damned fascists! Put that in your pipe and smoke it! "

4

The battles in April after that memorable crossing during which I had a dip in the sea were the fiercest of all that were fought on Little Land. And it is about them I shall tell you now.

Operation *Neptune* was intended by the fascists to liquidate our beachhead. A strike force of 27,000 men had been formed for this express purpose under the command of Wetzel and it was to go into action supported by 1,200 planes and hundreds of guns and mortars. The Germans had also planned another operation—from the sea— under the no less significant code name Box. The Box force included torpedo boat and submarine flotillas. Their task was to cut our sea communications and destroy the Soviet troops after they had been driven into the sea. That was how they saw it all in their plans.

The fighting on Little Land, which began on April 17, was steadily increasing in intensity; the enemy was moving up reinforcements every day. Early in the morning German heavy batteries would open fire and at the same time planes would appear in the sky. They would literally hover overhead all the time, coming in waves of from 40 to 60 aircraft, dropping bombs over the entire depth and along the whole front of our defences. After the fast bombers came dive bombers—also in waves—and then came the assault aircraft. All this went on for hours and then enemy tanks and infantry began the attack.

They would attack confidently, quite sure not a soul had survived in the solid smoke that blanketed Little Land. But their attacks would meet furious resistance and they would roll back, leaving hundreds upon hundreds of their dead. Then it would begin all over again. Again the heavy batteries would start pounding away, again dive bombers screeched and again the assault aircraft wreaked their fury. This would be repeated several times a day.

The bombers and assault planes had fighter cover. Because the enemy had considerable superiority in the air our fighters, though they inflicted losses on the Germans, were unable to halt the bombing. Soviet bombers did not appear over enemy positions and so the fascists were able to regroup and prepare for fresh attacks. This went on for three days up to April 20, the deadline the German fascist Command had set for the final liquidation of Little Land.

Determined to throw us into the sea Hitler staked everything on this sector of the front. A grave situation arose. The Military Council of the Eighteenth Army drafted an appeal to the men of Little Land—actually it was I who did it. The appeal went round all the trenches and dug-outs and men cut their hands to sign it in their blood. Later on I sent a copy to Stalin so he could see how our men were fighting.

"We have called the plot of land we took from the enemy near Novorossiisk 'Little Land'," said the appeal. "Though small, it is our land, Soviet land: it is drenched with our sweat and blood and we will never surrender it to any enemy... We vow by our battle flags, by our wives and children, by our beloved homeland, we vow to stand firm in the forthcoming battles against the enemy, to grind down his forces and clear the fascist scum from Taman. Let us make this Little Land a big grave for the Nazis! "

On the first day of the fascist offensive we received strict orders from General Headquarters to hold the beachhead at all costs. Seeing it as a key to liberating the Taman Peninsula, GHQ attached great importance to it and was closely following the course of the battle.

On April 18 staff officers from GHQ, headed by Marshal G.K. Zhukov, flew to the headquarters of the North Caucasian Front, commanded by Col.-Gen. I.E. Petrov. That same day together with People's Commissar for the Navy N. G. Kuznetsov and Air Force Commander A. A. Novikov they reached Eighteenth Assault Army Headquarters. One of the staff officers, a colonel who had come to Little Land, told me about this and added:

"The Marshal wanted to see you."

"Is that an order?" I asked.

"I had no such order from him," the colonel replied, "but he said he would like to have a talk with you."

To be frank, I also wanted to talk with him: we were all very worried about enemy air superiority. I had expressed my views on this to our commander, Konstantin Nikolayevich Leselidze, on the very first day the Germans attacked. I insisted on having air support. I had also spoken about this to Semyon Yefimovich Kolonin, a member of the Military Council, for whom I always felt great respect. Both were men of courage, principle and experience, both had agreed with me and I believed they would certainly report the air situation to Zhukov. As for myself, it was better that I should stay at the beachhead at such a difficult time. And that is what I did: I remained with the fighting men on Little Land.

Later Zhukov wrote in his memoirs: "We were all worried then about one thing—whether Soviet soldiers would be able to hold out in this unequal fight against an enemy attacking day and night from the air and shelling the beachhead." The Marshal went on to say he had wanted my opinion on that very point. Could our men stand that hell for another day or two at least, because GHQ had already taken serious steps to help us.

Within two days the situation did indeed change radically. Three air corps from the GHQ reserve arrived one after another, each joining battle the moment it arrived. Above all, the red-starred fighters protected the sky over Little Land. Bombs began to rain down on enemy positions. Equal forces were now fighting in the air, then when our airmen succeeded in destroying several enemy airfields we gained air superiority.

It's frankly difficult for me to describe what was happening in the sky. Wherever you looked Soviet and German planes singly or in formation were engaged in deadly combat. One crossing another, the black smoke trails of shot-up planes descended to the ground.

In three days of fighting our airmen brought 117 enemy planes down over Little Land. A. I. Pokryshkin, who took part in those furious battles, has described them in detail in his book.

The fate of Novorossiisk and Taman was being decided on our beachhead and the Nazi Command kept throwing new forces into battle. The men on Little Land fought for a nightmarish eight days and nights until the enemy's strength gave out and the remnants of his forces crawled back to their original positions. But the climax of the battle came on April 20, 1943, and strange as it may seem, I have an amusing recollection of that day.

M. K. Vidov was head of the political department of the 225th Marine Brigade. He fought with skill and daring, he carried very great weight with the men and, when reproached by his commanding officer for needlessly risking his life, he replied: "I'm a commissar, not a milksop!" So in the early hours of April 20 Mikhail Vidov called the political officers together, summed up the battle situation and asked if they had any idea why the fascists were attacking so furiously. It was the Führer's birthday the next day, he explained. "They want to finish us off and report their victory to him as a birthday present," he said. "It wouldn't be a bad idea if we also mark the day somehow! "

While various suggestions were being discussed Boris Prorokov, an artist not very well known at that time, made a rough sketch which everyone immediately approved. Overnight on a sheet he painted a hoglike monster running away from the Caucasus. The hog had Hitler's characteristic moustache and forelock. It was a perfect caricature. The sheet was fastened to a frame and the whole thing was put up at a spot in no-man's-land that was already in our sights, and firmly propped up.

On the morning of April 20 from all their positions in the hills around the Nazis could not fail to see this message of congratulations. As we had anticipated, the Germans could not bring themselves to fire on their Führer. Quite some time elapsed while they pondered what to do about it. At long last the fascists began crawling towards our caricature from three directions, but we had the whole place in our sights and a good half of them were killed: the remainder retreated as fast as they could. They made two further attempts that day, then finally their artillery opened fire on the "birthday present".

"That's the way," our men roared with laughter. "Hit him good and hard! "

Laughter is a mighty force, proof of optimism and a stout heart.

I was walking along a trench with Dorofeyev after an attack had been beaten off in one of the sectors and again we heard laughter near a firing point. We drew closer and saw a young sergeant, a political instructor, talking with a few men.

"Summing up the results of the fighting, comrade colonel," he reported.

"And what are the results?"

The men crowding round the machine-gun urged the sergeant: "Go on, tell him! " Embarrassed at first, he was emboldened by the men's enthusiasm:

"Hitler boasted he would push us into the sea today and I quoted a Ukrainian folk tale to show what success he had. A fellow went hunting, killed a bear, skinned a fox, brought home a rabbit, his mother dressed a duck and boiled up some jelly. He tasted it and it turned out to be sour..."

Along with the men I listened to this cheerful fellow with pleasure. At that moment his simple tale probably meant more and was more effective than a very serious analysis of the battle would have been, especially as that day proved to be the grimmest we ever experienced on Little Land.

The ground was blazing, boulders were smouldering, metal melted, concrete crumbled, but the men, true to their vow, did not budge an inch. Companies withstood the onslaught of battalions, battalions ground down regiments. Machine-gun barrels grew red hot, wounded men pushing medical orderlies aside attacked tanks with grenades and wielded rifle butts and knives in hand-to-hand fighting. There seemed to be no end to the battle. Where the ground all round was already strewn with enemy dead, fresh lines would advance. They too would be cut down but again and again grey-green figures appeared. So it is no wonder a soldier of the Eighth Guards Rifle Brigade exclaimed during one of the attacks: "Are they growing out of the ground or something! "

The fascists that day heavily outnumbered us and we sustained heavy losses. Many a time the thought flashed through my mind: how many of our lads would remain lying there, how many would never return home? The question of pity in wartime is a complicated one. War is a cruel business and deaths are inevitable. To spare one man means sending another in his place. There is only one moral justification here—to be together with the fighting men when it's toughest, to face the same dangers and to do everything you can to spare them needless risks and to lessen the hardship.

Among the documents that survived the war years there is a directive bearing my signature. It was sent to all the political bodies and to every political worker later, towards the end of 1943, during the fighting near Kiev. But the principles there stated were for me of the utmost importance throughout the war.

"Pay constant attention to the physical fitness and health of the soldiers. They must be regularly supplied with hot food and hot water. There must be the strictest control to ensure that everything the state issues for men and officers reaches them. People who are negligent or passive in this respect must be severely brought to account. Particular attention should be paid to the medical corps. The political departments of units should detail special personnel to be responsible for evacuating the wounded from the battlefield and giving them prompt medical aid."

And today, many years after those battles, no matter how busy we may be with other things, it is our duty constantly to remember war veterans. Give them every care and attention, help them in their daily lives—that is the moral obligation of our government bodies and of all our citizens: it is a guiding law of our life.

5

The reader, I think, is expecting me to talk about Party and political work, but, as a matter of fact, that is precisely what I have been speaking about all along.

Because the very staunchness of the soldiers on Little Land was the result of that work. Because the well-organised way of life on the beachhead, the care taken for the soldiers to be strong and fit, the timely appearance of air support, the men's good humour during lulls in the fighting and their selfless courage during attacks, and the fact that to the very end people never lost their humanity—all this was the result of that Party and political work. So it is difficult and hardly necessary to treat it separately in my narrative.

How is one to gauge or assess a political worker's efforts at the front? A sniper picks off ten Nazis—all praise to him; a company repulses an attack and stands its ground—all praise to the company commander and his men; a division breaks through the enemy lines and liberates a community—the divisional commander is named in orders of the Supreme Commander-in-Chief. But great services are also rendered by the political worker who gives the men ideological weapons, who fosters in them noble feelings of love for their country, builds up their self-confidence and inspires them to acts of heroism.

A true political worker in the army is a man round whom all others rally, a man with deep knowledge of the soldiers' mood, their needs, hopes and dreams; he inspires them to self-sacrifice and to heroic deeds. If we bear in mind that the fighting spirit of troops has always been considered a very important element of their courage, then the most effective weapon of the war was in the hands of the political workers. It was they who steeled the soldiers' hearts and minds and without that nothing—not tanks, guns or planes—would have won victory for us.

It was the same everywhere and on the difficult sectors of the front, such as Little Land, the importance of their work could scarcely be exaggerated. There were moments when the men felt cut off from the mainland and they had to be made to realise that cut off did not mean cast off, that separated did not mean forgotten. They had to be shown that the war against fascism was being waged on all fronts and that the whole country was behind us. The attack they had just repulsed had to be linked with the great battle all the Soviet people were fighting.

No ringing speeches were needed here (and anyway there were no halls in which to deliver them), but a frank man-to-man and, I would say, heart-to-heart, talk. I attended most of the Party meetings held in formations and units and, simply, was often among the men. I usually managed to find a common language with them, though I didn't use any special techniques to achieve this. Whether we were discussing something serious or just joking I always tried to be natural and unaffected. I always spoke the truth no matter how bitter. I'd like to note that one sometimes came across officers who tried to pass themselves off as one of the lads. The soldiers were of course quick to see through their affected familiarity and would not be frank with them.

The majority of our political department men, political instructors, Komsomol organisers and propagandists managed to strike the right note, they carried weight with the soldiers and, what is most important, the men knew that when things got tough those who called on them to stand their ground would be at their side, would stay with them and advance together with them, gun in hand and in the lead. The word of the Party uttered with deep feeling and reinforced by deeds and by personal example in battle was thus our main weapon. That was why the political workers became the heart and soul of the armed forces.

They naturally helped prepare offensive and defensive operations; no military operation was planned without them. I, for one, can't remember a single case of General Leselidze, or any other army commander I worked with, ignoring my point of view or my amendments, which were quite substantial on occasion. But in war the commander gives the orders, it is his prerogative and, though the political worker may also issue orders, he should, I think, exercise that right only in exceptional cases.

Here is an example. During a Party meeting, which I had occasion to conduct, people were sitting in rows on the ground. In the middle of my report an enemy shell burst somewhere behind me, not very far away. We had heard it whistling. We were used to this and I didn't stop speaking. Then a minute or two later a second shell burst, this time ahead of us. Not a person budged though they were all battle-seasoned and realised that the enemy artillery had "bracketed" us. The third shell, as they said at the front, would be ours. So I straight-away gave the order:

"On your feet! Depression 300 metres to the left at the double!"

We finished our discussion there and the third shell really did land where we had just been. On our way back from the meeting political officer V. Tikhomirov and I were silent.

"Not one of them budged," was all he said. "That's the sort of people they are..."

I was thinking the same myself.

In an emergency like that, whether in battle or during a lull, the political worker has a right and the duty to issue orders. But in his day-to-day work he should not order people about—only explain and persuade. And that too has to be done with intelligence and tact. Even when a person is in the wrong no one has a right to abuse him by shouting. I detest the habit which, though not widespread, some still have of shouting at people. Neither a business nor a Party executive should ever forget that subordinates are subordinated to him only in their official capacity and that they serve not the director or the manager but the interests of the Party and state. In that respect all are equal. Anyone who permits himself to deviate from this immutable law of our society utterly compromises himself and loses his authority in other men's eyes. Yes, whoever commits an offence must bear the responsibility—Party, administrative or legal responsibility—every kind. But on no account should you subject a person to indignities or wound his self-respect.

That's my view today and that was the rule I followed in the war years and it was the attitude I sought to foster in the staff of the political department I headed. I feel it my duty to say that the department was a close-knit team of officers schooled in Party work, men of experience and knowledge, noted for their initiative and personal courage, men who risked their lives in battle when the situation called for it. Not all of them lived to see victory, but each one of them did his duty honourably.

I have warm memories of these men. During the war I thanked many of them officially, I signed many citations and never once, so far as I remember, did I reprimand anyone. And not at all because I was "soft"—quite the contrary. I did not go easy on them, even when we had to work round the clock. It was simply that I knew I could safely rely on each one of them and they never let me down. To give the reader some idea of our people I'll mention at least a few.

One of my deputies was S. S. Pakhomov, head of the political education department. Calm in any situation and even a bit slow-moving at first sight, when the need arose he would become a bundle of energy and display exceptional resolve. He had a knack of finding the one word the soldiers needed most of all at any particular moment. That's why I enlisted his help more often than that of others in drawing up Military Council appeals and other important documents.

Major A. A. Arzumanyan, a most charming man, was a lecturer and propagandist with not only vast knowledge but also a fine sense of humour, something that always comes in useful. Already then he was quite obviously a man of outstanding ability. I was not at all surprised but very pleased to learn after the war that Arzumanyan had become an Academician and later a member of the Presidium of the USSR Academy of Sciences.

I. P. Shcherbak, an historian who had gained the degree of Candidate of Science before the war, was a fine propagandist, like Arzumanyan. G. N. Yurkin was also deeply knowledgeable. From him you may judge the courage of the political department staff. In the Novorossiisk offensive operation the commander of the Black Sea Fleet awarded him the Order of the Red Banner right on the battlefield. And since I've run so far ahead in my story, I might add that the contribution made by all the workers of the Eighteenth Army political department in that operation was no less highly appraised.

We had an army newspaper of our own, *Znamya Rodiny*, which swiftly reported all the news on Little Land. The men in the trenches eagerly looked forward to the paper and passed it round. Many were the times I attended short editorial meetings and had talks with the editor, V. I. Verkhovsky, and other editorial staff members. I came to respect the journalists because I knew they were always with the troops in the fighting, that they went along in the landing operations, joined sabotage groups and took part in the capture of enemy soldiers for information.

The newspaper staff and its contributors were first-rate. Besides full-time workers, like *Pravda* correspondent Sergei Borzenko, later to be a Hero of the Soviet Union, Boris Gorbatov, the author, and the poet Pavel Kogan wrote for us.

Other well-known writers also visited our army.

Finally, may I say how our soldiers appreciated an apt line of verse by a home-grown poet of our own, or a drawing in an unpretentious, frontline news-sheet because that line of verse and that drawing spoke directly to them. I remember returning once from the forward area at dawn and seeing two young women coming up from the seaward side. One was shortish, smartly belted, a flaming redhead. We saluted and I drove on. I had promised my assistant for Komsomol affairs that at five in the morning I would see several young people for approval as Komsomol organisers in place of fallen comrades. That same redheaded girl came along with several sheets of paper rolled up.

"Where are you from?" I asked her.

"From the sailor battalion."

"How do you get on with them?"

"Fine."

"They're not rude to you?"

"No, of course not! "

She liked to draw, it appeared. There and then she unrolled her news-sheets. I clearly remember a drawing captioned: "Why so bashful, Vassya?"

This young woman, Maria Pedenko, had volunteered for Little Land and had been with the task force from the very first days of the landing. She carried the wounded from the battlefield under fire and, when things quietened down a bit, made the rounds of the trenches with newspapers, envelopes and writing paper, gave talks and recited poetry. She was known and loved by all the fighters and she was considered to be one of the best propagandists. The handwritten newspaper, *Polundra*, was her idea. She even managed to "print" several copies of it and the soldiers would read them to tatters. Wherever these news-sheets were seen and read, general laughter followed.

Maria was wounded later in the fighting for Novorossiisk, but she quickly recovered and returned to frontline units. Her heroism earned her three combat decorations. When the fighting in Kiev was at its fiercest, she asked to be sent there. I once came across an article of hers entitled "Love", in a newspaper (*Pravda* or *Izvestia,* I don't remember which). From the title I expected something sentimental. But it wasn't so. It was an article about the homeland and love for one's homeland.

For the sake of her homeland Maria Pedenko spared neither her youth nor her own life. Her diary, which was later published, had some notes about Little Land: "You crawl from under the ground to take a look at the world outside and your heart gladdens. You feel such a love for life! But all around you the fields are ploughed up by the cruel machine of war. Everywhere you see buildings in ruins and blotches of rusty-red blood on the minced and mutilated earth. You've hardly time to enjoy the sun before you hear 'Air raid! ' Again you're back in the cave where the damp hits you in the face and you can hardly recognise your friends in the soot from lamps made of shell cases."

Like many heroes of ours, Maria has not lived to the present day. Remembering this fine woman, I think of the many other daughters of our country who shared all the hardships of war with our men. I see embodied in them the greatness of Soviet woman.

6

The offensive... After the April battles the entire army, from rank-and-file soldier to commander, lived with the thought of it. We had all known the grief of abandoning our villages and towns to the enemy; the long months of siege had embittered us against the invaders and our thirst for revenge was almost unbearable.

"When will it be, when?" soldiers, officers and political workers kept asking without mentioning the word "offensive" because everyone knew what was meant. There was only one word we could say in reply: "Soon." The date and plans of the offensive were kept a close secret. But it was impossible to conceal the fact that it was being prepared, and there was really no need to.

A very favourable situation was building up for delivering a crushing blow. The Red Army now held the initiative on every front. The fascist Command had irrevocably lost the advantages it had gained from its surprise attack and preponderance in arms. In 1943 the heroic Soviet workers in the rear sent 24,000 tanks and self-propelled guns, 35,000 planes and 130,000 guns to the front. We already had more sophisticated weapons than the enemy, and more of them. The outcome of all this was that, having won a series of major battles in the summer of 1943, the Red Army advanced 300 kilometres West in the central sector of the front and 600 kilometres here in the South.

What was the situation when the idea arose of storming Novorossiisk?

After the battle of Stalingrad Hitler felt he might find himself even more disastrously surrounded and so he clung to his southern bridgehead with particular tenacity. He realised that the loss of the Taman Peninsula would mean losing the Crimea and would put his troops in the Ukraine in great danger. To retain Taman the fascists built a powerful defence line. It ran from the Black Sea to the Sea of Azov and consisted of two zones strewn with minefields, anti-tank obstacles, blockhouses, pill-boxes and armoured gun emplacements.

A. A. Grechko's army was fighting alongside ours and he was the first to experience the fury of fascist resistance. He would capture one hill and have to stop, then capture another hill and again stop. I remember Leselidze, Kolonin, Colonel Zarelua and I were lying on a Caucasian cloak discussing the military situation during a rest period and Leselidze said:

"You know what? The key to Taman and the Crimea is not in these hills but in the storming of Novorossiisk. Let's ask Supreme Command for reinforcements of 17-20,000 men. We'll put the operation in hand and storm the city."

That is exactly what we did. Leselidze telephoned Moscow, the Supreme Command approved our initiative and gave us Gladkov's division. That's how it all began.

Novorossiisk was the main core of German resistance. Besides powerful fortification along the frontline they built many strongpoints in the city itself. Large apartment houses, industiral plants, the grain elevator and the railway station were heavily armed, communicating trenches crisscrossed whole residential blocks and districts, and barricades blocked streets. The port defences were specially strengthened.

The Nazi Command thought it knew Soviet army tactics well: we would not attack major centres of resistance head-on but bypass them. So, while they fortified Novorossiisk, they did not really expect it would be stormed. Here they miscalculated. A special feature of our tactics was their flexibility. One of the reasons prompting us to breach the enemy's defence lines at Novorossiisk in particular was the factor of surprise.

The Eighteenth Army had by now gained considerable experience in landing operations and we felt the city could be attacked simultaneously not just from two sides, as thought earlier, but from three—from the right and left shores of Tsemesskaya Bay, that is to say, from Little Land and from the side of the cement works and also from the seaward side with a large landing force which would take the enemy completely by surprise. This very plan was adopted.

Yet another surprise was being prepared. A large landing ought naturally to be carried out by big ships and the Germans were keeping a very close watch on them. We decided to use small boats to put our men ashore. A torpedo strike at coastal fortifications was also planned. Torpedoes had never before been used to strike at shore targets: they were designed for sea battles and striking ships. The torpedo-boat crews had to work very hard to make sure the torpedoes would go off as planned.

It is common knowledge that a plan which the enemy has divined is already half-doomed to failure. So our first major concern was to preserve absolute secrecy. We forbade all correspondence about the forthcoming operation. A minimum number of people were involved in planning it. Thorough reconnaissance began and it was conducted on a very broad front so as to confuse the enemy. Steps were also taken to misinform the Germans: a number of skilfully executed moves made them think another landing near Yuzhnaya Ozereika was again being prepared.

Party and political support for the operation was considered just as important as its military preparation. It was decided that by the time the attack began absolutely every unit should have a full-fledged Party organisation. To this end Communists were assigned to the vital sectors of the offensive. Special care was taken in selecting men for the task forces: from 60 to 70 per cent of them were Communists and Komsomol members.

I also gave much thought to a more sensible placing of political department workers: each of them was attached to a particular unit for the whole operation. Meeting them later in their divisions and regiments, I saw they were fighting with great zeal, inspiring others with their militant spirit. We drew a large number of political workers from the reserve too, so we·could swiftly replace those who fell in the fighting. Each Party organiser had two assistants and each Komsomol organiser—three. In this way we managed to have Party and Komsomol leaders with every unit all the time.

As became clear after the liberation of Novorossiisk, the Landing-Troops Handbook which we had compiled stood us in good stead. A few introductory paragraphs told of the successes of the

Red Army on all fronts and of Nazi atrocities; at last, it said our time had come to deliver the enemy a crushing blow and revenge ourselves for all his crimes. Then followed practical advice. Each member of the force was briefly reminded how to behave during embarkation, aboard the landing craft, during the landing and, finally, in battle. Our aim was to teach people in advance what to do in unforeseen circumstances. The handbook was given to every man.

I copied the idea of a handbook from soldiers on the Southern Front during the Civil War, when Lenin showed considerable interest in such a handbook and marked particularly important passages. By the way, in all our Party and political work we adopted a number of points to which Lenin drew particular attention. Here as an example are a few lines from the handbook:

"Comrade Communist!.. You must be first to join battle and last to leave. You have been called to the front to educate the Red Army masses. But you must be ready to take up a rifle at any minute and to show by your personal example that a Communist is able not only to live nobly, but to die bravely! "

I remember the days and nights of preparation for the attack as a period of very intensive work and of terrific responsibility. But how different it all was from the days and nights of the siege on Little Land! The work was not burdensome, the responsibility was pleasant and every meeting with people was heartening. A separate marine battalion commanded by the heroes of the first landing on Little Land, V. A. Botylyov and N. V. Starshinov, his deputy for political affairs, volunteered to be the advance guard of the landing. It was to this battalion that a flag was handed to hoist on the first high building retaken from the enemy in Novorossiisk. Petty Officer 2nd Class Vladimir Smorzhevsky, a young Communist Party member, accepted the flag as a great honour. Deeply moved by such trust, this bold scout and battle hero of the first landing on Little Land, vowed to his comrades: "I shall uphold the honour of the Navy! "

At last Army Commander Leselidze summoned all the commanders who were to lead troops in the assault and announced zero hour—the hour and minute of the assault on the night of September 9. The final details of each officer's task were decided here. Then twelve hours before the operation the Commander-in-Chief of the North Caucasian Front, I. E. Petrov, called an extended conference of army and navy commanders where each reported his state of readiness.

One hour before the offensive meetings were held in all the rifle units and task forces and on the ships. The men had to be told a great deal and this could not have been done earlier. So now one had to choose the words that were most needed. I attended many meetings and I saw for myself that the soldiers greeted the order for the offensive with great satisfaction, I would even say, with joy.

The moment we had waited for 225 days and nights had finally come. The Commander's observation post was set up on Markotkhsky ridge from which there was a clear view of Tsemesskaya Bay, the port and a large part of the city.

Night fell. There was still some time to go before the operation began, but many people had already assembled—the Army Commander, Chief of Staff General N. O. Pavlovsky with a group of staff officers, Artillery Commander General G. S. Kariofilli with his aides and the commanders of other arms of the services. The tense silence was interrupted by telephone calls. Scouts were reporting that no movement could be observed on the enemy side. Single shots of gunfire could be heard from time to time, a stray shell would burst somewhere and again all would be quiet. For some reason everyone spoke softly, almost in a whisper. Officers and generals kept glancing at their watches.

Finally zero hour came—at 2.44 a.m. I knew that 800 guns and 227 Katyushas would open fire at that moment and that 150 bombers would be airborne. Naturally I had some idea of the force of that blow. But what I heard astounded me. It was as if the whole earth were shaking.

The artillery barrage lasted fifteen minutes. In that time thirty-five thousand shells were fired at previously sighted targets. Marine and rifle units from Little Land rushed into the attack—not for nothing had we held that precious strip of shore for so long. On the other side an offensive was launched from near the cement works. A landing force from the sea engaged the enemy as planned.

The glow of fires breaking out in the city lit Tsemesskaya Bay. I peered hard into the darkness in the direction of Gelendzhik, but only near the port could I see the first group of break-through boats flashing by at terrific speed, destroying the obstructions. This happened six minutes after the artillery barrage began. An agreed signal appeared—"the way is clear". A few minutes later torpedo boats tore into the bay at high speed and started firing heavy torpedoes at the western and eastern wharves. It was a shattering blow that played havoc with the coastal fortifications. Smoke and cement dust blanketed the shore. This screened our landing craft from the enemy and in exactly fifteen minutes, that is to say, at the very moment the artillery barrage ended, Botylyov's battalion was already fighting on the quayside. In the space of half an hour 800 men armed with heavy machine-guns, mortars and antitank rifles landed under fierce enemy fire.

Tsemesskaya Bay was in utter confusion. Boats were racing in all directions, raising sheets of water as they turned, and it seemed they might collide any minute. But everything was following a strict time-table. In the wake of the torpedo boats came gunboats, patrol boats and seine-boats, each following its own route. The Lesnaya, Elevator-naya, Neftenalivnaya and Importnaya wharves were attacked in suc-cession. The flames of the explosions and fires brightly lit up the bay around the port. The water was literally seething.

At about the same time as Botylyov's battalion attacked and cap-tured the Lesnaya wharf, the 1339th Rifle Regiment under S. N. Kadanchik descended upon the Tsementnaya wharf. And though not all the regiment managed to land, the men who did get a hold on the shore attacked the enemy fortifications in a massive rush. By dawn they had seized an important strongpoint—the Proletary cement works. The rest of the regiment joined them the following night.

The telephones never stopped ringing at the observation post. Reliable contact was maintained with all units. The Army Commander directed the battle with magnificent calm and resolve. As the battle progressed he swiftly regrouped units, moved up reserves and sent reinforcements wherever a dangerous situation arose.

Stunned in the first few minutes, the enemy recovered his wits. Every building, every block spat fire. Ascertaining the extent of the bridgehead we had seized, the Nazis started shelling it. But our artil-lery too was supporting our advancing units. Our pilots had planned operations so that they could continuously bomb enemy-held terri-tory. Our attack aircraft were in the sky all the time, making from six to seven sorties a day.

On the second night the 1337th Regiment went ashore near the power station. Col. V. A. Vrutsky, commanding the 318th Rifle Division, landed together with the regiment but contact with him was lost. I noticed that the Army Commander was worried. Not just a company or a battalion but almost a whole division, and one sent in the direction of the main blow, had been lost track of.

Leselidze decided to send a senior officer to the power station area to find Vrutsky, grasp the situation there and report back imme-diately. After some reflection I suggested that the Commander entrust this mission to my deputy, Pakhomov. The Commander knew him well and quickly agreed, but ordered the chief of operations department to send Capt. Pushitsky, an officer from his department, along with Pakhomov.

"Take my jeep," the Commander added.

They had to make their way into the city through the forward area, passing through a zone the enemy kept under heavy fire. Then they had to find Vrutsky, appraise the situation with an experienced eye, mark it on a map and return as soon as possible. Luckily they both returned safely, though the Commander's jeep, which they had parked near the Oktyabr works, was blown to smithereens. Overcoming a great many obstacles and making their way along a drain-pipe that had been laid on the edge of the coast, they reached a small patch of open ground facing the power station. To the right was a long building from which the fascists were firing continuously. Some 70 metres had to be covered to reach the power station but the only way there was across the open space or along the building behind some heaps of coal. They took a quick decision. Pushitsky started crawling behind the mounds of coal, while Pakhomov dashed across the dangerous stretch at lightning speed. He later gravely assured us that a world champion sprinter could not have caught him. Despite the danger they returned the same way and with not just one but two maps and reports to make sure the information would reach the Army Military Council. They also brought sad news: Col. Vrutsky had suffered severe concussion, lost an eye and been wounded in the arm. Steps were immediately taken to help the division's units which were making slow but sure headway. The divisional commander's duties were temporarily entrusted to the divisional Chief of Staff.

Fighting was continuing in the streets. Reports were coming in one after another: the railway station had been taken and a naval flag hoisted there; the "Grey Mansion" had been taken; the "Red House" had been seized; our men had forced their way into the school; the 103rd district had been liberated... Each report was accompanied by bitter news: Lieut. Gol. A. Tikhostup, political department head of the 318th Division, had been killed... Major P. Isayev, army political department instructor, had been killed... Major A. Tsedrik, army political department inspector, had been killed... A short while before this M. Vidov was killed and also later near Anapa K. Lukin, head of the 83rd Marine Brigade's political department.

I remember going with him into one of the Romanian dug-outs that had been built right on the beach. It was very hot and Leselidze, Zarelua, Lukin and I were looking for a spot of shade. But inside the

dug-out we heard a kind of rustling sound, a continuous low whir-
ring, so I said:

"It sounds like a timing device. They've probably planted a bomb
here. Let's get out."

We emerged into the open, walked a short distance from the dug-
out, spread a large Caucasian cloak and lay down. Lukin also lay
down not far away. Odd shells would whistle past, the whole shore
was churned up. When the thunder of detonations ended, we rose and
I called my friend:

"Lukin! Lukin! "

Not a sound. We went up to him—he was dead. Not a scratch,
nothing. He had been killed by blast.

> *He's just no longer at your side.*
> *Oh, he never dies, your comrade.*
> *He cannot take the flask you offer*
> *Or share your roof at eventide...*

The poet put it very aptly. With my mind I understood that a
battle was being fought and sacrifices were inevitable. But in my
heart I refused to accept this and it ached insufferably. I have myself
written letters to widows, I have thrown handfuls of earth on the
graves of my comrades and I have fired my gun in many a funeral
salute. Loyal sons of the Party in the name of that Party led men into
mortal combat, called on them to fight to the death for their homeland. In battle they were the first to do what they expected of others,
giving a lead to the soldiers. They fulfilled Lenin's behest to the very
end—by their own example they showed that a Communist is able
not only to live nobly but to die bravely.

7

The fighting continued in Novorossiisk for six days and nights.
I will not list the units and formations here, nor give figures—the
storming of the city has been described in detail in history books
about the war. I want to note something else: the enthusiasm in
attack and the righteous fury of the men were such that nothing
could stop them now. Every day and even every hour we witnessed
heroic military exploits. I must tell you about one of them at least.

A company of marines had attacked some fascist fortifications
three times without success. Company Commander Ivanov decided

to form a volunteer assault force to make a breakthrough. The group numbering eleven men was headed by company Party organiser Valliulin and four other Communists. They breached the enemy defences with a hard strike and the others followed at a rush. But at the far end of the street flanking fire again halted them. Valliulin then said to Sgt. Maj. Dyachenko: "When the machine-gun stops firing lead the men into attack." And he crawled off. Right at the cellar window from which the machine-gun fire was coming he was hit. Covered in blood he threw himself on this window to block it. The enemy line was taken.

I had known Salakhutdin Valliulin back at Little Land. He was one of our best Party organisers. As I signed the order for his military decoration, I thought about the nature of feats such as this. There is no doubt he knew he was going to certain death. But it is unlikely he said to himself at that moment: "I am now going to do a heroic act." No, there was no show of heroism in his bravery. It was reticent, unostentatious, I'd even say modest bravery, the kind Leo Tolstoy particularly appreciated, judging by his *War and Peace.* His exploit was an exploit in Tolstoy's sense of the word: a man does what he has to do despite everything.

To feel fear in the face of death is, of course, only natural. But the decision a person makes at the critical moment comes of itself, as it were, prepared by the whole of his previous life. So there's a certain point, a certain moment in the life of a patriotic soldier when the sense of duty to his homeland overcomes his feelings of fear and of pain and his thoughts of death. This means that an act of heroism is not an unaccountable deed but springs from firm conviction of the rightness and greatness of the cause for which a person consciously lays down his life.

"The conviction that the war is a just cause," Lenin wrote at the time of the Civil War, " and the realization that their lives must be laid down for the welfare of their brothers, strengthen the morale of the fighting men and enable them to endure incredible hardships... The reason is that every mobilized worker and peasant knows what he is fighting for and is ready to shed his own blood for the triumph of justice and socialism."

These wonderful words of Lenin's fully and precisely reveal the source of the people's moral strength, the source of the immortal feat our people performed in the years of the Great Patriotic War so that justice and socialism might triumph.

On September 16 Moscow fired a salute in honour of the valiant men of the North Caucasian Front and the Black Sea Fleet. The great confrontation had come to an end. On a bare patch of land with the little settlement of Stanichka our men had withstood a seven-month siege and triumphed. The Nazis had occupied a big city which they had turned into an impregnable fortress—and we had driven them from it in six days.

The nation rewarded the unparalleled courage and valour of the liberators of the city with nineteen formations and units being conferred the title of "Novorossiisk units". Thousands of soldiers and officers were decorated with military orders and medals of the Soviet Union. Scores of them, who had performed outstanding feats of valour, were awarded the most honoured title of Hero of the Soviet Union.

The Novorossiisk landing operation, in which every branch of the services took part, was one of the biggest in the Great Patriotic War.

The Battle for Novorossiisk has gone down in the history of the Second World War as an example of the Soviet people's unshakable determination to win victory, of their fearlessness in battle and of their boundless devotion to the Party of Lenin and to their socialist homeland.

I heard the Supreme Commander-in-Chief's Order of the Day over the radio in a half-destroyed building where the city Party committee had set up its offices. We didn't call a meeting of citizens—there were no people left in the city. We went out into the streets—but there were no streets. Only shambles. The whole city was nothing but smouldering ruins. An old woman and a cat were found in a basement, but no one else. I remember there was a grain elevator and a seamen's club nearby. On the previous day the fascists had rounded up our people, herded them here, poured kerosene over them and burned them alive. A monstrous sight.

Sappers worked hard, defusing and removing thousands of mines, land mines and unexploded bombs and shells. They were also tearing down signs such as: "Any citizen found in the city will be shot on sight." The fascists were afraid of our people... There was a potato field in front of the seamen's club and I moved ahead of the others. Kolonin asked:

"What are you sticking your neck out for?"

"You're a member of the Military Council," I replied, "I'm head of the political department. I should be two steps ahead of you."

It would have been nice to pause for a while to recover one's breath after the liberation of Novorossiisk but we could not stop even for an hour. The capture of Novorossiisk facilitated the advance along the entire bridgehead. Hard-pressed by our troops, the Germans were literally on the run. We captured the Chortovy (Devil's) Gates and the road to Anapa lay open before us. The Nazi Command was forced to scrap Operation *Kriemhild* (a planned trooplift from the Taman Peninsula) and launch instead Operation *Brunhild* (a hasty evacuation). But even that mythical lady was unable to help them.

We were racing along the road at daybreak when we learned that our planes were attacking German units ahead of us. There were four of us in the car: Kolonin, Zarelua, adjutant Kravchuk and I. It was probably the sixth sense of people long under fire that made me shout:

"Get down! They're going to bomb us! "

We stopped, jumped out and lay down beside the road but were all the same nearly hit by our own planes. One can't really blame the pilots. So great was our eagerness to go onto the offensive and our desire to advance that we just could not hold back.

On September 21, 1943, tank and infantry formations of our army struck a crushing blow and liberated the city and port of Anapa, the enemy's main centre of resistance on the way to the Crimea. The attack was so swift that the invaders abandoned all their gear and equipment, all the loot they had taken and even sixteen ships loaded with oil that were ready to sail.

The enthusiasm of our troops for the offensive increased with every passing day and this enthusiasm, combined with their battle experience, proved to be an irresistible force. But by no means can one say it was easy going. We had to fight embittered, strong and well-armed Nazi units. Playing for time, they had painstakingly fortified their last lines on the approaches to the Crimea, clinging to every habitation and every height with the fury of the doomed. Only by the unceasing pressure of the armies of the North Caucasian Front and of the ships, marines and aircraft of the Black Sea Fleet and the Azov flotilla was the whole of the Taman Peninsula finally liberated by October 9, 1943.

We witnessed a scene of shocking Nazi cruelty from the shores of the Kerch Strait. Together with a group of commanders I was watching the enemy's transports sailing away. They could hardly be discerned even with the aid of field glasses but we clearly saw our bombers and fighters cutting across to intercept them. But on reaching their target the planes turned and flew away. We simply could not understand why they had not attacked. The pilots later reported that the decks of the ships were packed with women and children. The pilots could not drop their bombs: the civilians forced onto the decks at gunpoint were a shield for the fascists hiding in the holds.

Ahead of us lay the Crimea. Order No. 51 of the commander of the North Caucasian Front, dated October 9, 1943, was read out to the troops.

"The road traversed by the Eighteenth Army is a glorious and famous one," it ran. "Heroic battles on Little Land, Myskhako, in the mountains near Novorossiisk, and the bold and daring storming of the city and port of Novorossiisk mark the Eighteenth Army's path of glory. Capturing the cities of Anapa and Taman, troops of the Eighteenth Army were first to fulfil their combat mission of driving the enemy from the Taman Peninsula."

In the early hours of November 1, 1943, landing craft with men of the 318th (now the Novorossiisk) Infantry Division entered the waters of the Kerch Strait. Weathering stormy seas and passing through a 30-kilometre minefield under constant enemy gunfire, they made a successful landing on the shores of the Crimea by the fishing village of Eltigen, near Kerch.

Before the landing, Marshal S. K. Timoshenko, the representative of the Supreme Command, said a successful landing of the 318th Division would ensure the liberation of the Crimea. He proved to be absolutely right.

That is, strictly speaking, all that is linked with my memories of Little Land. One page in the history of the Great Patriotic War. Just one page, but an unforgettable one.

On the orders of the Supreme Commander-in-Chief we entrained to place ourselves at the disposal of the Third Ukrainian Front. After the fighting on Little Land and after the storming of Novorossiisk this seemed to us almost like a holiday. But life in wartime is subject to swift changes and fate had something else in store for us.

After liberating Kiev on November 6, 1943, our troops advanced 150 kilometres West in ten days and drove the enemy from a great many centres of population, including Zhitomir and Fastov. Important enemy lines of communication linking the South and Centre Army groups were severed. It was obviously a dangerous situation for the Nazis. Bringing fresh forces from France, the Nazi Command concentrated fifteen armoured, motorized and infantry divisions South of Zhitomir and Fastov. The Nazi plan was now quite obvious—to attack from the South-West, destroy our bridgehead on the right bank of the Dnieper and recapture Kiev. The fascists managed to break through and recapture Zhitomir.

Our Eighteenth Army, Katukov's tank army and a number of other units were ordered to seal the breach and halt the enemy advance. So en route we turned off to the First Ukrainian Front, commanded

by General N. F. Vatutin. By then the enemy was already 74 kilometres along the Zhitomir highway, heading for Kiev, the Ukrainian
capital.

The train carrying the Military Council, Army Headquarters staff
and the political department started first. Troop trains with the
Army's formations and units followed. We travelled rapidly, stopping
only to change engines. During the night we passed the railway station of Baglei—just six kilometres from Dneprodzerzhinsk. We stopped
at yet another station, also very near the city. So here I was back on
home territory.

I stepped down from the carriage and peered into the night. It
was windy, cold and pitch-black. Suddenly I thought I could scent
the smoke from our own Dzerzhinka—the plant where my father
worked and where I also began my working life, where I worked as
a stoker and later as an engineer in the power house. I felt a great
longing to drop in at home if only for a day, an hour or just a few
minutes. Only the previous day I had received a letter from my
mother: she had already returned from evacuation. From her letter
I could tell she had had a very hard time.

But the engine blew a short blast in its whistle, I had to jump
back into the carriage and only much later, when the war was over,
was I finally able to return home and see my near and dear ones...

8

We detrained at Gostomel station and headquarters was set up in
the village of Kolonshchina.

I was rarely there because of all the travelling I had to do to
nearby stations to help speed up the detraining of troops and especially the artillery so it could be deployed in the strips of forest along
the Zhitomir-Kiev highway.

At about 1 a.m. on December 12, I received a telephone call from
Lieut. Col. N. A. Soloveikin, deputy head of the Army Headquarters
operations department: the enemy had broken through near the
village of Stavishche. This was just a few kilometres away from us.

I got in touch with Leselidze and Kolonin. The Army Commander
had already ordered a rifle regiment to move off and tanks were
moving in that direction, but it would take them at least an hour to
reach the area of the enemy breakthrough. Pending their arrival,
we decided to rush almost all the headquarters' officers to the danger
point. This extreme step had to be taken so as not under any circum-

stances to allow the enemy to block and occupy the Kiev highway.

Immediately after Soloveikin's call I alerted all the officers of the political department. I had been speaking with the Commander for about three minutes and when I put down the receiver I was pleased to see that about thirty men were already ready with submachine-guns and grenades. We decided who was to go where.

Adjutant I. Kravchuk and one submachine-gunner were to accompany me. Our thoughtful driver had already loaded three dozen grenades into the car. Cars were starting up all down the street. We headed for the nearest regimental command post where we received the information we needed and then rushed on. About a kilometre and a half from the front line we had to leave the car because of heavy enemy mortar fire. We pushed on quickly in the direction of the firing and soon came to a trench. Wounded men were groaning and a youngish lieutenant was shouting something. Leaning on the breast-work, about two dozen submachine-gunners were firing short bursts. Suddenly a frightened voice was heard in the darkness: "We've got to fall back! " Whereupon the lieutenant shouted: "Shut up, coward! "

At that moment I did not yet know what the situation was. I didn't know that after the fascist attack this second line of trenches had now become the forward one. I didn't know that the enemy had decided not to let us dig in and was again attacking. I realised this only when I caught sight of fascists under the desultory fire of our infantrymen advancing in short rushes, firing their own submachine-guns and dropping to the ground whenever our machine-gun opened fire.

Reassuring the lieutenant, I told him to pass down the line the news that they had to hold out only a few minutes more, because a rifle regiment was on its way in lorries and tanks were coming at full speed. His face lit up, he rushed off to his men and Kravchuk dashed off in the other direction with the same news. I remember how he kept endlessly repeating: "That's the commissar, the head of the political department! "

A considerable time had passed since the institution of commissars was abolished in our armed forces, and the very word c o m m i s- s a r had not been heard among the troops for a long time, but to Kravchuk it seemed the most fitting word to use at that moment.

This was not the first or the last time that I saw the enemy so close, but I have particularly vivid memories of that night's battle. Using the unevenness of the terrain to take cover, the Nazis dashed from one hillock to another in the light of flares. They drew closer and closer and it was mainly our machine-gun that held them off. As the Germans made yet another dash, the machine-gun opened fire again, then suddenly fell silent. Only a thin line of soldiers was now firing. The Germans were no longer dropping to the ground but, urging themselves on with shouts and continuous submachine-gun fire, they were running towards our trenches without even bending down. Our machine-gun remained silent. I noticed a soldier dragging the dead gunner to one side. Without wasting precious seconds, I dashed straight to the machine-gun.

At that moment the whole world for me narrowed down to the strip of ground across which the fascists were running. I don't remember how long it lasted. A single thought dominated my whole being: they had to be stopped! I don't think I even heard the roar of battle or orders shouted around me. But at some point I suddenly noticed that enemy figures I hadn't even been aiming at were dropping to the ground: they were being cut down by the fire of the men who had come to our assistance. One of them touched my arm: "Let a machine-gunner take over, comrade colonel."

Turning round, I saw that the trench was full of soldiers. They were taking up their positions in their usual efficient and business-like manner and, though I was seeing these men for the first time, they seemed very near and dear to me. We halted the Nazis, of course, and in a short while, descending upon them in full strength, Soviet troops liberated Zhitomir and continued their advance.

I would like to dwell briefly on the spirit of brotherhood and friendship that reigned among our troops and the strong attachment the soldiers felt for their units.

Every battle and every engagement, no matter where it is fought, spells fire, blood and death. Yet, when I recall the fighting in many places from the Dnepropetrovsk region to Prague, the scenes vary. The Barvenkovo-Lozovaya operation—and here, before my eyes men up to the waist in snow are swept by an icy-cold wind; the fighting on Little Land—small boats filled with troops are tossed from side to side in the waters of Tsemesskaya Bay that is being churned up by shell-bursts; and the Sukhumi highway: solid dust all the way to the coast. The dust hung in the air, enveloping houses, guns and trucks, and lying thickly on plants and trees, bending the branches low. It managed to seep in through boot-tops to one's toes and through clothing to one's skin. We swallowed it with our water and our food and in its pure unadulterated state.

It was along such a dust-laden scorching road with shells whining overhead that I was heading in a car for a division getting ready for battle. We got stuck in a traffic jam, I got out to seek a detour and came upon a sergeant and a soldier loudly arguing at the roadside. This is what I discovered.

The soldier had been posted to a reserve unit on discharge from hospital. On the way he had deliberately fallen behind the group and slipped away. The sergeant ordered to find him had caught up with him in another unit—the one with which the soldier had served before being wounded. Realising what the argument was about the company commander had told his former soldier: "It can't be helped —you must go along with the sergeant." And off they had gone. But on the way the soldier had rebelled and said flatly: "I won't go and that's that. I'm returning to my unit."

"He was posted to our regiment," the sergeant told me in reply to my question. "He disobeyed orders and is in breach of oath. He ought to be court-martialled and here he is jibbing."

"There's no breach of oath, comrade commander," the soldier pleaded. "I didn't run off to the rear, I rejoined my own unit."

"And where is it?"

"In the thick of the fighting, expecting a Nazi attack any moment, while they," he cast a hostile glance at the sergeant, "are just frittering their time away."

Consider this for a moment. The man was quite entitled not to rush into battle. He had been granted a respite, at least, and nobody could say when he might have to fight again. But that did not suit him, he was eager for battle. What conclusions follow from this random case? The soldier trusted his commanding officers and political leaders, he trusted the fellow soldiers with whom he went on reconnaissance or into battle, otherwise why should he be trying to rejoin his unit? Besides, he must have showed up well in action. A coward would be only too glad to transfer to another unit where no one had seen his faintheartedness. Would he be anxious to rejoin his mates if he were a slovenly soldier, not respected by his comrades?

Perhaps his was a special company and that was why he was so drawn to it? Nothing of the sort! From one end of the Soviet-German front to the other, in all the field hospitals of the Soviet armed forces we heard the same cry: "I want to return to my unit! " The men regarded their own company, regiment or division as something special, as the very best, their own in every sense of the word. So one had the impression that our whole army consisted of "special" units.

I recall another even more striking case. This was also at the time of our advance; troops were entraining and I decided to visit a nearby hospital. In the first ward there were about thirty men, mostly walking patients. I said goodbye to them, told them we were moving on to clear out the fascists and said I hoped they would soon get well and catch up with us. They all started talking at once: to be sure they would catch up with us. The second ward was full of grave cases. The doctor warned me that the first patient on the right, a lieutenant, was doomed. Gas gangrene could not be arrested. I went up to him. Handsome wavy black hair, dark eyebrows and blue eyes gazing from a burning face. I asked if I could do anything for him.

"Yes, comrade colonel, you can. Put a word in for me, please, I want to go back to my own unit if I don't die."

I did not answer right away. Taking grip of myself, I gave a definite promise to put a word in for him. I told him not to worry. I asked what unit he had fought with and how he came to be wounded. I took leave of him and was moving away when I heard him say:

"So you're not going to put a word in, comrade colonel?"

"Didn't I promise you I would..."

"Yes, but you haven't got my name."

Words again failed me but the nurse saved the situation.

"I wrote it down," she pointed to her pad, "your name and rank, and the number of your unit. Here you are! "

I took the slip of paper and read: "It's time to go now." Slipping it into my map case, I glanced at the lieutenant again. He was all smiles. A lump rose in my throat. Many times during the war I heard people say: "I want to rejoin my unit." But never will I forget that lieutenant with his peacetime phrase about "putting a word in", and that stubborn soldier on the Sukhumi highway.

What nobility of spirit! What unostentatious but boundless love of their country, what eagerness to defend it without thought of one's own life! It was not so much the soldier's request itself that shook me as the way he put it. He was not parading his heroism, it was almost as if he was apologising, begging for some very personal, very private favour, for something only he needed.

What could I have said to the soldier by the dusty roadside? By all the regulations and laws of military discipline he was in the wrong. No one may choose where he will serve in wartime. No one may leave the service "of his own will" or transfer elsewhere. Keeping to the laws and regulations in force, I was duty-bound to order him to report to the unit to which he had been posted. But I hesitated.

"What am I to do with you then?" I asked the soldier, being myself truly at a loss.

"Send me back to my own unit, Comrade Commander. I'm going to be admitted to the Party! I've already failed to make it once because I landed in hospital. And this time I had just put in my application when those damned fascists got me again. As for them," he nodded again in the sergeant's direction, "nobody there knows me."

These last words dispelled my doubts. I asked my adjutant to note the soldier's name and the numbers of both units. I promised the soldier that by the next day at the latest there would be an order posting him back to his own unit. But meanwhile he should go with the sergeant, because no one may disobey an order. It would be by order that he would return to his mates. The soldier couldn't and didn't even try to conceal his joy. He braced himself, straightened up and saluted smartly:

"May I leave?"

Again and again one discovers how right Lenin was when he pointed to the great importance of keeping in close touch with the masses, of mixing with workers, peasants and soldiers. Many serious and important conclusions were drawn from talking with soldiers during halts on the march, in rest periods and at battle stations. This was also the case after that hospital meeting and my chance talk with the soldier on the Sukhumi highway. I kept my promise, of course. But an official decision was also taken that whenever and wherever possible men should return to their own units on leaving hospital.

February 11, 1944, was a bitter day for me. I was seeing our gravely ill commander off to Moscow. The doctors said there was almost no hope for him. Ten days later Konstantin Leselidze died.

At the front you very quickly get to know people. There you see the true worth of a person straightaway. Leselidze was a talented military leader who embodied the best features of our Soviet people. Stern and merciless towards the enemy, kind and gentle with friends, a man of honour and a man of his word, a man of keen intellect and one who loved life and was very brave—that is how this friend and brother-in-arms of mine lives in my memory.

Much could be said about what followed, a whole book could be written because thousands of kilometres and long months of war still lay ahead of us. But today I would like to stress one thing again: the memory of Little Land, the steeling and experience of Little Land were a help to me and my comrades-in-arms to the very last shot of the war. The patriotism, enthusiasm and boundless courage of our soldiers were enhanced by their presence of mind, maturity, prudence and skill, and all this taken together brought us final victory.

Fighting fiercely, liberating towns and villages, we advanced through the Kiev, Vinnitsa, Khmelnitsky, Chernovtsy, Lvov and other regions of the Ukraine and reached the Carpathian Mountains. Taking advantage of the terrain there, the fascists had built their mighty Arpad line of defence. But there were no longer any barriers the Soviet army could not surmount. Drawing upon our experience in the Caucasus, we forced the Carpathian mountain passes and smashed the seemingly impregnable line of enemy defences.

Now indeed the political workers knew no respite by day or night. The fighting was continuous and Party and political work among the troops never ceased for one minute. At the same time we had to help local comrades, Communists who had been working underground up to now, to organise life anew. Major political events were held one after another: a Party conference, trade union congress, youth conference and women's conference. The new atmosphere of freedom roused the entire population of the Transcarpathian Ukraine to political life. We were received as brother liberators. People's committees were set up everywhere and were preparing to hold their first congress. Attending this congress later I witnessed the great enthusiasm with which participants adopted the historic decision to reunite Transcarpathia with its own people.

It's hard to forget the joy with which the peoples of Romania, Hungary, Poland and Czechoslovakia greeted the arrival of our troops. The Eighteenth Assault Army also helped to liberate those countries. That was a time when political work was of special importance. The imperialists had slandered our Party for decades. For decades they had been spreading all kinds of monstrous lies about Soviet life and people. Now Soviet people appeared in Europe as liberators and it was very important not to discredit this humane mission in any way. Our soldiers were equal to it. Everywhere they proved themselves noble, humane, fair and battle-hardened men.

In the hardest year of the war, 1941, we had been sure victory would come. Now we knew that it was just round the corner. The entire course of events had prepared us for it. Yet when victory did finally come our joy was simply overwhelming. To my mind no one has yet been able adequately to express that joy in words. Nor do I have words to convey to you what filled our hearts on May 9, 1945. All I can say is that it was the happiest day of my life.

The last day of war for our Eighteenth Assault Army came in fact a little later—on May 12. The Act of Unconditional Surrender by fascist Germany had already been signed but we were still destroying remnants of enemy forces which continued to resist on the territory of Czechoslovakia.

Nor will I ever forget that great act of triumph—the Victory Parade in Red Square. With pleasure and pride I read the order that General Brezhnev, head of the political department of the Fourth

Ukraine Front, had been appointed commissar of the Front's combined regiment for the parade. To this day I cherish the sabre with which I marched with our commanding officers in that parade at the head of our combined regiment.

That's how my dream of seeing victory came true. It was the dream of millions of Soviet soldiers who not only fought to the last in defence of their country but honourably carried the banner of victory through all the ordeals of war and hoisted it over the Reichstag in Berlin.

* * *

Our victory was a great milestone in the history of mankind. It showed the greatness of our socialist homeland and the omnipotence of Communist ideas, it produced wonderful examples of selflessness and heroism—all this is indeed true.

But let there be peace, because peace is what the Soviet people and all honest people all over the world very much need.

To the very last day of the war we were burying our loyal comrades. All along the roads of war we saw evidence of fascist atrocities. We saw weeping mothers, inconsolable widows and hungry orphans. If I were asked today what is the main conclusion I drew from the war which I went through from beginning to end, I would say: There must be no more war. Never again must there be any war.

Happy indeed is the politician, happy is the statesman who can always say what he really thinks, do what he really thinks necessary and work for what he really believes in. When the Soviet Union put forward the Peace Programme and when at many international gatherings our country came forward with initiatives aimed at eliminating the threat of war, I did, I worked for and I said what I believe in as a Communist with all my heart.

That, I think, is the main conclusion I have drawn from the experience of the war.

Translated by Pavel Shikman

Anatoly Ananyev
(b. 1925)

Ananyev volunteered for the army in 1942. Upon finishing an intensive course at an anti-tank artillery military school, he found himself on the front line at the height of the Kursk Battle. There he received his first medal and first wound. Only twenty years later, in *Attacked by Tanks,* a novel which won him popularity (selections are published in this edition), did Ananyev recount what he went through that summer of 1943.

After the war, he worked at a plant and simultaneously studied by correspondence at an agricultural school. Later he worked on a collective farm, again studied, and, finally, became a journalist. His first book of stories appeared in 1958. Ananyev is a winner of the State Prize of the Russian Federation and the author of five novels and a number of novellas.

Attacked by Tanks*

Major Griva's battalion had been stationed in Solomki for over a month and had got so used to this deserted, half demolished little village, and so used to the stillness, that they could hardly believe that soon the fighting would start again, that once again, as at Moscow and on the banks of the Volga, the earth would rumble with gunfire, peasant huts would burst into flames, and tanks with yellow crosses on their sides would crawl amid the acrid smoke across deserted fields and meadows, crushing the young wheat that had just begun to ear, and that the sky, that clear blue summer sky, would be blotched with ack-ack shell bursts; they could hardly believe that again, as in 'forty one, and that memorable summer of 'forty-two, the columns of retreating troops would stretch out across the Donside steppes and the wooded slopes of the Kursk country, heading for the river crossings, that the stations would be jammed with trains, and thousands of refugees in creaking wagons, driving and carting everything that could be driven or carted, would flow eastwards along the dusty cart-tracks in a terrifying flood. Somehow they just couldn't believe it. When they thought of the coming battle, the men thought of an offensive. Many were counting on the second front—surely the Allies would open that long-awaited front at last! But the Allies were about to take a different decision. In those tense days the British prime minister, Winston Churchill, was aboard a battleship, making a top secret voyage to Washington. He sat in his comfortable cabin and his pen quietly scratched a letter to Moscow: "I am in mid-Atlantic on my way to Washington to settle the further stroke in Europe after "Husky"... Barring accidents, my next cable will be from Washington."** Nothing did happen to him on the voyage, he arrived safely at his destination and, true to his word, having conferred with the President, wrote again to Russia. In calm tones he informed the Soviet Government the Allies could not open a second front that year because it had been "hoped that twenty-seven Ameri-

*English translation © Raduga Publishers 1985

**Correspondence between the Chairman of the Council of Ministers of the USSR and the President of the USA and the Prime Minister of Great Britain during the Great Patriotic War of 1941-1945. Vol. I. Foreign Languages Publishing House, Moscow 1957, p. 129.

can divisions would be in Great Britain by April 1943, in fact, there
is now, in June 1942, only one, and there will be by August only
five," and also because the landing craft had "been drawn into the
great operation now impending in the Mediterranean". Churchill
considered Operation Husky—the invasion of Sicily—so important
that it might, in fact, had already "led to the delay of Hitler's third
attack upon Russia, for which it seemed great preparations were in
existence six weeks ago". In conclusion Churchill wrote: "It may
even prove that you will not be heavily attacked this summer".*
It is difficult, of course, to imagine that the British Premier knew so
little about the true state of affairs. At the very time when he wrote
his message, in Russia, along the two edges of the Kursk salient,
the Germans had concentrated powerful assault forces: one in the
Orel area, north of Kursk, and the other near Belgorod, south of the
city. The respective commanders, Field Marshal von Manstein and
Field Marshal von Kluge, had received their final instructions from
Hitler and flown out to their troops.

Meanwhile life at the front followed its usual course. After long
months of defence the men had grown used to the lull and they could
not and would not believe that battle was imminent.

At about midnight Lieutenant Volodin noticed a strange disturb-
ance on the field of buckwheat in front of his positions. It seemed to
be suddenly crowded with men and machines. Junior Sergeant Frolov,
when sent to investigate, soon returned with the report that an infantry battalion and the batteries attached to it were retiring, that
they had been ordered to pull back behind Solomki, and that there
were now no our troops at all in front. The buckwheat field was
mined, except for a narrow corridor running along the edge of a birch
grove and sappers were now directing the battalion along the corridor.
The rumble of moving trucks and machinery went on for a long time,
almost till daybreak, and the dark, stooped figures of weary men
made their way in a thin straggling line along the ridge, disappearing
into the dip, then reappearing on the other side and melting away
into the darkness. Volodin could see them well while they were on
the ridge. He watched them sadly, without anger. With cool indifference he reflected that now in front of his positions there was no
fortified defence line, which only yesterday had seemed so impregnable, no covering forces, not a single Soviet soldier. Instead there

Ibid., pp. 140-141.

was the enemy, the no man's land between two lines of trenches, the no man's land that began just beyond the parapet of his trench; he could reach out and touch it.

There had been moments when Volodin had passionately wanted the fighting to blaze up right here, on the approaches to Solomki. But now, when the mental picture had actually materialised, when the enemy had actually advanced right up to the edge of Solomki and might at any minute attack his trench, he felt none of his former determination; when he thought of the impending battle, he thought mainly about how many guns, mortars and machine-guns there were in Solomki and where they were mounted (he tried to remember everything he knew and had seen); he thought of the anti-tank battery in the birch grove. Lucky that it was not far away, that it had not been pulled back and was not being pulled back, that the men there were probably great guys and could be counted on to help if it come to a crunch ... lucky there were mortars in the dip... Before he knew it he had dozed off, but even in this drowsy state he went on thinking about the battle. He did not hear Captain Pashentsev enter his emplacement from the communication trench, did not hear him talking to Signaller Ukhin, a sharp-witted, crafty fellow, who had been a boatman on the Irtysh. Volodin was awakened by the intense stillness, ringing in his ears. While he was rubbing his eyes and trying to get his bearings, while he stared in surprise at the captain's straight back, recognising and yet not recognising his company commander, the early morning stillness was broken by a sound, flabby at first but growing rapidly louder, which ended with a deafening roar as a heavy shell burst behind the trench. Then the white flame of an explosion rose in front of him, almost on the parapet, and the whole line began to rock with the impact of exploding shells. The shells landed close together and burst with such a mind-shattering roar that, though he tried to put on a bold front, Volodin could not help crouching against the wall of the trench. He kept his eyes on Pashentsev (the captain had not turned round and only his straight back was visible), and to Volodin he appeared to be completely oblivious of the fire; only when a shell landed very close did the captain duck down for a moment, then stood up again and clamped his glasses to his eyes, watching the field ahead.

Volodin made an effort and went up to his commander.

"Feeling scared?" the captain asked.

"Yes! "

"That's good! "

Volodin wondered what could be good about his being scared.

Perhaps the remark had referred to something else that only Pashentsev could see or knew? He took his field glasses out of their case and, like the captain, observed the field. It was wrapped in clouds of dust and scarcely anything was visible.

The bombardment grew steadily fiercer; Junkers started dive-bombing the positions with a terrifying howl and both Pashentsev and Volodin had to take cover in a slit. All around the command post as far as the main road and further, right up to the crossroads the ground became a seething mass of fire.

Today was the same in many ways as yesterday. Volodin was still only sitting it out in his trench, as he had done the day before, and might die in just the stupid way he had imagined and was afraid of; the trench was the same with its crumbling grey walls and choking stench of TNT, mingled with that of human flesh and blood, and there was the same paralyzing crash and roar all around. But today was battle, not just a minor action on the other side of the wood, as it had been yesterday, and he, Volodin, was in the middle of it. Putting together everything he had heard from eye-witnesses and knew himself from the minor engagements he had taken part in, Volodin tried to guess the true nature of the fighting that had now blazed up round Solomki. Clearly the Germans were concentrating for an attack under cover of artillery fire. He would have to keep a look-out so that not to be caught unawares. He was surprised and disturbed by Pashentsev's cool composure. Apparently the captain had no intention of going to the command post. At times Volodin thought he could hear the clattering roar of approaching tanks and stared at Pashentsev, trying to guess from the look on the captain's grimy face what he could hear. But the captain's expression did not change.

Captain Pashentsev was well aware of something that Volodin in his excitement had forgotten. There would be no attack until the artillery softening-up was over, and the Germans could not come very close because the buckwheat field in front was mined. Yes, he was happy enough on that score. What worried him was the fact that the bombardment had already lasted twenty minutes without any let-up; that meant either that the Germans lacked the muscle for a powerful blow and were therefore trying to crush the defence with their artillery, or that they had chosen this sector for the main blow and were throwing in everything they had to ensure a clean break through to the main road. Since he could not be sure which assumption was right Pashentsev chose the more dangerous of the two, and now his thoughts were centred on his own positions, on the long, staggered line of the main trench with its side-slits and reserve emplacements, which he could not see at the moment, but which he felt like his own hand, like a part of himself; and from the barely perceptible signs that he could make out amid the din of battle he tried to assess what losses the company was suffering and how it would meet the attacking enemy; he was already beginning to realise that they would probably not be able to stop an all-out attack by enemy armour, and that they would have to let some of the tanks through and mow down the infantry advancing behind them; he felt sure about that because the gunners themselves had proposed this plan of action, and also because his company had got through its "running-in" period and every man knew what to do if the tanks broke through to the main trench, and every section and platoon commander knew what to do, and Volodin, whom Pashentsev considered to be inexperienced and who only yesterday, the day before the battle, had unexpectedly lost his reliable assistant—Senior Sergeant Zagrudny—was at his side and, to the captain's great satisfaction, was standing firm...

The whole company, the whole battalion, the whole Solomki defence, muffled in dust and yellow TNT smoke, was waiting tensely for the air-raid to end.

But what the Solomki men had yet to see—a black spearhead formation of tanks—was already clearly visible from the divisional command post. This huge black rhombus, like a piece of the forest that had broken away from the main mass, was moving towards the buckwheat field.

"Tanks! "

"Tanks! ..."

"Tanks! ..."

The signallers bawled the news over the field telephones.

The tanks were steadily gaining speed, but from a distance they seemed to be crawling, as they heaved their massive bodies over the hillocks. A small light tank was leading the formation, bouncing along like a rubber ball. It seemed to be feeling its way. When it turned to left or right, the whole formation changed course with it.

When Volodin and Pashentsev climbed out of the slit trench and went up to the command post, the small light tank was not far from the buckwheat field. At first they saw only this small tank plunging through the dust and Pashentsev, who had expected the worst and resigned himself to it, but now saw something quite different, something so paltry and insignificant, gave a cheerful whistle; but a moment later the heavy tanks showed up through the thinning clouds of dust and in another few seconds the whole attacking formation with its hundreds of rumbling caterpillar tracks came clearly into view. Pashentsev whistled again, but without the cheerful note of a moment ago; now, like Volodin, he too stared at the rapidly approaching tank formation, but whereas Volodin, who was seeing a tank attack for the first time, was impressed by the grandeur of the spectacle, Pashentsev, who had at once noticed the unusual rhomboid formation and the exceptionally good order and synchronisation, tried to guess the enemy's plan. In the centre of the rhombus there were light tanks, self-propelled guns and tracked personnel vehicles carrying submachine-gunners, and along each side there were heavy tanks, which shielded the great mass of fighting machines with their armour. For Pashentsev this was not just the astonishing sight it was for the beginner Volodin; Pashentsev had very definite ideas about tank attacks: tanks advanced in extended order with the infantry running behind them. This was the kind of attack he had been prepared to face with confidence; but what he saw now was quite different from his experience of previous engagements, and it made him nervous. He knew that his men would also feel the same nervousness at the sight of this great black phalanx bearing down in them, and that they were expecting him to give them the "requisite command"; he racked his brain for such a command and it wouldn't come, and this made him even more nervous because he realised that his hesitation might prove fatal for the company. Pashentsev's face paled and if Volodin, who was aware of nothing but the tanks coming towards him and could think of nothing but the voice inside him shouting "Smash them! Stop them...", if Volodin had been able to ignore even for a moment the clanking roaring monster that held his attention, he would have felt the company commander's shoulder trembling and would have seen a face quite different from the one he knew so well—the face of a stranger, dejected, drained of blood.

The attacking force was coming on fast; the small light tank had already reached the field of buckwheat and was tearing its way through the corn, but suddenly a spout of flame shot up from under one track and the tank span round like a top and caught fire. And as if at a signal, the whole formation stopped. This happened so unexpectedly that for a moment Pashentsev was baffled, but then he remembered the minefield and felt some relief. And the minefield was only the first obstacle; there were also the anti-tank guns and anti-tank rifles... The company's anti-tank riflemen ought to be firing at the personnel carriers, to make those submachine-gunners jump out, then it would not be so hard to "cut them away" from the tanks... "At the personnel carriers! At the personnel carriers! " Pashentsev repeated to himself, getting a clearer picture of the battle and rejoicing that the "requisite command" had occurred to him, that at least he had got that far, even if it wasn't the best solution, but at least the tanks had stopped and there was time to think and make a decision; the captain's confidence was returning, he straightened his shoulders and, when Volodin turned to him and shouted in desperate jubilation, "It's burning! " the captain's face was calm once again.

"It's burning, Comrade Captain! "

"I can see that."

"And the tanks—they've stopped! "

"It's too soon to rejoice, Lieutenant, this is only the beginning..."

But Volodin already had some more joyful news to communicate.

"Our heavies are pounding 'em! "

The heavy howitzer batteries had opened up and were getting the range on the tank formation halted in front of the mined field of buckwheat. But the tanks and the self-propelled guns had begun to answer the batteries' fire, reluctantly, lazily at first but with increasing persistence. By the look of it the Germans had no intention of retiring; nor were they doing anything about clearing the minefield. And this indecision or confusion worried Pashentsev and put him on his guard. He felt that there must be a definite plan behind all this, but he could not get to the bottom of it; his nervousness returned and his mind raced with anxiety; he watched the enemy tanks, the gun flashes and shell-bursts, the grey-blue fringe of forest on the horizon, trying to spot something that would help him to guess the enemy's intentions; then he looked up at the sky and saw Junkers. The first thing he thought of was that the Germans were going to clear the minefield under cover of a dive-bombing attack. But the Junkers's target was not the battalion's positions but the buckwheat field. Volodin came out at once with the joyful assumption, "They're bombing their own lot! " But Pashentsev, although the same thought had occurred to him, treated the idea with caution. The Germans could not have overlooked their trench from the air; besides they were bombing according to a definite pattern, hurling their deadly loads in a straight line in front of the formation. "They're demining the field with bombs! They radioed for air support to clear the minefield! " Pashentsev decided at last. Now the picture was quite clear, now he knew how to fight this battle; the Junkers were still diving on their target, but the captain had other things to attend to; he bent over signaller Ukhin and gave him the command to transmit: "Prepare anti-tank grenades and incendiary bottles! "

"If they get close, let the tanks through and then pelt them with bottles and grenades! "

"Anti-tank riflemen, aim at the personnel carriers! "

"Machine-gunners and submachine-gunners, cut away the infantry! "

The captain's voice was firm and clear, and Ukhin scarcely had
time to repeat his commands.

Lieutenant Volodin was still standing by the parapet, watching.
Amid the din of battle he heard neither the captain's nor the signaller's
voices; he had not even noticed that the captain had left the parapet
to speak to the signaller. He was still enthusing over the way the
Germans were "pulverising their own lot", and when the next Junkers
went into a dive over the stinking cloud of smoke and dust that hung
over the buckwheat field, Volodin was ready to shout his encouragement to the pilot. At first, during the artillery attack Volodin had
tried to think out what was going on, but when he saw the rhomboid
tank formation and later, when the formation stopped, and especially
now, when in his view something incredible but very fortunate for
him and all the Solomki men was happening—now Volodin could
neither think nor assess the situation, and was entirely in the grip of
enthusiastic impulses, and everything that was rumbling and moving,
all these noises, from the short bursts of automatic fire to the boom
of the heavy howitzers—all this seemed to him not the opening but
the final chord of the battle. So he was naturally confused when
Pashentsev called him over and ordered him to go at once to the
machine-gun emplacements.

"Stand to the last man! "

"But they're..."

"They're demining the field with bombs, they'll be attacking
any minute now... Act, Lieutenant! "

As soon as Volodin, in obedience to Pashentsev's order, left his
emplacement and ran along the communication trench to the machine-
gun emplacement, the joyful excitement that had seized him at the
start of the battle, when the rhombus of tanks had halted on the edge
of the buckwheat field, and the Junkers had started demining it,
this joyful excitement, which had given him cheerfulness and energy,
at once abandoned him. He ran along the half demolished trench,
sliding into shell-holes and scrambling over mounds of earth; he felt
the decisive moment was approaching and fear of that moment, and
the desire to be fearless and daring, now stopped him and made him
listen to the roar of battle, the clatter and howl of engines, now got
him moving again and drove him forward. Wounded men were lying
in the trench and no one was attending to them; the noise drowned

their feeble groans. They turned their ashen, pain-racked faces to
the lieutenant as he ran past, and Volodin found it hard to recognise
his own men. "Where's Zhikharev? Why isn't anybody attending
to the wounded?.." But at that very moment Volodin almost tripped
over the company's medical instructor, who was lying at the
entrance to one of the side trenches, a small figure with his knees
pulled up to his chin and a white, drawn face. Lumps of reddish
clay from the walls of the trench sprinkled into his ear, over his
white cheek and forehead and stuck to his moist dead eyes. His
first-aid bag and shattered helmet were lying beside him. And just
opposite, in a small emplacement, a team of anti-tank riflemen were
hard at work.

"That's the fourth! ..." gun-layer Volkov shouted at the top of
his voice and his mate Shchegolev scratched a stroke on the side of
the trench.

And again Volkov's booming voice was heard,

"Bullets! ..."

The trench was alive: dusty figures, almost invisible in the dust,
the men were doing the difficult job that war demanded of them;
they had no time for the wounded or the dead, the living were thinking of life, of repelling, breaking, swamping with fire the attack by
enemy tanks and infantry. Volodin stepped across Zhikharev's dead
body and ran on. The machine-gun emplacements were only about
ten metres away, round two bends of the trench. When he got round
the last bend he discovered that the machine-guns were silent. When
had they stopped firing? Now or a minute ago? Why? He ran out to
the emplacements, which were under heavy fire from the enemy's
self-propelled guns; he plunged into an inferno of explosions, forgetting fear and death and thinking only of one thing, "Why? Why?.."
But the machine-gun nests were empty. As soon as he realised that the
German gunners had got them "taped", Junior Sergeant Frolov
had moved his crews out of the line of fire to their reserve positions,
and the German guns were now pounding empty emplacements.
Shells burst with blinding flashes all round Volodin and he crawled
the last few metres, using his elbows frantically.

Three machine-gun nests, three emplacements, linked by communication trenches. The floor was scattered with empty abandoned drums,
half buried in earth. In one of the emplacements Volodin noticed
a wounded man. Machine-gunner Razmakhin was dragging himself
towards the main trench, both legs shattered.

Volodin dashed up to him. "Where are the machine-guns?"

Razmakhin scrabbled on the loamy floor of the trench and raised

his head a little; his arms, shoulders and head shook with the effort
and pain.

"Where's Frolov? Where're the guns?"

Razmakhin said nothing and slumped forward. It was no use
asking him. What should he do? Go back? No machine-guns. Empty
emplacements. Volodin backed away slowly from Razmakhin's
prostrate body; it was frightening to be here amid these high grey
walls, and he was backing away from the emptiness of it, from the
terrible sense of isolation that had assailed him. At the back of the
emplacement a row of anti-tank grenades stood ready and waiting,
like a rank of soldiers. Volodin noticed them and counted—six. "Six!
Six! Six! .." he repeated to himself, counting and rocounting the
row. "Run! Run! Run! .." another, stronger voice repeated and
made him back away further. Volodin was just about to climb out
of the emplacement but he hesitated; perhaps Razmakhin was still
alive and needed his help? He went over to the prostrate machine-
gunner and was still making up his mind—should he bandage him or
run back to the main trench?—when he heard the chatter of machine-
guns. The fire was coming from the reserve emplacements. The over-
heated guns sang out their tune unsteadily, as though competing
with each other in haste. "They're alive, alive, alive! " the song echoed
joyfully in Volodin's mind. He straightened his back, walked into
the emplacement and looked over the parapet—and saw tanks. A lot
of tanks. But his eyes focussed on only one of them, the nearest.
The long gun barrel was swaying like a pendulum and the tank was
swaying with it and bellowing as it crawled towards him out of the
dust, a great black shape against the backdrop of the pale-blue morning sky. Behind the tank, amid the smoke and dust, he saw the dark
figures of the submachine-gunners in their angular helmets. Volodin
was looking at them from below and they, too, seemed to him big
and dark against the blue strip of sky. The figures fell and thinned
out, but the tank crawled with terrifying steadiness towards the
emplacement. Hurriedly Volodin groped for one of the anti-tank
grenades hitched to his belt, unclipped it, and going cold as he braced
his whole body, threw it well ahead of him, as he had done at grenade
practice. It went off with a great bang and Volodin, confident that
the tank had been crippled, but ready with a second grenade just
in case, looked over the parapet again. Undamaged and even bigger,
fully visible right down to the handles on its sides, the tank was coming straight at him. This time Volodin threw his grenade without
looking, from the bottom of the trench and crouched down, waiting
for the explosion; instinctively he unclipped a third grenade and in

his confusion began groping for the pin, as if it were an ordinary infantry hand-grenade; his eyes roved distractedly round the emplacement; the grey walls struck him as low and unreliable, apt to crumble, they wouldn't take the weight of a tank, they'd collapse and crush him. Was this the end? Would he never see the sky, the fields again? No, surely there was something he could do, try, some action he could take right now, this moment... He racked his brains, trying to think of something, but it was no good and he sat with the grenade in his hands, groping vainly for the pin. It would be more dangerous to run out of the trench than to stay there, and he realised that, but a voice seemed to be urging him to run. "Escape! " The voice impressed him and he tried to guess how many paces he would have to take to get out of the emplacement and how many after that to reach the main trench, the nearest fox-hole, how many seconds. Would he make it? He didn't make it—the bottom of the tank was already jutting over the edge of the emplacement. He dropped flat beside Razmakhin and froze to the ground, hearing and understanding nothing, but clearly aware of the clods of damp cold soil piling on to his shoulders, his legs...

The tank swung round over the trench and stopped, crippled by the artillery; a pale tongue of flame slithered over its armour and in a moment the whole tank was ablaze and belching black smoke.

Just as after a nightmare, a man wakes up suddenly and is delighted to find that it was all only a dream and his thoughts begin to run smoothly and calmly, while his body still retains that horrible sense of falling—just as after a nightmare, Volodin opened his eyes under the doomed tank, dazed and clamped down by the dislodged soil; he lay in total darkness, like in a cellar with the hatch closed, and with Razmakhin's stiffening body beside him, and all the sounds of battle, that a few moments ago had been so deafening, now came to him faintly, as if from afar, and told him almost nothing about how the battle was going. But the machine-guns in the reserve emplacements had not given up and even now Volodin could pick out their muffled chatter and realised with relief that the company had not retreated, that the fighting was here, on their line of trenches, and that this was very good, and it was good that he, Volodin, was still alive, and all he had to do now was to think calmly, without hurrying, how to get out from under the tank. At first all his movements were unhurried, deliberate—cautiously he freed his shoulder and legs from the heap of clay that had fallen on him, then peered round in the darkness and made out a narrow crack between one track and the ground and crawled towards it, trying not to touch Razmakhin;

but then the trench became filled with acrid, choking smoke and he began to hurry; his hands moved faster and faster as he raked away the earth, he coughed and panted, but he went on raking, digging his fingers into the dry lumpy clay and, feeling no pain, struggled towards the fresh air that filtered in a thin stream through the narrow crack; shells began to explode inside the tank, after one or two bangs the crack was choked with smoke and dust, heat poured down on him from the bottom of the tank and there was nothing at all to breathe, and Volodin no longer breathed; he swallowed the choking fumes, but even as he began to faint, he went on struggling spasmodically towards the crack, his boot soles slipped, he tried to get a leverage somewhere and his boots kicked and dented the helmet that had fallen from the machine-gunner's head. Now Volodin had no coherent thoughts; for him there was no battle, no burning tank, nothing that had happened before this moment; there was only this moment, and then death; he was face to face with death, in the grip of panic and terror; he imagined he was still doing something, crawling, struggling forward, towards the air, but actually he was feebly twitching his fingers and sliding to the bottom of the trench. For the last time, somewhere in the far depths of consciousness he caught a glimmer of the thought that he was dying the inglorious, foolish, absurd death that he had feared most and that had got him after all; for the last time somewhere in the depths of consciousness he felt pity for himself, regret at the failure of his hopes and then everything fizzled out, evaporated, and was masked by a glittering black curtain...

"Take that!.."
"And that! .."
"And that! .."
This was Yefim Safonov as he pressed the trigger of his light machine-gun. He was shooting calmly, in long steady bursts, swinging the barrel of his gun to any spot where German submachine-gunners appeared; he saw the battlefield over the sight of his machine-gun and everything that happened in the narrow frame of the sight seemed hazy and distant, as if seen through a blue curtain of rain. The tanks were moving amid blue puffs of smoke, and so were the submachine-gunners, and with the butt of his gun jigging cheerfully against his shoulder Safonov sliced through this swirling blue fog with fiery tracers. The tanks did not frighten him; some of them were already on fire, and those that were still moving (he was sure) would also be set ablaze. That was the job of the anti-tank gunners, but he had

his own job to do... He was one of those calm, stolid Russian soldiers, who get bawled out on parade and in barracks, but who perhaps just because of their stolidity turn out to be steady and invaluable in battle. When an enemy tank that no one had set fire to did nevertheless loom up in front of the emplacement, Safonov lifted his machine-gun off the parapet and, holding the gun in his arms, dropped to the bottom of the trench, not forgetting to cover the breech with his hand, as he had been taught, so that it would not get bunged up with earth and dust and the cartridges would not jam when he tried to fire it afterwards. He did everything just as he had been taught and demanded the same efficiency from his assistant, the young soldier Cheburashkin. As soon as the tank had passed over his trench, Safonov lifted the gun back on to the parapet and hugged the butt; he threw no grenades after the tank that had broken through, he didn't even look at it; not even when he heard the fierce roar of an anti-tank grenade behind him—as a machine-gunner it was his job to cut down the infantry, and he kept at it with steady persistence. What had happened behind him—Junior Sergeant Frolov and Private Shapovalov blowing up the tank with grenades and preparing to meet another in the same fashion—was only what should have happened and Safonov couldn't imagine anything else happening. Cheburashkin was squatting at his feet, packing the next drum with cartridges. The empty cases flew out of the gun and landed on his helmet and the top of the drum and the soldier grumbled and waved them off like flies.

"Take that! "

"And that! .." Yefim Safonov repeated, still without haste, but pressing the trigger with bitter anger. He scarcely took his eyes off the emplacement where the badly wounded Razmakhin had been left behind, and where platoon commander Volodin was now (Safonov had seen the lieutenant dodging his way through the barrage to get there). Safonov had been shooting at the submachine-gunners who were following the tank, running in short dashes towards that emplacement. He had forced the Germans to take cover and the tank had turned round over the emplacement and caught fire.

"Chebuk! " Safonov stopped firing and called to his assistant.

"Another drum, Uncle Yefim?" the young soldier responded quickly.

"The lieutenant's under the tank! .."

"Yeah?.."

Both men stared at the huge German tank, wreathed in smoke. The turret hatch opened and the head of a tankman appeared, then his shoulders; clearly the German meant to jump out of the burning tank, but he was hit at once and clumped over the turret. Somebody in the turret was trying to tip him out. But the battery was keeping the tank under fire. An armour-piercing shell ripped off the hatch, then two shells hit the turret... The calm, easy-going Safonov and the impulsive energetic Cheburashkin watched in awe as the metal seethed with ominous black smoke. Both of them were overwhelmed by the spectacle and for a moment forgot who they were and what they were here for, and they both failed to notice the German submachine-gunners taking advantage of the lull to crawl forward and then make a whooping rush at the main trench.

"What's up, Safonov? Why aren't you shooting?" the junior sergeant's deep voice boomed behind them. "Is it jammed? Give it here!.."At that moment Safonov felt Frolov's powerful hand tugging at his shoulder.

But now he had seen what was happening in front. He pressed his cheek to the gun and, gritting his teeth, squeezed the trigger. "Take that," he muttered fiercely.

As soon as the sergeant went away, Safonov called Cheburashkin again. "Chebuk! "

"Want a drum, Uncle Yefim?"

"Listen, Chebuk," Safonov said between bursts of fire. "Can you get to that tank?"

"What for?"

"To bring out the lieutenant and Razmakhin. They'll choke there... Go on, I'll give you covering fire."

Cheburashkin stared apprehensively at the tank, and at the shell-torn, half demolished trench, as though working out whether he could pass along it or not, and, having reached the conclusion that this was impossible, gave Uncle Yefim a dirty look and said nothing.

"What's up ?" Safonov asked again between bursts, noticing the young soldier's hesitation, "Are you scared?"

"Why should I be?" Cheburashkin responded. His face paled and began to twitch quite noticeably, but he straightened his thin, boyish shoulders challengingly, as if to prove that he was no coward and capable of far more than some people might imagine. He climbed out of the emplacement and, instead of crawling or darting forward, drew himself up to his full height and walked along the trench towards the tank. "Look, I'm not scared of bullets, but you were wrong to send me and you'll be sorry when I get killed..." his whole appearance—straight back, chin up, submachine-gun held casually at the ready—seemed to be saying. His blood ran cold with fear and happiness because he was able to walk like this, unbowed by bullets, and was really ready for death and was sure he would not come through alive, and was aware of nothing but his own body and where the bullet would hit him. In the chest? The stomach? Or perhaps in the leg, and then... At first everything he did was guided by resentment against Uncle Yefim, who had sent him out to the tank, into this hell of flying bullets, but when he found himself in the line of fire, and heard their venomous buzzing and whining and realised that he was not afraid of these sounds or the bullets themselves, Cheburashkin wanted to throw down a challenge in front of Uncle Yefim and everyone else. He wanted to do this because he had been so offended by what he had been made to endure at that moment. "I'll get killed. Look, you people, at what a horrible thing you've done to me! .." But the bullets missed him and smacked quietly into the clay, and he walked on, moving faster with every step, and soon the desire to live overcame resentment, and the thought that people would be horrified when they saw him, the young soldier Cheburashkin, dead, receded into the background and faded out altogether; he hurried to the bend in the trench—once round that bend he would be able to get his head down and run forward in short dashes, and no one, Uncle Yefim or anyone else, would see him. He must get to that bend quick...

"Keep down! " Safonov shouted after him. "Keep your head down, you bloody fool, you'll get killed! "

But Cheburashkin was already round that bend and for some time there was no sign of him. "They got him," Safonov muttered angrily to himself, and, as though taking his revenge on the Germans for Cheburashkin's death, he fired off a whole drum at them without stopping.

What happened after that Safonov could never remember. The Germans got up and charged, then took cover again and charged again, and he fired drum after drum at them. There was no time to think of Cheburashkin or the lieutenant or Razmakhin, it was such a mix-up, and the only thing he could remember was the sweat on his hands. The heated stock of the machine-gun was unpleasantly sticky to the touch, the drums slipped out of his fingers; he hastily wiped them on his tunic, but then wiped his brow with his hand and it was wet and sticky again. Safonov was the only one still shooting. Both the other machine-guns in the platoon were silent. But Safonov was running out of ammunition and he looked round worriedly for his section commander. There seemed to be nobody in the slit trench from which Junior Sergeant Frolov and Shapovalov had been throwing grenades; but Safonov simply hadn't spotted them; the sergeant had been slightly wounded in the head and Shapovalov was hurriedly bandaging him.

"Hurry," the sergeant begged. "Hurry up, there's not a gun firing!"

He stood up and ran to the machine-guns without waiting to be bandaged. In the emplacement manned by Corporal Kokorin's crew, both the machine-gunner and his loader were dead; the barrel of the gun, buckled by a direct hit, was sticking up out of a heap of clay. In the third emplacement the machine-gunner had also been killed, but the gun stood undamaged on the parapet and the number two, Shcherbakov, instead of taking over and firing himself, was sitting barefoot on the ground, trying a new white footcloth to his sub-machine-gun. When Junior Sergeant Frolov appeared, the terrified pale-faced loader, who had obviously expected to see nothing but Germans and his own death, dropped the gun and backed away, holding up his arm as if to shield himself from a blow. For a second Frolov stood at the entrance, staring at the submachine-gun lying on the ground and the white footcloth tied to it, then bent down, ripped off the cloth, threw it away, pushed Shcherbakov aside, and ran to the machine-gun. He guessed what Shcherbakov had meant to do, and in his anger was ready to hit or even shoot him, but German submachine-gunners were nearing the trench, their voices were audible, and there was not a second to be lost; only when he had fired a long burst did Frolov look round and grunt, "Drums, you bastard!"

Barefoot and pale as death, Shcherbakov suddenly get to work with more alacrity than he had ever shown in his life.

Pashentsev was lying on the grass, several paces away from his emplacement; although he had not lost consciousness for a second while the fight was on, had not been wounded or shell-shocked, now, as he listened to the clatter of tanks heading away in the direction of the crossroads, and the hush that had suddenly fallen over the field, he felt the happy awakening of life that always comes after a spell of intense effort. The feeling was in everything: in the dry earth that smelled of heat, to which he was pressing his cheek, in the morning sun that was warming his back, in the unexpected breeze that had crept inside the collar of his tunic and was cooling his sweating neck; it seemed to Pashentsev that he had been lying like this for a long time, but in fact it was not more than a few seconds—this was the lull between two waves, after one had broken and the next was billowing, and this next wave was the German submachine-gunners who had lagged behind their tanks. They were running close together in line and not shooting because they were confident that the way had been cleared for them. But the Solomki men were already scrambling out of their flattened half demolished slits and shaking off the dust and the fear generated by the tank attack they had just experienced, and all along the trench, like a crackling of branches, there was a clicking of breach-bolts and the parapet bristled again with the barrels of machine-guns, rifles and submachine-guns that were still not cool from the recent action. Now they would slash the advancing enemy line with hot lead... Pashentsev was lying awkwardly with one arm tucked under him; his sweating fingers felt the warm sticky stock of his submachine-gun. A scorched blade of grass stood motionless before his eyes. An ant was crawling on it. It looked wonderfully pellucid and tender in the sunlight, its brown body seemed to be quite transparent. It climbed up and down the stalk, as though it too felt uncomfortable on this huge bare stretch of land, and could find nowhere to settle. Under the stalk lay a big jagged shell splinter, still steaming. Beyond the splinter there was more scorched grass, and on it lay the body of a soldier blocking the whole horizon. "Pyatkin! That's Sergeant-Major Pyatkin! " In the hand thrown back behind the sergeant-major's head, Pashentsev could see a dust-sprinkled bundle of grenades, lightly held by the unclenched fingers. The grenades were tied with a belt. The buckle gleamed like a mirror in the sunshine and Pashentsev noticed the gleaming surface of the belt, polished by use as a razor strop, and the congealed blood on the fingers and finger-nails; for a few seconds he stared at the bundle as if it could explain the sergeant-major's death... Not far away stood a crippled tank, big, spotted, with a ripped-off track and its engine still running.

"I've seen all kinds of tanks. Black, the way they come off the production line, probably, and white, with whitewash poured all over them..." This one was spotted, like a reconnaissance scout's camouflage cape. Its armour plating was like a map with dark lowlands, yellow deserts, and the brown zigzags of mountain chains, and on those chains—the swastika, the badge of death, its spidery legs reaching down into the valleys... Perhaps the turret actually did have the five continents mapped on it, expressing Germany's fanatical concept of *Lebensraum*, the mad idea that so many generations of Germany have had injected into their brains like some elixir of life, the idea that Hitler developed into the absolute concept of *world domination*; perhaps Germany herself, crushed and strangled by the swastika, was represented dozens of times on that revolving turret; or perhaps they were just shapeless yellow, green and brown patches, daubed by some careless painter for camouflage; and this tank was approaching, a huge spotted object, clearly visible from far or near (the man who did the camouflaging didn't know the Russian country-side), scarred by bullets and shells. It was coming straight at the em-placement; it had come here from the Rhein, this spotted Tiger that had been whelped in the Krupp factories; marching tunes blared out when it was loaded on its truck, thousands of hands touched its cold armour plating, thousands of Burghers and their buxom Fraus, infect-ed by the same *Lebensraum* madness as the Führer, gazed at it with reverence and hope as the train began its eastward journey; thousands of curses were showered in its wake when, under its tarpaulin covers it crossed the land of Poland; a sentry appeared beside it when the truck crossed the Russian border; near Smolensk a train ahead of it was blown sky high; in the goods yard of Belgorod station the partly sawn through supports of the unloading platform collapsed under it; at night, in a village near Tamarovka, a boy's hand slipped an old rusty infantry hand-grenade under one of its tracks; even before it had fired a single shot, like hundreds of its spotted brothers, it had scattered its road from the Rhein to the Northern Donets with corpses —all those who, intentionally or unintentionally, had been near the train were rounded up, hanged, shot, gassed in concentration camps; its armour was spattered with blood and the painter had the wrong idea when he daubed it yellow, green and brown. This "tiger" was now bearing down on the emplacement, and two vision slits, the driver's and the commander's, were staring straight at Pashentsev. Who was behind those slits, who was driving the tank? A convinced Nazi or a bamboozled Burgher, whose *Lebensraum* at home was far more spacious than the narrow grave with a birchwood cross at the head that awaited him in Russia? Or was it steered by the poet who didn't want to die himself and desired no one else's death, that smiling N.C.O. Raimund Bach, about whom fifteen years later Heinrich Bohl would write pityingly, "He was burned to death in a tank, turned into a charred mummy..." Fifteen years after the was the Germany des-cribed by Bohl and Remarque would evoke compassion among those who had never seen bombs bursting, earth burning and soldiers dying. "The lost generation, the lost generation! " ...It was lost in 1914, and again in 'forty-one! In the ancient town of Murom, sitting by a window with a view of the red-painted station water-pump fifteen years after the war the retired Colonel Pashentsev would say to his grandson, "You've started on Remarque before you've even read Tolstoy. You don't know what war is! " And standing by that win-dow with a view of the water-pump he would think, "The streets of

Bonn are full of soldiers, the idea of *Lebensraum* has been taken out
of the cupboard and dusted down. Once again the madness is spreading through Germany and the drum-beat echoes across Europe. The
columns are marching past under the windows where Heinrich Bohl
writes his novels. Again the lost generation, the widows and orphans
of war... But what about the battle at Barvenki? And the Battle of
Kursk? When will it all end? Whose fathers will put an end to it?.."
He would stand by that window and watch the trains go by; the war
had not marked his house with death, he had a wife and a grandson,
a wife who spent six months of the year in a TB hospital, and a grandson who enjoyed reading Remarque... All that was to come, and the
retired colonel would set about writing his memoirs, but as yet he
had no idea of what was to come. The Tiger was only five metres
from the parapet; Pashentsev could almost see the eyes of those who
were steering this clanking monster towards his position, aiming the
barrel of the gun. Another second and the black bottom would clamp
itself over the emplacement, another second and everything would be
buried in dust and acrid smoke. In every engagement there was a
moment when Pashentsev could not command his company because
nothing was visible to the right or left, in front or behind; every emplacement became a small individual fortress; consciousness disappeared
and only the thousand-year-old instinct of one's ancestors survived:
"Them or me!.." Pashentsev had time to glance at the emplacement, to assess the strength of its walls, and to see what Ukhin and
Pyatkin were doing: the sergeant-major was tying a bundle of grenades
with his belt, and Ukhin, pale-faced, was blowing into his telephone
receiver; he had time to reflect that the sergeant-major had always
been a brave fighter, and he would definitely throw that bundle of
grenades and blow up the tank, and that in the engagement before
this he ought to have been recommended not for a "valour" medal
but for a "star", but Ukhin, he wouldn't perform any feat of bravery,
even before this he had had to be sent out to mend the line at gun
point, Pashentsev had time to remember, "Father was killed in the
first world war. Mother knew the day and hour when he was killed,
she knew even before she got the official letter. That day she had
been out in the fields, reaping; she had collapsed on the ground, holding her heart; the neighbours brought her round with water. For the
rest of her life Mother had talked of her premonition... "What will
happen to my wife and Andryushka, if that tank crushes me here and
now?" He had time to think even of that and even to picture his
own home, the front door, the room with a view of the water-pump—
it would be morning there too, Andryushka would be looking out of

the window and his wife would have clutched at her heart and sat down on a chair. "What's the matter, Mummy?" "Never mind, son, it's just that something may have happened to Father." She would say that, and for the rest of her life she would remember her premonition... The Tiger lumbered over the emplacement with a grinding roar and covered it with its bottom. The feeling was like a train plunging into a tunnel at full speed, but louder, more enclosed, and the smoke from the locomotive was all round him and the yellow lights of the tunnel lamps were blinking before his eyes, and his sense of danger was alerted—suppose the tunnel collapsed? But this danger seemed absurd because tunnels never collapsed, thousands of trains had gone through this one, and so would thousands more because— how many times had Pashentsev let enemy tanks pass over his trench, then thrown grenades after them. And this was what he was going to do now, but Sergeant-Major Pyatkin beat him to it. The sergeant-major jumped out of the emplacement—Pashentsev saw him jump and swing his arm to throw the bundle of grenades, and then fall to one knee and try to throw from there, but then only manage to lift his arm helplessly and fall back on the grass. "Killed! " the word burst into Pashentsev's brain a moment later. "The sergeant-major's down, the tank'll get through! " The thought threw him out of the trench like a wave, he ran a few paces and hurled a grenade at the tank.

Suddenly he felt as if someone had touched his elbow, then he heard the clatter of a submachine-gun on the hard ground, and the rustling sound of a man scrambling to his feet. He raised his head and saw signaller Ukhin. Ukhin was poised like a runner on the starting line and his massive figure was bathed in the sunlight; the morning rays seemed to rejuvenate the old Irtysh boatman's grey, always gloomy face. It was not the sweat-stained tunic that suddenly looked newer in the sunshine, not the gnarled veiny hands, not the burnished gleam of the submachine-gun they held, but the face, Ukhin's face, that astonished Pashentsev with its amazing straightness and clarity of thought. The signaller only just now had seemed pale and wretched, and in that other battle he had had to be forced at gun point to go and mend the line, but that had been in *that* battle, when Ukhin was a beginner, and after that battle Pashentsev couldn't remember Ukhin ever having shown fright; his face went pale but he went out to the line; once he had even volunteered; and now, looking at the signaller's poised massive figure, like a runner on the starting line, the captain remembered all this. Ukhin was watching a German who had jumped out of the tank (the tank with a broken track and its engine still running was gradually being enveloped in flames) and was running away into the smoke. Pashentsev sensed the determination in the old boatman's narrowed eyes, narrowed more from hatred than because of the brilliant sunlight, in the grim set of his mouth, in his jutting chin; Ukhin was ready to go after that German and grab him, but because he was a crafty man, who always made sure of his mark, he was waiting for the right moment to attack. And Pashentsev read that determination in the signaller's face.

Ukhin darted forward and disappeared in the black smoke swirling round the tank, and only just above the ground under the curtain of smoke was there a glimpse of his boots and, a little lower, the boots of the running German. Round the revived main trench the Germans were still attacking, now blasting full out with their sub-machine-guns, and bullets were snicking over the dry grass, humming like wasps. The battle raged fiercer. Pashentsev turned and looked round at the smoking field; the whole trench, all the emplacements and slit trenches, along its entire yellow length, from the birch grove to the sports stadium, the shell-torn parapet was alive and fighting, seething with the white flashes of automatic fire.

"They're holding! " Pashentsev whispered, applying the word simultaneously to the light machine-guns firing from the reserve positions, which he imagined were under the command of the lieutenant he had sent there, and to the right flank, which was fiercely resisting the oncoming Germans, and to the left, to the whole company, to the whole Solomki defence.

"They're holding! "

"They're holding! "

"They're holding! "

Though they had never been written down in any set of regulations, those words were used by everyone that day, from soldier to general, in all units—infantry, artillery, air force, on all sectors of the Voronezh and Central fronts; they were repeated in shattered gun emplacements, in burning tanks, on shell-ploughed gun positions; they were awaited impatiently at command posts and headquarters, just those two words—"They're holding! " They were passed from mouth to mouth on dusty roads. They were repeated by front commanders, reading the combat reports from their units; those two brief words, which embodied the fate of whole regiments, divisions and armies, were on that day, the first day of the Battle of Kursk, the measure of true heroism and glory.

Translated by Robert Daglish

Alexei Tolstoy
(1883–1945)

Alexei Tolstoy was born in a small Volga town near Samara (now Kuibyshev).

During the First World War he was a front-line correspondent. After the downfall of the monarchy in February 1917, Tolstoy, in trying to comprehend the development of Russia, turned to historical subjects. He worked on his novel, *Peter the Great,* till his last days.

The writer did not understand and accept the Socialist revolution immediately, but after recognising its importance and justice, he devoted himself to portraying and affirming the new realities. Academician Alexei Tolstoy, whose works are considered classics of Soviet literature, is the author of the trilogy, *Ordeal,* which was translated into many languages, as well as of novellas, stories and plays. *The Russian Character* is part of the cycle *Ivan Sudarev's Stories*, written during the Second World War.

The Russian Character

The Russian character! It is too impressive a title, of course, for a story of no great length. But there it is, it happens to be the Russian character that I want to talk about.

Yes, the Russian character—describe it, if you can! I could tell you about plenty of heroic feats, but there are so many that I should be at a loss which to choose. Luckily, however, a friend of mine has come to my rescue with a story from his own life. I shan't tell you how he fought the fascists, though he wears the Gold Star and sports a row of medals across his chest. He is a simple, quiet, ordinary man— a collective farmer from a village on the Volga in Saratov region. But he used to stand out among others because of his powerful physique and good looks. You just couldn't help staring when you saw him climb out of the turret of his tank—a veritable god of war! He would leap to the ground, pull off his helmet, freeing his thick hair, now damp with sweat, wipe his smudged face with a rag, and then—he always did it—smile with the sheer joy of being alive.

When a man's at war and constantly facing death he rises above his ordinary self. All the trashy stuff that doesn't matter peels off him, like dead skin after sunburn, and only the kernel, the real man, is left. Of course, the kernel is tougher in some men than in others, but even those with a few flaws in them are trying hard, because everyone wants to be a good and loyal comrade. But my friend, Yegor Dromov, was strict in his ways even before the war—he had enormous respect for his mother, Maria Polikarpovna, and his father, Yegor Yegorovich. "My father's a man of dignity. The first thing you feel about him is that he has self-respect. 'You'll see a lot of things in the world, son,' he says, 'and you'll go abroad, but mind you always keep your pride in being a Russian.' "

Yegor was going to marry a girl from the same village on the Volga. Our lads talk a lot about their girls and their wives, especially when it's quiet on the frontline, and cold, and there's a fire in the dugout and they've had their supper. The things you hear sometimes, it's enough to make your ears curl up. Someone starts off, for instance: "What's love?" "Love arises out of respect," says one. And another'll say: "Nothing of the kind! Love's a habit. A man doesn't just love his wife, he loves his father and mother, he even loves animals." "Blow me, what a fool! " says a third. "When a man's in love, he's throbbing with it. He goes about as if he's drunk." And they keep it up like that for an hour or two till the sergeant-major chimes in with his voice of authority and goes right to the heart of the matter.

Yegor Dromov, no doubt because he was embarrassed by such discussions, only dropped me a hint about his girl. She was, he told me, a very good girl, and if she said she'd wait for him it meant she'd be there when he came, even if he came back on one leg.

Nor did he like to talk much about his battle record. "I don't like recalling such things," he would say with a frown and pull hard at his cigarette. We heard about the battle exploits of his tank from the crew. Driver Chuvilyov told a particularly impressive story.

"...We'd only just turned round and what did I see coming over the hill... 'Comrade Lieutenant,' I shouted, 'a Tiger!'. 'Step on it! ' he shouts back. So off I went, weaving through the fir trees, making use of what cover there was. The Tiger groped about with its gun like a blind man, then fired and missed. But the lieutenant let him have it right in the side—what a wallop! Then he got another shot in on the turret and the Tiger toppled back with its snout in the air. And with the third shot the smoke started pouring out of every slit, and then the flames shot up about three hundred feet high. Out comes the crew through the escape hatch and Ivan Lapshin mows 'em down with his machine-gun... Well, that cleared the road for us, and in five minutes we came tearing into the village. What a lark! The Nazis went scuttling all over the place. And it was muddy, mind you, so a lot of 'em lost their boots and went hopping around in their socks, making for the barn. So Comrade Lieutenant gave me the order: 'Ram the barn! ' We turned our gun round back to front and went smack into it—Gor! There were beams and bricks and planks crashing down on us, and the Nazis who'd climbed into the loft. I swung round and went in again to iron the place out. The ones that were left put their hands up and yelled 'Hitler Kaput! ' "

And that was how Lieutenant Yegor Dromov fought until he had a stroke of bad luck. During the Battle of Kursk, in the later stages, when the Germans were hard pressed and had begun to give way, his tank, which was stationed in a wheat field on a hill, was hit by a shell that killed two of the crew outright. The next shell set it on fire. Driver Chuvilyov, who had escaped through the front hatch, climbed back onto the turret and managed to pull out the lieutenant—he was unconscious and his clothes were burning. Chuvilyov had only just dragged him clear when an explosion ripped the tank to pieces and hurled the turret about fifty yards away. He threw handfuls of loose earth on the lieutenant's head and clothes to smother the flames, then dragged him from one shell hole to another till he found a first-aid post. "Why did I do it?" Chuvilyov said afterwards. "Because I could hear his heart still beating..."

Yegor Dromov survived and didn't lose his sight, although his face was so badly burned that the bones were showing in places. He was in hospital for eight months. Plastic surgery restored his nose, lips, eyelids and ears. When the eight months were over and the bandages taken off, he looked in the glass at a face that was his, yet no longer his. The nurse who had given him the little pocket mirror turned away and cried. He gave the mirror back to her.

"I've known worse," he said. "I can get by."

But he never asked the nurse for her mirror again. Instead he would often feel his face, as though trying to get used to it. When the medical board declared him fit for non-combatant service, he went straight to his general and asked permission to return to his regiment. "But you're disabled," said the general. "No, I'm not. I'm disfigured, but that doesn't matter. I'll soon be able to fight as well as I ever did." (Yegor noticed that the general tried to avoid looking at him during the interview, and this brought a grim smile to the blue slit that was his mouth.) He was granted twenty days' leave to complete his convalescence and went home to see his father and mother. That was last March.

He had expected to get a cart at the station but had to walk the ten miles to his village. The ground was still covered with snow. It was damp and deserted everywhere. The biting wind kept dragging open the flaps of his greatcoat and howling loneliness in his ears. It was growing dark by the time he reached the village. Yes, there was the well with the long wellsweep creaking to and fro in the wind. The sixth cottage down the street was his father's house. Suddenly he halted, pushed his hands into his pockets and shook his head. Instead of going up to the front door, he cut across the patch of ground round the house and, sinking kneedeep in the snow, crouched by the low window and looked in at his mother. By the dim light of an oil lamp she was laying the table for supper. She still wore the same dark shawl on her head, still looked as quiet, unhurried and kind, but she had grown older, and her shoulders were very thin. If only I'd known, he thought, I'd have written every day, even if it was only a few words. She prepared her simple meal—a bowl of milk, a piece of bread, two spoons and a salt-cellar—and then, standing at the table with her thin arms folded under her breast, she seemed to become lost in thought. As he watched his mother through the window, Yegor Dromov realised that he couldn't possibly give her such a fright, that he mustn't let her poor little face crumple in despair.

Very well then! He opened the gate, stepped into the yard and knocked at the door. He heard his mother's voice ask from inside who was there. "Lieutenent Gromov, Hero of the Soviet Union," he replied.

His heart was thumping so violently that he had to lean against the door-post. No, his mother hadn't recognised his voice. He himself felt as if he was hearing it for the first time, it had changed so much after all his operations. It was thick and hoarse.

"What do you want, son?" she asked.

"I've brought you greetings, Maria Polikarpovna, from your son, Senior Lieutenant Dromov."

Then she opened the door, rushed out and grabbed his hands.

"Is he really alive, my Yegor? Is he well? Come inside, dear, come inside."

Yegor Dromov sat down on the bench at the table in the very place where he had sat in the days before his legs were long enough to touch the floor, when his mother would sometimes stroke his curly head and say: "Eat up, my little swallow." He started telling her about her son, about himself. He told her in detail what he ate and drank, how well and happy he was, and free of hardship, and only briefly did he mention his tank battles.

"But tell me, isn't war frightening?" she interrupted, staring into his face with eyes that were focussed elsewhere.

"Yes, mother, of course, it is," he replied, "but you get used to it."

Yegor Yegorovich, his father, came in. He had also aged; his beard looked as if it had been sprinkled with flour. He eyed the guest, kicked the snow off his battered felt boots against the doorstep, slowly unwound his scarf, took off his overcoat, and walked over to the table and shook hands—ah, how well Yegor knew that broad, just hand of his father's! Asking no questions, because it was quite clear without that why this man with a row of medals was here, he sat down and also began to listen, with half-closed eyes.

The longer Lieutenant Dromov sat there unrecognised and talked about himself as though he were someone else, the more impossible it became to throw off the pretence, to stand up and say: "Can't you recognise me, father and mother, disfigured though I am! " At his parents' table he felt both happy and hurt.

"Well, mother, let's have supper. Bring us something for our guest." Yegor Yegorovich opened the door of the little dresser. Yes, the matchbox full of fishhooks was still there, and so was the teapot with its chipped spout and the dresser still smelled of bread crumbs

Into battle, and don't spare your lives!

On the Orel-Kursk Bulge, 1943

German soldier on the carriage of
a wrecked gun. July 1943

The first artillery salute in Moscow to mark
the liberation of Orel and Belgorod, 1943

Exhibition of captured war materiel in
Moscow, 1943. In the photograph: a
German heavy Tiger tank, hit in the recent
battle on the Kursk Bulge

French flyers of the Normandy-Niemen
squadron and Soviet soldiers fought against
the Nazis together

A group of Byelorussian Komsomol partisans

◄

The Southern Front. A respite between
battles. 1943

Left to right: Konstantin Simonov,
Roman Karmen and Boris Tseitlin in liberated
Vyazma, 1943

The people's avengers

Partisan bread

Commanders of Ukrainian partisan units S. Malikov
and A. Fyodorov (centre) working on a plan for
joint battle operations

Partisans crossing the river

In partisan country

Partisans restoring Soviet power in the district from which they have
driven the fascist occupiers

and onion peel. Yegor Yegorovich took out a small decanter of vodka— only enough for two glasses—and sighed because he wouldn't be able to get any more. They sat down to supper, as they had in years gone by. And only after a while did Lieutenant Dromov notice that his mother was following every movement of the hand in which he held his spoon. He gave a short laugh; his mother raised her eyes, and her face quivered with pain.

They talked of one thing and another, of what the spring would be like and whether the farmers would manage the sowing in time, and Yegor Yegorovich said that they might expect to see the end of the war this summer.

"Why do you think the war may end this summer, Yegor Yegorovich?"

"The people have got their dander up," Yegor Yegorovich replied. "They've been through death itself. There'll be no stopping them now. The fascists are finished."

Maria Polikarpovna asked: "You haven't told us when they'll give him leave to come home and see us. We haven't seen him for three years. I expect he's got much bigger and has grown a moustache. And being near to death every day, like he is, I dare say his voice has got harsher."

"Yes, when he comes back you mayn't even recognise him," said the lieutenant.

They made up his bed on the ledge over the stove, where he remembered every brick, every chink in the log wall, every knot in the ceiling. It all smelt of sheepskin and bread, of that home comfort that a man never forgets, even in the hour of death. The March wind whistled and murmured under the eaves. Behind the wooden partition his father snored gently. But his mother sighed and stirred restlessly on her bed; she was not asleep. The lieutenant lay still with his face in his hands. How can it be that she didn't recognise me, he was thinking.

In the morning he was wakened by the crackle of burning wood; his mother was quietly tending the stove. His footcloths, which she had washed, were hanging on a rope stretched from wall to wall. His boots had been cleaned and were standing by the door.

"Do you like millet pancakes?" she asked him.

He didn't answer at once. He climbed down from the stove, put on his tunic and belted it, and sat down on the bench barefooted.

"Does a Katya Malysheva live in your village? Andrei Malyshev's daughter?"

"She finished her course last year, she's our village schoolteacher. Do you want to see her?"

"Your son asked me to make sure I passed on his regards."

His mother sent the neighbours' daughter for her. Before the lieutenant had time to pull on his boots, Katya Malysheva was there. Her wide grey eyes were shining, her brows raised in wonder and her cheeks flushed with joy. The lieutenant almost groaned when she threw back her shawl onto her broad shoulders. If only he could kiss that warm, fair hair! This was just how he had pictured her. Fresh, tender, merry, kind, beautiful—so beautiful that the whole cottage seemed to glow like gold when she entered it.

"Have you brought greetings from Yegor?" (He was standing with his back to the light and he merely nodded because he couldn't speak.) "Tell him I'm waiting for him day and night."

She came closer. Her eyes met his and she fell back a pace, as though something had struck her in the chest; she was frightened. That made up his mind—he wouldn't stay a day longer.

His mother made some millet pancakes with baked milk. He talked again about Lieutenant Dromov, this time about his deeds of valour. He spoke harshly, without looking up at Katya, so that he shouldn't see in her sweet face the reflection of his disfigurement. Yegor Yegorovich wanted to go and ask for one of the collective farm's horses, but the lieutenant went off to the station on foot, as he had come. He was so overwhelmed by what had happened that he kept stopping and pressing his hands to his face, muttering hoarsely to himself: "What shall I do now?"

He returned to his regiment, which had been brought back to the rear for reinforcement. And there he got such a welcome from his friends that it shifted the load off his heart. He decided that his mother needn't know about his misfortune for some time yet. And as for Katya—he would tear that thorn out of his heart.

About two weeks later he received a letter from his mother:

"My darling son! I am afraid to write to you, for I hardly know what to think. We've had a visit from a man who said he came from you. He was a very good man but his face was badly disfigured. He was going to stay with us for a while but he changed his mind and left suddenly. And ever since, my son, I haven't been able to sleep a wink, because it seems to me that man was you. Yegor Yegorovich scolds me, 'You must be out of your mind, old woman,' he says. 'If it had been our son, do you think he wouldn't have told us? Why should he pretend if it was he? A man should be proud to have such a face as he had.' Yegor Yegorovich tries to talk me round, but my mother's heart knows otherwise—it was him, it was him, it tells me. That man slept on our stove and I took his greatcoat out in the yard to clean it, and I held it to my breast and wept because I knew it was you. Dear Yegor, please, for the love of Christ, write to me, tell me what happened. Or perhaps I have really gone out of my mind."

Well, Yegor Dromov showed this letter to me, Ivan Sudarev, and, as he told me his story, he wiped his eyes on his sleeve. I said to him: "That's a clash of character for you! You're a fool, man, you're a fool. Write to your mother and ask her forgiveness. Don't drive her mad. A lot she cares about your appearance! She'll love you even more as you are now."

He wrote a letter the same day. "My dear parents, Maria Polikarpovna and Yegor Yegorovich, forgive me for my foolishness. It really was me, your son, who came to see you..." And so on and so forth, for another four pages, in small handwriting. He'd have written twenty, if he had had the time.

Some time later we were on the proving ground together, when a soldier came running up. "Someone wants to see you, Captain Dromov," he said. Though he was standing stiffly at attention, the soldier looked as if someone was just about to treat him to a drink. We went down to the hut where Dromov and I were living. I could see he was uneasy—he kept coughing and clearing his throat. He may be a tank soldier, I thought, but he's got nerves. He went into the hut ahead of me and I heard his voice:

"Hullo, mother, it's me." I saw a little old woman clinging to his chest. When I looked round I noticed there was another woman in the room. Well, there must be other beautiful women about, she's not the only one, I'm sure, but I've never seen another like her.

He freed himself from his mother's embraces and turned to this girl. As I said before, his magnificent physique made him look like a god of war. "Katya! " he said. "Why did you come? You promised to wait for another man, not this—"

And before I went out into the porch, I heard her say: "Yegor, I'm going to live with you for ever and ever. I will love you truly, with all my heart. Don't send me away."

Yes, that's the Russian character! A man may seem ordinary enough, but when trouble comes, he is endowed with a mighty strength —the beauty of the human heart.

Translated by Robert Daglish

Vladimir Bogomolov
(b. 1926)

Bogomolov was born in a village of the Moscow Region. When the war broke out, he gave his age as older than he actually was and was sent to the front. He went through the war first as a soldier and then as a reconnaissance officer, and was badly wounded several times, each time returning to the ranks.

His first short story, *Ivan*, published in 1958, brought him fame and has been translated into more than thirty languages.

Bogomolov's short stories and novellas that followed—*First Love, A Cemetery Near Belostok, Second-Rate, There Are People All Round, The Man in the Next Bed, My Heart's Pain* and *Zosya*—were regarded as new graphic pages of Soviet literature dedicated to the war theme.

In 1974, Bogomolov published a new novel, *A Moment of Truth (In August, 1944...)*. His short story, *Ivan*, is included in this edition.

Ivan

1

I intended to check the battle outposts that night, and giving orders to wake me at 4.00, I turned in a little after eight.

I was awakened earlier, however—the hands on the luminous dial pointed to five minutes to one.

"Comrade Senior Lieutenant... Comrade Senior Lieutenant." Someone was shaking me hard by the shoulder. In the dim light of the lamp glimmering on the table I saw Lance-Corporal Vasilyev of the outpost platoon. "I have a detainee here. The Junior Lieutenant told me to bring him to you."

"Turn the light up! " I ordered, and swore to myself. Surely they could have handled this themselves without bothering me.

Vasilyev turned the wick up, then faced round to me and reported:

"He was crawling about in the water near the bank. Refused to give any explanation, and demanded to be taken down to headquarters. He won't answer any questions. Says he'll only speak to the commanding officer. Looks done up, but maybe he's only kidding. The Junior Lieutenant ordered me to bring him here."

I swung my feet over the side of the bunk and sat rubbing my eyes. Vasilyev, a burly powerful fellow, stood in front of me, water dripping slowly from his sodden cape.

The brightening light illumined the spacious dug-out, and right by the door I saw a thin boy of about eleven, all blue and shivering with cold. His wet shirt and trousers clung to his body; his bare feet were caked with mud up to the ankles. The sight of him made me shiver.

"Go and stand by the stove," I told him. "Who are you?"

He came forward and stared at me with a fixed guarded look of his large wide-set eyes. He had prominent cheekbones, and his face was dark-grey with the dirt that had eaten into the skin. His wet vague-coloured hair hung down in tufts. There was a strained, suspicious and hostile look in his peaked face with its tightly compressed blue lips.

"Who are you?" I repeated.

"Tell him to go out," the boy murmured through chattering teeth, motioning to Vasilyev with his eyes.

"Put some more wood in and wait outside," I ordered Vasilyev.

Leisurely, so as to prolong his stay in the warm dug-out, he raked the stove, filled it with short billets, and slowly went out. Meanwhile, I had pulled on my boots and was looking expectantly at the boy.

"Well, why don't you speak? Where do you come from?"

"I'm Bondarev," he said quietly in such a tone of voice as if the name could mean something to me. "Notify staff headquarters, Number Fifty-One, at once that I am here."

"I see! " I couldn't help smiling. "And then what?"

"That's their business. They know what to do."

"Who are 'they'? What staff headquarters have I got to notify and who's Fifty-One?"

"Army headquarters."

"And who's Fifty-One?"

He did not answer.

"The staff of which army do you need?"

"Military post forty-nine five-five-o."

Unerringly he had given the number of the military post of our army staff. No longer smiling, I looked at him in surprise, wondering what it was all about.

The dirty shirt reaching to his hips and the short narrow trousers were old country-cut garments of coarse cloth, probably homespun, for all I knew. He spoke correctly, however, with the noticeable accent of the Muscovite or the Byelorussian. Judging by his speech he was a town-bred boy.

He stood in front of me sniffing and shivering, eyeing me with a scowling, guarded look.

"Take your things off and give yourself a rub down. Snap into it! " I ordered, handing him a towel that had seen cleaner days.

He pulled off his shirt, exposing a thin body with the ribs showing through and dark with dirt. He glanced at the towel dubiously.

"That's all right, use it. It's dirty."

He started to rub his chest, back and arms.

"Take your trousers off, too," I ordered. "You're not shy, are you?"

After a silent struggle with the damp knot, he untied the tape that served as a belt and threw off his trousers. He was quite a child yet, with narrow shoulders and thin legs and arms. He did not look more than ten or eleven, at most, although, judging by his sullen face with its look of unchildlike concentration, and his crinkled forehead, one would not give him less than thirteen. He picked up his shirt and trousers and tossed them into a corner by the door.

"Who's going to dry them—uncle?" I said.

"They'll bring me all I need."

"Is that so?" I said doubtfully. "Where are your clothes, then?"

He did not answer. I was about to ask him for his identity papers, when it suddenly dawned on me that he was too young to have any.

From under the bunk I got out an old quilted jacket belonging to my batman, who was at the battalion aid post. The boy stood by the stove with his back to me. A large birthmark, the size of a five-kopeck coin, stood out darkly between his thin protuberant shoulder-blades. Slightly above the right shoulder-blade there was a red scar, the result of a bullet wound, as far as I could tell.

"What's that on your back?"

He looked at me over his shoulder, but said nothing.

"I'm asking you—what's that on your back?" I said, raising my voice as I handed him the jacket.

"It's none of your business. And don't you shout at me! " he answered belligerently, his green eyes blazing like a cat's. Nevertheless, he took the jacket. "Your business is to report that I am here. The rest does not concern you."

"Don't teach me! " I shouted, somewhat ruffled. "You don't seem to understand where you are and how to behave. Your name doesn't tell me anything. Until you tell me who you are and where you come from and what you were doing down by the river, I shan't stir a finger."

"You'll answer for it! " his voice held a threat.

"Don't try to frighten me—you're not big enough. And this game of silence won't get you anywhere. Seriously now, where do you come from?"

He wrapped the jacket around him—it came down almost to his ankles—and turned his face away, saying nothing.

"You'll sit here all day, three days, five days, but until you tell me who you are and where you come from I'm not going to report you anywhere! " I declared flatly.

He looked at me coldly and turned away again.

"Are you going to speak?"

"You must report at once to Fifty-One at staff headquarters that I am here," he repeated doggedly.

"I must do nothing of the kind," I said irritably. "And until you explain who you are I shall do nothing. Now put that in your pipe and smoke it. Who's Number Fifty-One anyway?"

He maintained a surly concentrated silence.

"Where do you come from?" I demanded, barely able to control my rising anger. "You've got to tell me if you want me to report about you."

After a long pause of tense reflection, he squeezed out through his teeth:

"From the other side."

"The other side?" I couldn't believe it. "How did you get here, then? How can you prove you are from the other side?"

"I am not going to prove it. I'm not going to say anything more. You have no right to question me—you'll answer for it. And don't say anything on the phone either. The only one who knows I'm from the other side is Fifty-One. You must report to him at once that Bondarev is here. That's all. They'll send for me," he shouted.

"Still, maybe you'll explain who you are to have them sending for you?"

He was silent.

I studied him for a while, thinking hard. His name told me nothing at all, but they might possibly know about him at army staff headquarters. The war had taught me not to be surprised at anything.

He looked miserable and worn out, but bore himself with an air of independence, and spoke to me in a tone of assurance, I would even say authority. He did not ask, he demanded. His grim, frowning air of unchildlike concentration and watchfulness, produced a very odd impression. His statement that he had come from the other side struck me as being a barefaced lie.

I had no intention, of course, of reporting directly to army headquarters about him, but it was my duty to report to regimental HQ. I figured that they would send for him and go into the matter themselves. I'd be able to get an hour or two's sleep before going out to check the outposts.

I turned the handle of the telephone and called regimental HQ.

"Hullo, Number Three here," I heard the voice of Captain Maslov, the Chief of Staff.

"Comrade Captain, this is Number Eight reporting. I have Bondarev here. Bon-da-rev! He demands that we should report to 'Volga' about him."

"Bondarev?" Maslov queried. "What Bondarev is that? Not the major from O.P.D. on a check up, surely? What's he doing at your place?" Maslov fired off his questions, obviously disturbed.

"No, not the major. I don't know who he is myself—he doesn't want to speak. Demands I should report to 'Volga', Number Fifty-One, that he's here with me."

"And who's Number Fifty-One?"

"I thought you knew."

"We haven't got 'Volga's' call signs. Only divisional. What's his job, Bondarev's, and what's his rank?''

"He has no rank," I couldn't help smiling as I said it. "He's a boy, you see, a boy of about twelve."

"Are you trying to be funny? Who's leg are you trying to pull?" Maslov roared into the telephone. "What's this, a circus show? I'll show you a boy! I'll report it to the Major! Are you drunk, or you've got nothing else to do? I'll—"

"Comrade Captain," I shouted, flabbergasted at the turn things had taken. "Comrade Captain, I give you my word of honour it's a boy. I thought you knew about him..."

"Well, I don't and I don't want to know! " Maslov shouted angrily. "And don't you bother me with trifles. I'm not a boy to be made game of! I'm up to my ears in work, and..."

"But I thought..."

"Thought your grandmother. Stop thinking! "

"Very good! Comrade Captain, but what should I do with the boy?"

"Do with the boy? How did he get there?"

"He was detained on the bank by our outpost."

"What was he doing on the bank?"

"From what I can gather..." For a moment I hesitated. "He says he's from the other side."

"He says," Maslov mimicked. "Came in on a magic carpet, I suppose? The fellow talks out of his hat, and you swallow it all. Put him under guard! " he ordered. "And if you can't handle this thing yourself, turn him over to Zotov. It's their job, anyway, let them do it."

"Tell him if he doesn't stop shouting and doesn't report at once to Fifty-One, he'll answer for it," the boy suddenly said in a loud incisive tone.

But Maslov had put down the receiver, and I slammed mine down, too, annoyed with both the boy and Maslov.

The fact of the matter was that I was only temporarily fulfilling the duties of battalion commander, and everyone knew that I was a "temporary". What's more, I was only twenty-one, and, naturally, I was treated differently from other battalion commanders. Whereas the regimental commander and his assistants were careful not to show it, Maslov—incidentally, himself the youngest of my regimental superior officers—made no bones about the fact that he regarded me as a boy and treated me accordingly, although I had been fighting since the early months of the war and had wounds and awards.

Maslov, of course, would not have dared to speak to the command-

er of the First or Third battalions in such a tone. With me it was
different. He had gone up in the air without knowing what it was
all about. I was sure that he was wrong. Nevertheless, I said to the
boy, not without malicious glee:

"There, you asked me to report you, and I did. I've got orders
to put you under guard. Satisfied now?"

"I told you to report to Fifty-One at army headquarters, but you
didn't."

"You 'told' me! I can't apply to army headquarters over the heads
of my superiors."

"Let me ring them up then," the boy said, his hand shooting out
of the jacket and grasping the receiver.

"Don't you dare! Who are you going to phone? Who do you know
at army staff headquarters?"

He was silent for a while, still gripping the receiver, then muttered
sullenly, "Lieutenant-Colonel Gryaznov."

Lieutenant-Colonel Gryaznov was Army Intelligence Chief. I knew
him not only by hearsay, but personally.

"How do you know him?"

Silence.

"Who else do you know at army headquarters?"

Silence again, then a swift sullen glance and a muttered: "Captain
Kholin."

Kholin, an officer in Army Intelligence Section, was known to
me too.

"How do you come to know them?"

"Let Gryaznov know at once that I'm here," the boy demanded,
ignoring my question. "If you don't, I will."

I took the receiver from him, and after a moment's reflection,
turned the handle. I was put through to Maslov again.

"Number Eight again, Comrade Captain. Please hear me out,"
I said firmly, trying to control my agitation. "It's about this Bondarev
again. He knows Lieutenant-Colonel Gryaznov and Captain Kholin."

"How does he come to know them?" Maslov asked wearily.

"He doesn't say. I think this ought to be reported to Lieutenant-
Colonel Gryaznov."

"If you think so, then report it," Maslov said indifferently. "You're
always worrying your superiors with all kinds of nonsense. Personally, I see no reason for bothering headquarters, and at night of all
times. It's frivolous! "

"Allow me to phone them, then?"

"I'm not allowing anything, and don't drag me into this. On second thoughts, you can ring up Dunayev. I've just been speaking to him, he's not sleeping."

I rang up Major Dunayev, Chief of Divisional Intelligence, and told him that I had Bondarev here, and that he wanted us to report him at once to Lieutenant-Colonel Gryaznov.

"Okay," Dunayev interrupted me. "I'll report and ring you back."

Two minutes later the phone buzzed sharply.

"Number Eight?" 'Volga' on the line," said the telephone operator.

"Galtsev? Hullo, that you?" I recognised the deep gruff voice of Lieutenant-Colonel Gryaznov. It was a familiar voice to me. Gryaznov had been our Divisional Chief of Intelligence until the summer, and I was liaison officer at the time. I came in touch with him very often. "Is Bondarev with you?"

"Yes, Comrade Lieutenant-Colonel."

"Good boy! " For the moment I couldn't make out whether he meant me or the boy. "Now listen to me carefully. Chuck everybody out of the dug-out. Don't let anybody see him or bother him. No questions, and no talk about him. Get me? Give him my regards. Kholin is going out to pick him up. He'll be down in about three hours, I should think. Meanwhile, see that he has everything he needs. Treat him with tact, he's a touchy kid, you know. First of all, give him paper and ink or a pencil. Send his message to regimental HQ in a sealed envelope by reliable messenger. I'll give orders to have it forwarded on to me immediately. Make him comfortable and don't bother him. Give him some hot water to wash in and something to eat. Let him get some sleep. He's our chap. Get me?"

"Yes," I answered, although many things still puzzled me.

* * *

"Have something to eat?" was my first question.

"Later on," the boy murmured without looking up.

I then put some paper, envelopes, ink and pen on the table, went outside and ordered Vasilyev to his post, then came back again and shut the door on the hook.

The boy was sitting on the edge of the bench with his back to the red-hot stove. The wet trousers, which he had thrown into a corner, now lay at his feet. From a pinned pocket he pulled out a dirty handkerchief, unfolded it and shook out onto the table an assortment of wheat and rye grains, sunflower seeds and pine and fir needles, which he arranged in separate little heaps. Then, with an air of great concentration, he counted the contents of each heap and wrote it down on the paper.

At my approach he quickly turned over the sheet of paper and darted a hostile glance at me.

"I'm not looking, don't you worry," I said hastily.

I phoned to battalion headquarters and gave orders for two pails of water to be heated immediately and brought down to my dug-out together with a wash pot. I caught a note of surprise in the sergeant's voice as he repeated the order back to me. I told him I wanted to have a wash. As it was half past one in the morning, he must have thought, like Maslov, that I had had a drop too much or had nothing else to do. I also gave orders for Tsarivny, a smart soldier from the Fifth Company, to get ready to deliver a message to regimental headquarters.

While speaking on the telephone, I stood sideways to the table and saw, out of the corner of my eye, that the boy had ruled the paper off in lines and columns and was writing out in the extreme left column in a large childish hand: "2...4,5..." I never got to know what those figures stood for and what else he wrote down.

He wrote a long time, for about an hour, scratching away at the paper with his pen, breathing hard and covering the sheet with his sleeve. His fingers were scratched and bruised, and his nails bitten off short. His neck and ears had not been washed for a long time. Now and again he stopped, nervously biting his lips, thinking or trying to remember something, then went on writing again. Hot and cold water had been brought in—I had carried the pails and the pot into the dug-out myself without letting anyone in—but he was still scratching away with his pen. To keep the water hot I put one of the pails on the stove.

When he had finished writing, he folded the written sheets, slipped them into an envelope, licked the gummed edge and carefully sealed it. Then he took a larger envelope, put the other one into it and just as carefully sealed it.

I handed the envelope to the messenger, who was waiting outside.

"Deliver this at once to regimental headquarters. It's urgent. Report back to Krayev."

I then went back and poured some cold water in one of the pails to cool it. The boy slipped out of the jacket, got into the pot and started to wash.

I felt guilty towards him. By refusing to answer my questions he had no doubt been acting in accordance with instructions, and I had shouted at him, bullied him, tried to get information out of him that it was not my business to know. Scouts, as everyone knows, have secrets which even superior staff officers are not allowed to pry into.

Now I was prepared to wait on him like a nurse. I even wanted to wash him myself, but I couldn't bring myself to do it—he was not looking in my direction and I might not have been there for all the notice he took of me.

"Here, let me scrub your back," I offered hesitantly.

"I'll do it myself," he snapped.

There was nothing for it but for me to stand by the stove holding a clean towel and a cotton shirt, which he was to put on, and to stir the millet porridge and meat in the billycan—my supper, which, as luck would have it, I had not eaten that evening.

Washed, he turned out to be fair-haired and fair-skinned. Only his face and hands were darker from the wind or sunburn. He had small, pink, delicate ears, which, I noticed, were asymmetrical, the right one being flattened while the left one stuck out a bit. A noteworthy feature in his face were his eyes—they were large, greenish, and set very wide apart. I had never seen such wide-set eyes before.

He rubbed himself dry, and taking the shirt from my hand—I had warmed it by the stove—he put it on, carefully rolled up the sleeves and sat down at the table. His face had lost some of its hostile remoteness. He looked tired, grave and thoughtful.

I expected him to attack the food, but he only nibbled at it seemingly without any appetite and pushed the billycan away from him. Then he drank a mug of very sweet tea—I did not stint the sugar—with a biscuit from my combat rations, and got up, saying in a low voice: "Thank you."

In the meantime I had taken out the pot—the water in it was as black as ink with only greyish soap suds on top—and beaten up the pillow on the bunk. The boy got into my bed and lay down with his face to the wall and his hand under his cheek. He took everything I did for granted, and it dawned on me that this was not the first time he had returned from "the other side", and that he knew that as soon as army headquarters got to know of his arrival orders would be issued immediately to give him "VIP treatment". I covered him up with two blankets and tucked him in from all sides, like my mother used to do for me when I was a kid.

2

Taking care not to make a noise, I put on my helmet, slipped the cape over my greatcoat and went out on tiptoes, telling the sentry not to let anybody in without my order.

It was a bleak night. Although it had stopped raining, a gusty north wind was blowing, and it was dark and cold.

My dug-out was in the underbrush within half a mile of the Dnieper, which stood between us and the Germans. The high bank opposite commanded the terrain, and our main line stood back in more favourable positions. In the immediate vicinity of the river we had our outpost sub-units.

I made my way through the underbrush in the dark, guided mainly by the light of the distant flares from the enemy bank. They shot up here and there all along the German lines. Every now and then machine-gun bursts splashed into the stillness of the night. Every few minutes the Germans raked our riverside zone and the river itself by way of "preventive measure", as our Regimental Commander put it.

Coming out to the Dnieper, I made my way to the trench where our nearest outpost was located and sent for the commanding officer of the outpost platoon. When he came up, breathless, we went out together along the bank. He asked me straightaway about the "kid", probably thinking I had come in connection with the boy's detention. I quickly changed the subject, but my own thoughts kept returning to the boy.

I peered into the pool of the river, hidden in the dark. It was about half a mile wide at this spot, and I simply couldn't believe that little Bondarev had come from the other side. Who were the people who had taken him across and where were they? Where was the boat? How could the outpost patrol have missed it? Maybe they had slipped him into the water at a considerable distance from the bank? But how could they have let such a thin weak boy take the water in this cold autumn weather?

Our division was making ready to force a crossing of the Dnieper. The manual I received—and I had studied it until I knew it almost by heart—this manual, intended for grown-up healthy men, said: "But if the temperature of the water is below $+15^{\circ}C$ even a good swimmer will find it extremely difficult to swim across, and in the case of broad rivers, impossible." And what if the temperature was $+5^{\circ}$ instead of $+15^{\circ}$?

No, obviously the boat had come close to the bank, but in that case why had no one spotted it? How could it have sheered off after putting the boy ashore without being observed? I couldn't make head or tail of it.

The outpost was fully alert. Only in one fox-hole situated right next to the river did we discover a dozing soldier. He was taking a cat-nap standing up, leaning against the wall of the trench with his helmet cocked over his eyes. At our approach he clutched his tommy-gun still half-asleep, and all but triggered off a round of lead at us. I ordered him to be replaced immediately and punished, after swearing both at him and the squad commander under my breath.

After doing the rounds we sat down in a shelter recess on the right flank and had a smoke with the men. There were four soldiers in the trench, which was a large one with a machine-gun emplacement.

"Did you find out who that nipper was, Comrade Lieutenant?" one of them asked me in a husky voice. He was standing by the machine-gun, not smoking.

"What makes you ask?" I said guardedly.

"Nothing. I was just thinking there's more to this than meets the eye. You wouldn't turn a dog out o' doors in such weather, and here he goes and wades the river. Why should he do that? He may have been looking out for a boat to take him across to the other side for all we know. It looks fishy to me. I'd put the screw on that kid, I would, and make him come clean."

"It does look fishy," another soldier said rather uncertainly. "Just sits scowling like a wolf-cub and doesn't speak a word, I heard say. And why is he undressed?"

"The kid's from Novoselki," I lied, drawing slowly at my cigarette. Novoselki was a large village, half gutted, within four kilometres of us. "The Germans sent his mother away to Germany, and he doesn't know what to do with himself. The poor kid's desperate."

"Oh, so that's what it is! "

"He's heartsick, poor fellow," one of the men said with an understanding sigh. He was an elderly soldier, who squatted opposite me, smoking. The glow of his cigarette lit up his broad dark face covered with several days' growth of beard. "Must be taking it hard. Yurlov's always thinking bad of people, always trying to show how nasty they are. It isn't right," he said gently and judiciously, turning to the soldier who was standing by the machine-gun.

"I'm vigilant," Yurlov said doggedly. "And nothing you say can change me. I can't stand your goody-goody trustful people. It's because of this trustfulness that all the land from the frontiers to Moscow is drenched with blood. I've got my bellyfull! If you're so full o' the milk of human kindness, why don't you lent some of it to the Germans to grease their souls with! You tell me this, Comrade Senior Lieutenant—where are his clothes? And when all's said and done, what was he doing in the water? It's fishy, I tell you."

"Look at him, questioning his superior! " the elderly soldier said sarcastically. "Why don't you leave the kid alone? As if they won't be able to handle this without you. You'd better ask our command what they think about some vodka. It's freezing cold out here, and we've nothing to warm ourselves with. When are they going to issue some—ask him that. They'll deal with the kid without us."

I sat with the men a little longer, then recollecting that Kholin would soon be coming down, I took my leave and started back. I refused to be escorted, and shortly regretted it. In the dark I lost my way, and blundered on among the bushes, pulled up by the sharp challenging cries of the sentries. It was half an hour before I reached my dug-out, chilled by the wind.

To my surprise the boy was not sleeping.

He was sitting in his shirt, his feet lowered over the side of the bunk. The stove had long since gone out and it was pretty cold in the dug-out—you could see your breath in the air.

"Haven't they come yet?" the boy asked pointblank.

"No. You go to sleep. I'll wake you when they come."

"Did he get there?"

"Who?" I asked blankly.

"The messenger. With the dispatch."

"Yes," I said, although I did not know. After sending the messenger off I had forgotten all about him or the message.

For some moments the boy stared thoughtfully at the lamp, then suddenly, and, as it seemed to me, anxiously, he asked:

"Were you here when I was sleeping? Did I speak in my sleep?"

"No, I didn't hear anything. Why?"

"Nothing, I never used to speak. But now I'm not sure. I've become sort of nervy," he confessed.

Presently Kholin arrived. A tall, dark-haired handsome man of twenty-seven, he burst into the dug-out carrying a large German suitcase. He thrust the suitcase at me without stopping and ran up to the boy.

"Ivan! "

At the sight of Kholin the boy came to life immediately and smiled. It was the first time he had smiled, a joyful smile, like a child.

It was a meeting of friends, very good friends, and without a doubt at that moment I was one too many here. They embraced like grown-ups; Kholin kissed the boy several times, stepped back, then gripped his thin narrow shoulders, looked at him rapturous-eyed and said:

"Katasonov is waiting for you with a boat at Dikovka, and you are here."

"The place is lousy with Germans at Dikovka, you can't get near the bank," the boy said, smiling guiltily. "I swam from Sosnovka. Half way I was all in, and on top of it I got cramps. I thought it was the end."

"Don't tell me you swam across! " Kholin exclaimed astounded.

"Yes, on a log. Don't be angry, I couldn't help it. The boats were upstream and all of them guarded. Looking for that dinghy of yours in the dark would have been too risky. They'd have nabbed me in no time! I was all in, you know, and that log was twisting round and slipping away, and then my leg got cramps—well, I thought, I'm done for! The current—it carried me along, I don't know how I managed to fight clear."

Sosnovka was a hamlet upstream, on the enemy's side of the river, and the boy must have drifted nearly two miles. It was nothing short of a miracle that he didn't drown that dark October night, a weak little boy struggling in the cold stream.

Kholin swung round, shot out a muscular arm and shook hands with me. Then he took the suitcase, deposited it lightly on the bunk and clicked open the locks.

"Go and drive the car up, we couldn't get any closer. And tell the sentry not to allow anyone to come in here and not to come in himself—we don't want any witnesses. Get me?"

This pet phrase, "get me", of Lieutenant-Colonel Gryaznov had caught on not only in our division, but at army headquarters too.

Ten minutes later, after I had found the car and shown the driver how to drive up to the dug-out, I returned to find the boy transfigured.

He was wearing a little cloth tunic, evidently specially made for him, with an Order of the Patriotic War and a brand-new "For Bravery" medal pinned to it, a snow-white neckband, dark-blue breeches and neat high-boots. He looked now like a trainee—the regiment had several of them—except that he had no shoulder-straps to his tunic, and that the real trainees looked much stronger and healthier. He was perched sedately on a stool talking to Kholin. When I came in they fell silent, and I even fancied that Kholin had sent me out to see about the car so as to be able to have a talk without witnesses.

"Where have you been all this time?" he said nevertheless, looking displeased. "Get another mug and sit down."

The food he had brought with him was laid out on the table, which was covered with a clean newspaper. There was pork fat, smoked sausage, two tins of canned meat, a package of biscuits, two paper bags containing some eatables and a flask in a cloth cover. On the bunk lay a smart, brand-new, boy's size sheepskin coat and an officer's fur cap with earflaps.

Kholin cut the bread up into thin delicate slices, then poured vodka out of the flask into three mugs—half a mug each for himself and me, and a finger level for the boy.

"Here's to our meeting!" Kholin said in a brisk rollicking tone, lifting his mug.

"Here's to my always coming back," the boy said gravely.

Kholin threw him a swift glance, and proposed:

"Here's to your going to the Suvorov school and becoming an officer."

"No, that'll be afterwards! " the boy protested. "But while the war is on, it's to my always coming back! " he repeated stubbornly.

"All right, have it your way. Here's to your future. To victory! "

We touched mugs and drank. The boy wasn't used to vodka—he started coughing and tears came into his eyes, which he wiped with a furtive gesture. Imitating Kholin, he snatched a slice of bread and sniffed at it for quite a time before slowly chewing it.

Kholin deftly made some sandwiches and offered them to the boy. The latter took one and ate it slowly, reluctantly, as it were.

"You eat, come on! " Kholin said, attacking the sandwiches with relish.

"I've got out of the habit somehow," the boy sighed. "I can't."

He used the familiar "thou" in speaking to Kholin and did not seem to take any notice of me at all. Stimulated by the vodka Kholin and I were having a good tuck in, but the boy, after eating two small sandwiches, wiped his hands and mouth with his handkerchief, and murmured, "That'll do for me."   .

Kholin emptied a bag of chocolates in coloured wrappers on the table. The sight of the sweets did not bring the slightest sign of joyful animation to the boy's face, as it usually does with children of his age. He took one of the chocolates unhurriedly and apathetically, as if he had been eating chocolate candy every day of his life, unwrapped it, bit off a piece, then pushed the sweets back into the middle of the table, saying, "Help yourselves."

"No go, old chap. Not after vodka, you know," Kholin said.

"Then let's be going," the boy suddenly said, getting up and turning his eyes away from the table. "The Lieutenant-Colonel is waiting for me. Let's go! " he demanded.

"We'll go in a minute," Kholin said, somewhat disconcerted. He was holding the flask, obviously intending to replenish our two mugs, but seeing the boy get up, he put it back in its place. "We'll go in a minute," he repeated glumly and got up.

Meanwhile, the boy was trying on the fur cap.

"It's too big, drat it! "

"There wasn't any smaller size. I chose it myself," Kholin said half-apologetically. "It's only till we get there. We'll think of something."

He glanced with regret at the snacks on the table, picked up the flask, shook it, eyed me ruefully and said with a sigh, "Fancy all this stuff going waste, eh! "

"Leave it here for him! " the boy said with an expression of annoyance and scorn. "You're not hungry, are you?"

"Of course not! But this flask is class-2 supplies," Kholin turned it off with a joke. "And he doesn't need sweets."

"Don't be stingy! "

"Ah well, it can't be helped, I suppose," Kholin said, then turned to me. "Get the sentry out of the way. And take care that no one sees us."

I threw my soggy cape over my shoulders and went up to the boy. As Kholin did up the hooks of his sheepskin coat, he boasted: "I've got plenty of hay in the car—a whole haystack of it! I brought blankets and pillows, too. We'll tumble in and sleep all the way to HQ."

"Well, good-bye, Ivan," I said, holding out my hand.

"Not good-bye, but so long! " he corrected me gravely, giving me a tiny narrow hand.

The I. S.'s canvas-topped Dodge stood within ten paces of the dug-out. I could barely make it out.

"Rodionov! " I called quietly to the sentry.

"Yes, Comrade Senior Lieutenant," his hoarse voice sounded behind me, close at hand.

"Go to the staff dug-out. I'll call you in a minute."

The soldier disappeared in the darkness.

I walked round, but there was nobody in sight. The driver of the Dodge, wearing a cape over his sheepskin coat, slept or dozed over his wheel.

I went back to the dug-out, groped for the door and opened it. "Come on."

The boy and Kholin carrying the suitcase slipped past me into the car. There was a rustle of tarpaulin, a short conversation in whispered undertones—Kholin woke the driver—then the engine started up and the car moved off.

3

Sergeant-Major Katasonov, who commanded a platoon of the Division's Reconnaissance Company, turned up three days later.

He was a short lean man of over thirty, with a small mouth, a short upper lip, a small flattened nose with tiny nostrils, and grey-blue lively little eyes. It was a mildlooking, pleasant face whose gentleness reminded one of a rabbit. Katasonov was a modest, quiet, retiring man. He spoke with a pronounced lisp, and that may have been one of the reasons why he was so shy and silent in company. It was hard to believe that he was one of the army's best hunters after identification prisoners.

Seeing Katasonov reminded me of the boy Bondarev—he had often been in my thoughts these last few days. I decided, when an opportunity offered, to ask Katasonov about him. He ought to know, as it was he who had been waiting for him with a boat that night at Dikovka, where "the place was so lousy with Germans that you couldn't get near the bank".

Coming into the staff dug-out, he touched his crimson-edged trench cap and stood patiently by the door without taking off his kit-bag, waiting until I had finished telling off the clerks.

They were tied up in knots, and I was angry and exasperated, having just received a nagging lecture from Maslov over the phone. He rang me up almost every day, first thing in the morning, and always on the same business—forever demanding reports, statements, forms and diagrams in and out of schedule time. I had a suspicion that some of this accountancy is a routine of his own invention—he is a great lover of paper work.

Listening to him, one would think that if I delivered all those forms and papers to regimental headquarters punctually on time the war would quickly be over with us the victors. It all depended on me, it seemed. Maslov demanded that I put my "heart and soul" into the business. I did my best, but the trouble was we had no aides in the battalion, and no experienced clerk. As a rule, we were late and nearly always guilty of some mistake or other. I often caught myself thinking that it was easier to fight than to handle all this clerical work, and I looked forward to the time when they send us a real battalion commander who would take this job off my hands.

While I was swearing at the clerks Katasonov stood waiting quietly by the door, his cap clenched in his hand.

"Are you waiting to see me?" I asked, turning to him at last, although I had no need to ask. Maslov had warned me that Katasonov was coming, and told me to admit him to the observation post and give him every assistance.

"Yes," Katasonov said, smiling shyly. "I want to take a look at the Germans."

"All right, go ahead and look," I said graciously, after a slight pause designed to give my words more weight, and ordered the messenger to take him down to the battalion OP.

Two hours later, after dispatching my report to regimental head-quarters, I went to sample the food at battalion kitchen and made my way to the OP through the underbrush.

Katasonov was "taking a look" at the Germans through the stereo-scopic telescope. I had a look, too, although it was all familiar to me.

Across the broad sheet of the brooding Dnieper, which had a dark pitted surface in the wind, lay the enemy bank. A narrow strip of sand ran along the water's edge; above it was a terraced projecting ledge not less than a metre high and beyond it a sloping clayey bank with bushes growing here and there; at night it was patrolled by the enemy outposts. Farther up was a sheer bluff rising almost vertically about eight metres high. Along the top of this bluff stretched the trenches of the enemy's forward area. Just then only observers were on duty there, while the rest were relaxing in the shelters. By nightfall the Germans would crawl out into the trenches, keep up a desultory fire in the dark and let off flares until the morning.

On the sandy strip of bank on the other side lay five corpses. Three of them lying apart in different poses, were obviously decomposing—I had been watching them for over a week now. Two fresh corpses were seated side by side against the ledge directly facing my OP. Both were stripped of their outer clothing and had no boots on. One was wearing a striped sailor's vest which could be distinctly seen through the telescope.

"Lyakhov and Moroz," Katasonov said, his eyes glued on the eye-piece.

They were his comrades, both of them sergeants of Divisional Reconnaissance Company. He told me how it had happened in his quiet lisping voice, as he continued to look through the telescope.

Four days ago a scout party—five men—had gone over to get a prisoner. They had crossed downstream. They captured their pris-oner without making any noise, but on their way back they were spotted by the Germans. Three of them started retreating towards the boat with their captured Jerry and managed to get away. One of them was killed, though—blew up on a mine, and the prisoner was wounded by a machine-gun burst as they were getting away in the boat. The other two—Lyakhov (the one in the sailor's shirt) and Moroz kept the Germans at bay to cover their comrades' retreat.

They were killed in the fray. The Germans stripped them, dragged their bodies down to the river in the night and fixed them up so that we could see them from the other side—to teach others a lesson.

"They ought to be taken in," Katasonov finished his brief account with a sigh.

Coming out of the shelter with him I asked about Bondarev.

"Ivan?" Katasonov looked at me and a warm tender smile lit up his face. "Wonderful kid! Obstinate as they make 'em, though. Kicked up a shindy yesterday."

"Why?"

"War is no job for a kid like him, surely! They're sending him to school—the Suvorov Military School. The Commander has issued the order. But he won't hear of it. He has one answer—after the war. And now, he says, I'm going to fight, I'm going scouting."

"I can't see him doing any scouting now that the Commander has issued the order."

"Ah, there's no holding this fellow back. Hatred is burning him all up inside. If they don't send him out he'll go himself. He's done it before," Katasonov said with a sigh. Glancing at his watch he said hastily: "Oh, I've got to be off. Is this the way to artillery OP?"

A moment later he was slipping through the underbrush, carefully parting the bushes and treading noiselessly.

* * *

Katasonov spent two days and nights "taking a look" at the Germans from the observation posts of our battalion and the Third Battalion on our right, as well as from the battery lookout, and making notes and sketches in his notebook. It was reported to me that he had spent the whole night at the telescope at our OP, and he was there again in the morning, in the daytime and in the evening. I found myself wondering when the man slept.

On the third day, in the morning, Kholin arrived. He burst into the staff dug-out, greeting everyone boisterously. "Hold it, and don't say I'm stingy," he said, gripping my hand until the finger-joints crunched and I squirmed with the pain.

"I'll need you," he said, then picked up the telephone, asked to be put through to the Third Battalion and spoke to its commanding officer, Captain Ryabtsev.

"Katasonov will be coming down. See that he has every assistance. He will tell you all about it. And give him a hot meal. Now listen: if the artillerymen or anybody else ask for me, tell them I'll be at your HQ after 13.00. I'll be needing you too. Have the defence scheme ready and be on the spot."

He used the familiar "thou" in speaking to Ryabtsev, although the latter was ten years his senior. He treated me and Ryabtsev as his subordinates, although he was not our chief. It was the way he had. He spoke in exactly the same way with the officers at divisional HQ and with our regimental commander. To all of us, of course, he represented the higher staff, but there was more to it than that. Like most intelligence officers he was convinced that his particular arm of the service was the most important in the army and therefore everybody was obliged to assist him.

Even now, as he put down the receiver, he said to me in a tone of command, without taking the trouble to ask whether I was engaged or not: "Take the defence scheme and let's go and see your troops."

I did not like his offhand way of treating me but having heard a good deal about him from the scouts, who told me stories of his bravery and resourcefulness, I held my peace and forgave him what I would never have forgiven another. I had no urgent business in hand, but I purposely said I would be detained a little while at HQ, and he left the dug-out saying he would wait for me in the car.

In a quarter of an hour or so, after looking through the regimental orders file and the rifle cards, I went out. The Intelligence Section's canvas-topped Dodge was standing under some fir trees a little way off, its driver pacing up and down beside it with a tommy-gun slung from his shoulder. Kholin was sitting at the wheel with a large-scale map spread on it in front of him. Next to him sat Katasonov with the defence scheme in his hand. They were talking, but fell silent at my approach, their heads turned in my direction. Katasonov hastily jumped out of the car and greeted me with his usual shy smile.

"All right, go ahead," Kholin said to him, rolling up the map and scheme and getting out of the car. "See that everything's shipshape and have a rest. I'll be down in two or three hours."

I took Kholin down to the front line by one of the many paths. The Dodge moved off in the direction of the Third Battalion. Kholin was in a cheerful excited mood, and he strode along whistling a gay tune. It was a cold, quiet day, so quiet that you almost forgot there was a war on. But the war was there, right in front of us, with its freshly dug trenches along the edge of the wood, and a passage on the left leading down to the communication trench—a strong profile trench covered on top and carefully camouflaged with turf and shrubs and running right down to the bank. It was over a hundred metres long.

Undermanned as the battalion was, the digging of this trench at night-time (and by a single company at that) had been no easy job. I told Kholin about this, expecting appreciation of the job we had done, but he cast a cursory glance around and merely wanted to know where the battalion observation post and lookouts were located. I showed him.

"How quiet it is! " he remarked not without surprise, and took up a position behind some bushes near the edge of the wood, from where he examined the Dnieper and the bank through his field glasses. The knoll on which we stood commanded a clear view of the opposite bank. He did not seem to take much interest in my "troops", however.

Standing behind him as he examined the river, I was suddenly reminded of Bondarev.

"That boy who was at my place—who is he, after all? Where does he come from?"

"Boy?" Kholin queried absent-mindedly, his thoughts elsewhere. "Oh, you mean Ivan! Curiosity killed the cat, you know," he said. "Come on, let's try your Metro."

It was dark in the trench. Chinks had been left here and there to admit some light, but they were covered with branches. We moved through the semi-darkness with our heads slightly bent, and it seemed as if there would be no end to this damp and gloomy passage. Presently it grew lighter ahead of us and we found ourselves in the battle outpost trench within twenty yards of the Dnieper.

The young sergeant in command of the squad made his report to me as he glanced at the well set-up deep-chested figure of Kholin.

Though the bank of the river was sandy, there was squelchy mud ankle-deep in the trench, probably because the floor was at a lower level than the water in the river.

I knew that Kholin, when the mood took him, liked to chat and joke, and that is what he did now. He took out a packet of cigarettes and treated me and the soldiers to a smoke. Lighting up, he remarked cheerily:

"What a life you fellows have! You wouldn't believe there's a war on. Everything peaceful and quiet! "

"Sure, a rest-home! " machine-gunner Chupakhin, a lanky stoop-shouldered private in padded jacket and trousers said gloomily. Taking off his helmet, he stuck it on a spade handle and raised it above the parapet. Some seconds later shots rang out from the opposite bank and bullets whistled overhead.

"Sniper?" Kholin asked.

"Rest-home," Chupakhin repeated grimly. "With mud baths under the eye of loving relations."

We went back to the observation post by the same dark trench. Kholin did not like the idea of the Germans keeping such a close watch on our forward line. Although it was only natural for the enemy to be alert and watchful, Kholin suddenly grew gloomy and silent.

Back at OP he examined the right bank through the telescope for about ten minutes, asked the observers various questions, thumbed through the log-book, and swore at them for not knowing a thing and making meagre entries which gave no idea of the enemy's habits and behaviour. I did not agree with him, but said nothing.

"D'you know who they are there in the sand?" he said to me, meaning the dead scouts on the opposite bank.

"Yes."

"You mean to say you can't get them out?" he continued scornfully. "It's only an hour's job. Waiting for instructions from above, I suppose?"

Coming out of the shelter trench I asked him:

"What is it you and Katasonov are looking at all the time? Going on a raid?"

"Details will be supplied on application! " Kholin flung out without looking at me, and strode off through the wood in the direction of the Third Battalion.

I followed him.

"I don't need you any more," he announced suddenly without turning round.

I stopped, disconcerted, staring at his retreating figure, then turned back to HQ.

"Well of all the...! " Kholin's domineering manner annoyed me. Smarting from the insult, I swore under my breath. A passing soldier saluted me and looked back at me in surprise.

At HQ the clerk reported:

"The Major phoned twice. He ordered you to report."

I rang up our regimental commander.

"How are things with you?" was his first question, uttered in his calm slow voice.

"Normal, Comrade Major."

"Kholin will be calling on you. Please do the necessary and give him every assistance."

"Kholin be damned! " I said to myself.

After a pause the Major added:

"These are 'Volga's' orders. Hundred and One phoned me."

"Volga" was the Army HQ. Hundred and One was our Divisional Commander Colonel Voronov. "Who cares! " I thought. "Catch me running after Kholin! I'll do only what he asks me. I'll be hanged if I'm going to dance attendance on him! "

And so I went about my own business and dismissed Kholin from my thoughts.

In the afternoon I dropped in at the battalion medical aid post.
It was housed in two spacious shelters on the right flank next to the
Third Battalion. This arrangement was very inconvenient, but the
dug-outs and shelters which we occupied had been built and equipped
by the Germans, who least of all had us in mind.

The new medical officer, a pretty trim-looking blonde of about
twenty with bright-blue eyes, who had arrived ten days ago, saluted
awkwardly by putting her hand to the gauze kerchief tied over her
fluffy hair, and reported in a fumbling stammering way. I did not
say anything to her about it. Her predecessor, Senior Lieutenant
Vostrikov—an old army surgeon suffering from asthma—had been
killed a fortnight ago on the field of battle. He had been an experienced, brave, and efficient man. But she? So far I was anything but
pleased.

The military uniform—the spruce tunic drawn tightly round the
waist by a broad belt, the close-fitting skirt sitting snugly on her
strong hips, and the soft leather highboots on her shapely legs—
suited her admirably. Our new medical officer was a bit too good to
look at.

Incidentally, she and I were fellow countrymen—both Muscovites.
But for the war I would probably have fallen in love on meeting her,
and if she reciprocated I would have been the happiest man. I would
have dates with her in the evening, dance with her in Gorky Park and
kiss somewhere among the trees. But there was a war on, worse luck.
I acted as battalion commander and she was just the battalion M.O. as
far as I was concerned. And an M.O. who couldn't manage her job at that.

I told her in a brusque tone that there were cases of lousiness
again among the companies, that the men's underwear was not properly treated and bathing facilities had not yet been organised. I made
a number of other complaints and reminded her that she was a commanding officer, that she did not have to do everything herself, and
that she should make the company's stretcher bearers and medical
orderlies do their jobs properly.

She stood before me stiffly at attention, head lowered, reiterating
in a low, tremulous voice: "Very good ... very good ... very good"—
and assuring me that she was trying her hardest and "everything
would be all right" soon.

She looked so pathetic that I felt sorry for her. But I dare not
indulge that feeling—I had no right to pity her. That feeling was
permissible in defence, but with the prospect of our troops going into
action and forcing the Dnieper there would be dozens of wounded
in the battalion and their lives would depend a great deal on this girl

who wore the shoulder-straps of a medical service lieutenant.

It was with an uneasy mind that I left the aid post dug-out, the medical officer following me.

About a hundred paces from us, on the right, there was a knoll where the battery men had set up their OP. At the base of it, on the rear side, stood a group of officers—Kholin, Ryabtsev, battery commanders, the commanding officer of Third Battalion's mortar company, and two other officers whom I did not know. Kholin and two others were holding maps or schemes. Apparently, preparations for a trenchraid were afoot, and it looked as if it was going to be held on the section of the Third Battalion.

Seeing us, the officers turned and looked in our direction. Ryabtsev, the artillerymen and the mortar man waved a greeting to me. I waved back. I expected Kholin to hail me—seeing that I was to "give him every assistance"—but he stood sideways to me, showing the officers something on the map.

I turned to the medical officer:

"I give you two days. Put things in order and report to me."

She muttered something unintelligible. I saluted brusquely, and moved away, determined, at the first opportunity, to have her relieved. The new M.O. would definitely have to be a man.

I spent the whole afternoon in the companies, inspecting the dug-outs and shelters, checking the weapons, chatting with the men who had returned from the battalion aid post and having a game of dominoes with them.

It was nightfall when I got back to my dug-out to find Kholin there. He was fast asleep, sprawling on my bed in trousers and tunic. On the table lay a scribbled note: "Wake me at 18.30. Kholin."

I had come just in time to wake him. He opened his eyes, and sat up on the bunk.

"You know a good thing when you see it, young fellow-me-lad! " he said, yawning and stretching himself.

"What?" I said blankly.

"That medical gal of yours—nice bit o'fluff." Kholin crossed over to the corner where the wash-handstand hung and began to wash himself. "Take my advice, though, don't be seen with her in the daytime. It's no good for your reputation."

"Go to hell! " I shouted, losing my temper.

"Don't be rude, Galtsev," he said pleasantly, snorting and splashing water all round him. "Can't you take a joke? This towel of yours is dirty, she could wash it. I don't think much of your discipline."

He wiped his face on the "dirty" towel and enquired:

"Anybody asked for me?"

"I don't know, I wasn't here."

"Didn't anyone phone?"

"The Regimental Commander phoned about twelve o'clock."

"What about?"

"Asked me to give you assistance."

"*Asked* you? Now, fancy that! " Kholin said with a grin. "Pretty good arrangement, I must say." He considered me with a glance of mockery. "My dear fellow, what assistance can *you* give me! "

He lit a cigarette and went out, but soon came back again rubbing his hands and looking pleased.

"It's going to be a fine night, couldn't be better. God is merciful after all. I say, do you believe in God? Where are you off to?" he demanded. "No, don't go away, I may need you yet."

He sat down on the bunk and began to croon, repeating the same words over and over again with an air of abstraction:

> *Ah, the night's so dark,*
> *And I'm scared,*
> *See me home, Marusya.*

I spoke on the phone with the commanding officer of the Fourth Company, and when I put down the receiver I caught the sound of an approaching car. There came a tap on the door.

"Come in! "

Katasonov walked in, closed the door behind him, touched his cap and reported:

"We've arrived, Comrade Captain."

"Dismiss the sentry! " Kholin said to me, breaking off his song and getting up quickly.

We followed Katasonov out. It was drizzling. Close to the dug-out stood the familiar car under its canvas top. Waiting until the sentry had disappeared in the darkness Kholin unfastened the canvas from behind and whispered, "Ivan! "

"Yes," answered a low childish voice, and a small figure appeared from under the canvas and jumped to the ground.

4

"Good evening! " the boy said to me as soon as we entered the dug-out, and with a sudden friendly smile he gave me his hand.

He looked restored and stronger, and there was a healthy glow in his cheeks. Katasonov brushed the straw from his little sheepskin coat and Kholin enquired solicitously, "Maybe you'll lie down and have a rest?"

"What, after sleeping all day?"

"Then find us something interesting, will you," Kholin said to me. "Some magazine or something ... one with pictures in it."

Katasonov helped the boy off with his coat, and I laid out on the table several issues of *Ogonyok,* and illustrated army magazines. The boy had seen some of the magazines and he laid them aside.

Today he was unrecognisable—talkative, smiling every now and then, looking at me in a friendly way, and addressing me as he did Kholin and Katasonov, using the intimate "thou". I, too, had an extraordinarily warm feeling for this tow-headed boy. I reminded myself of a tin of fruit-drops that I had, and I got it out and placed it before him. Then I poured him out a mug of baked sour milk with a chocolate-coloured skin on top of it, and sat down next to him, looking through the magazines together.

Meanwhile Kholin and Katasonov had brought in from the car the already familiar German suitcase a big bundle tied up in a cape, two tommy-guns and a small plywood suitcase.

They pushed the bundle away under the bunk and sat down behind us, talking. I heard Kholin say to Katasonov in an undertone:

"You should hear the way he spouts Deutsch, like a regular Jerry. I wanted to use him as an interpreter last spring, and now he's commanding a battalion."

Obviously, he was referring to me. What he said was true. Kholin and Lieutenant-Colonel Gryaznov, hearing me once interrogate some prisoners by the order of Divisional Commander, tried to persuade me to go over to Intelligence Section as an interpreter. I refused and don't in the least regret it. I would have willingly taken a job in Intelligence, but not as an interpreter.

Katasonov poked the stove and murmured, "It's a wonderful night out! "

He and Kholin discussed the assignment in low tones and I learned that what they were planning was not a raid at all. It became clear to me that the boy was going behind the enemy's lines and that Kholin and Katasonov were to take him across the Dnieper that night.

For that purpose they had brought with them a "Shturmovka"—a small inflatable boat—but Katasonov was trying to persuade Kholin to take a flat-bottomed boat from my battalion. "They're handy little dinghies," he whispered.

They'd smelled it out, the devils! The battalion had five flat-bottomed fishing boats. We had been lugging them about with us these last two months. To keep them from being appropriated by the other battalions, which had only one boat apiece, I had them carefully camouflaged, kept them hidden under straw when on the march, and showed only two boats instead of five in the accountancy reports on available fording facilities.

The boy was eating candy and looking through the magazines, lending no ear to the conversation between Kholin and Katasonov. He put aside one of the magazines containing a story about scouts.

"I'm going to read this one," he said. "Haven't you got a gramophone, by the way?"

"I have, but the spring's broken."

"You people here live poor," he remarked, then suddenly asked: "Can you wiggle your ears?"

"My ears? No, I can't", I said, smiling. "Why?"

"Kholin can! " he announced with a note of triumph. He turned round, saying, "Come on, Kholin, show us the ear wiggle! "

"Anything to oblige! " Kholin sprang to his feet with alacrity, stood before us and began to wiggle his ears, while his face remained perfectly motionless.

The boy looked at me with a pleased triumphant air.

"Don't let it worry you," Kholin said to me. "I'll teach you how to wiggle your ears. And now come along and show us the boats."

"Will you take me with you?" I suddenly asked on the spur of the moment.

"Take you where?"

"To the other side."

"Look at him," Kholin said, jerking a thumb at me. "What do you want to go to the other side for?" Then, eyeing me over with an appraising look, he asked: "Can you swim, at least?"

"I can swim and row."

"How do you swim—downwards, in a vertical line?" Kholin enquired with a dead-pan expression.

"As good as you, at any rate."

"Could you swim the Dnieper, say?"

"Five times," I answered. And that was true, considering that I had in mind light-clad bathing in summer conditions. "I can swim it easily there and back five times! "

"The fellow's a rip-snorter! " Kholin said, and suddenly burst out laughing. They all three began to laugh. Rather Kholin and the boy laughed, while Katasonov smiled shyly.

Kholin suddenly grew serious.

"You don't happen to be an angler, do you?" he said.

"Oh, go to hell! " I said, losing my temper. I knew there was a catch in that question.

"There, you see," Kholin said, pointing at me, "goes right off' the handle. No self-control. Ragged nerves. And yet he wants us to take him over to the other side. Nothing doing, my dear chap."

"Then I won't give you a boat."

"We'll take the boat ourselves. Haven't we got hands of our own? If it comes to that I'll ring up Divisional Commander, and you'll lug that boat down to the river on your own hump! "

"Oh, stop it! " the boy intervened in a conciliatory tone. "He'll give us the boat. You will, won't you?" he said, looking up into my face.

"I'll have to, I suppose," I said, smiling ruefully.

"Then let's go and have a look! " Kholin said, taking hold of my sleeve. "You stay here," he said to the boy. "But don't play about, have a rest."

Katasonov put the plywood suitcase on a stool and opened it. It contained various tools, tins, rags, tow, and bandages. Before putting on my padded jacket, I hitched a commando knife with an ornamented handle to my belt.

"Gee, what a knife! " the boy exclaimed, his eyes lighting up with admiration. "Show me! "

I held it out to him. He toyed with it, then said:

"I say, let me have it! "

"I'm afraid I can't. It's a present, you see."

I wasn't deceiving him. The knife really was a present, a keep-sake from my best friend Konstantin Kholodov. Kostya and I had sat together at the same desk in school, had been called up together, had received our training at the same military school and had fought together in the same division, and later in the same regiment.

Sunrise on that September morning had found me in the trenches on the bank of the Desna. I saw Kostya with his company start ferrying across to the right bank—it was the first company in our division to do so. The rafts, made up of logs, poles and barrels, had passed midstream when the Germans opened up on the rafting site with their artillery and mortars. A white fountain of water spouted into the air over Kostya's raft. What happened after that I didn't see— the receiver in the telephonist's hand rasped: "Galtsev, forward! " I leapt over the parapet, followed by my whole company—a hundred odd men—and made a dash for the water's edge where similar rafts stood waiting. Within half an hour we were engaged in a hand-to-hand fight on the right bank.

I hadn't decided yet what I was going to do with the knife—whether to keep it, or to go down to that little street off Arbat when I got back to Moscow and give the knife to Kostya's old folks in memory of their son.

"I'll give you another one," I promised the boy.

"I want this one! " he said capriciously, peering into my eyes. "Give it to me."

"Don't be so stingy, Galtsev," Kholin flung out. He stood dressed, waiting for me and Katasonov. "Don't be mean! "

"I'll give you another one. One exactly like it," I said to the boy.

"You'll have a knife like that," Katasonov said, after examining it. "I'll get one for you."

"I'll give you one, upon my word of honour! " I assured him. "This one's a present, don't you understand—a keep-sake."

"Oh, all right," the boy said petulantly. "Let me play with it while you're gone."

"Leave him the knife and come along," Kholin said impatiently.

"Why should I go with you? What's the sense?" I said, thinking out loud, as I buttoned up my jacket. "You're not taking me with you, and you know where the boats are without me."

"Come along," Kholin pushed me. "I'll take you with me. But not today."

The three of us went out and made our way towards the right flank through the underbrush. It was raining—a cold fine drizzle of a rain. It was dark and overclouded, without a star in the sky.

Katasonov glided on ahead of us, carrying the suitcase. He trod noiselessly and so confidently that one would think he had been using this trail every night. I asked Kholin again about the boy and learned that Bondarev was from Gomel, but that before the war he had lived with his parents at a frontier post somewhere in the Baltic region. His father, a frontier-guard, had been killed on the first day of the war. His eighteen-months-old sister had been killed in the boy's arms during the retreat.

"He has been through more you and I could ever dream of," Kholin whispered. "He was with the partisans, too, and was in Trostyanets—a death camp. There's only one thing on his mind—vengeance to the last man. When he starts talking about the camp, or about his father and sister, he goes all atremble. I never thought a child could hate like that."

Kholin fell silent for a moment, then resumed in a barely audible whisper:

"We've been arguing with him for two days, trying to get him to go to a Suvorov school. The Commander has been trying too, with kind words and threats. In the end, he allowed him to go out on condition that it was the last time. The trouble is, if you don't send him out things are likely to misfire. When he first came we decided not to send him out. So he went himself. And when he was coming back our own men—the regimental outpost of Shilin's—fired on him. Wounded him in the shoulder. And you couldn't blame them. It was a dark night and nobody was in the know. You see, he does things no grownups could get away with. He brings in more than your whole Reconnaissance Company does. They nose around the German lines but can't get to the forward area. A reconnaissance party can't get behind the enemy's lines and stay there, say, for five or ten days. It is a rare scout who can manage to do that. The trouble is that an adult, no matter in what disguise, always arouses suspicion. But a kid, a homeless begging waif, is probably the best mask for reconnoitring behind the enemy's lines. You don't know him, he's an ideal kid for the job. It's been decided that if his mother doesn't turn up after the war Katasonov or the Lieutenant-Colonel are going to adopt him."

"Why not you?"

"I'd be only too glad," Kholin whispered with a sigh, "but the Lieutenant-Colonel is against it. He says I need educating myself."

I couldn't help agreeing with the Lieutenant-Colonel. Kholin was rather coarse, and sometimes inclined to be cynical. True, in the boy's presence he kept himself in check. Indeed, at times it even seemed to me that he was a bit afraid of Ivan.

About a hundred and fifty metres short of the bank we turned off into the bushes where the boats were hidden, covered up with fir branches. On my orders they were kept ready and had water sprinkled on them every other day to keep them from warping.

Kholin and Katasonov examined the boats in the light of their pocket torches, feeling over and tapping the bottoms and sides. Then they turned each boat over, got into it, put the oars into the rowlocks and began to row dry. Finally, they selected one, a small broad-sterned boat to seat three or four persons.

"We don't want these irons," Kholin said, taking hold of the chain as if he owned the boat and beginning to unscrew the ring. "We'll do the rest on the bank. First we'll try it on the water."

We lifted the boat—Kholin by the bow, Katasonov and I by the stern—and took several steps with it between the bushes.

"Oh, you're no good! " Kholin swore softly. "Heave it up! "

He hoisted the boat onto his back, bottom downwards, gripped

the gunwales with arms stretched out over his head, and strode down
to the bank in the wake of Katasonov.

I overtook them at the riverside to warn the outpost—apparently
that was all they wanted me for.

Kholin slowly stepped down to the water's edge with his burden
and stopped. Carefully, so as not to make a noise, we lowered the
boat into the water.

"Tumble in! "

We got in. Kholin shoved off and jumped in as the boat slid away
from the bank. Pulling with one oar and backing with the other,
Katasonov swung the boat round from side to side. Then he and
Kholin as if bent on capsizing it, flung their weight first on one side,
then on the other until they very nearly flooded it. After that they
got down on all fours feeling and stroking the bottom and sides.

"Handy little boat! " Katasonov whispered approvingly.

"She'll do! " Kholin concurred. "This chap's an expert at pinching
boats all right—he won't take any old rubbish! Confess, Galtsev, how
many boat-owners have you robbed?"

Every now and then bursts of machine-gun fire, like a deep hollow
bark, came across the water from the other side.

"Blazing away like mad," Katasonov whispered. "Jerry's supposed
to be a thrifty blighter, but look at all this waste! What's the sense of
blazing away blindly like this? Maybe afterwards, before dawn, we'll
be able to drag those poor boys out of it, Captain," he suggested ten-
tatively.

"Not today. Some other time."

Katasonov made for the bank, pulling an easy stroke. We all got
ashore.

"Well, we'll muffle the oars and grease the rowlock slots, and
that's that! " Kholin whispered to me. He sounded pleased. "Who
have you got here, in the trench?"

"Soldiers, two of them."

"Leave one man. A reliable one, who can keep his mouth shut.
Get me? I'll drop in on him for a smoke, and sound him out. Warn
the outpost platoon commander that at 22.00 the reconnaissance
party may possibly—don't forget to tell him that—possibly, cross
over to the other side. By that time all the posts have to be warned.
And let him be in the big trench nearest to the bank, where they have
the machine-gun," Kholin said, pointing downstream. "If they start
popping at us when we come back I'll twist his neck for him! And
not a word about who's going over, why and for what! Bear in mind,
you're the only man who knows about Ivan. I'm not taking anything

from you in writing, but if you give the show away, I'll..."

"You needn't try to frighten me! " I said resentfully. "What do you take me for, a baby?"

"Keep your hair on, old chap. There's no need to take offence." He slapped me on the shoulder. "I had to warn you. And now, get going! "

Katasonov was already busying himself with the rowlocks. Kholin went over to the boat and got busy too. I stood there for a minute, then walked off down the bank.

I ran into the outpost platoon commander a little way off. He was making the round of the trenches, checking the posts. I instructed him the way Kholin told me and went to Battalion HQ. There I gave various orders and signed some papers, then returned to my dug-out.

The boy was alone. He was all red, hot and excited. He had the knife in his hands and my field-glasses hanging from his neck. He had a guilty air. The dug-out was in disorder, with the table turned upside down and covered with a blanket and the legs of the stool sticking out from under the bunk.

"Please don't be angry," he pleaded. "It was by accident, honour bright it was! "

And then, on the floorboards, which had been scrubbed white only that morning, I saw a large ink stain.

"You're not angry with me, are you?" he said, looking up into my face.

"Of course not," I answered, although the disorder in the dug-out and the ink stain on the floor went against my grain.

I put everything back in its place without saying a word, the boy helping me. He glanced at the stain and said, "Could you get some water heated? Water and soap. I'll scrub it off."

"Never mind about that, we'll see to it."

I was feeling hungry and ordered supper for six over the phone. I felt sure that Kholin and Katasonov would be as hungry as I was after messing about with that boat.

Seeing the magazine with the story about the scouts I asked the boy, "Well, did you read it?"

"Uhu. A thriller. But things don't happen like that, if you ask me. They'd get the works right away. But these chaps get medals pinned to their chests afterwards."

"What did you get your medal for?" I asked.

"It was when I was with the partisans."

"Were you a partisan?" I said wonderingly, as if I were hearing it for the first time. "What made you leave?"

"They surrounded us in the forest, so I was flown out by airplane. Sent to a boarding school. But I soon did a bunk."

"Ran away?"

"Yes. I felt so miserable there, I just couldn't stand it any more. Eating good bread for nothing. And all you did was to cram: fishes are vertebrates, aquatic animals. Or the importance of herbivorous animals in the life of man."

"You've got to know these things too."

"You do. But what do I want it for now? What's the use of it? I stood it for nearly a month. I'd lie awake at night thinking, why am I here? What for?"

"A boarding school isn't quite the thing," I agreed. "What you need is the Suvorov school. Now if you could get into one of those! "

"Did Kholin teach you that?" the boy asked quickly, eyeing me with suspicion.

"What's Kholin got to do with it? It's what I think. You've done your share of fighting—with the partisans and in reconnaissance. You've made a name for yourself. What you need now is to take it easy and study. You know what a splendid officer you'd make?"

"Kholin taught you that! " the boy repeated with conviction. "But it's no use. I'll have plenty of time to become an officer. And while the war is on only a man who is of little use can take things easy."

"That's true, but you're still a little boy! "

"A little boy? Have you ever been in a death camp?" he suddenly demanded, his eyes blazing with a fierce, unchildlike hatred and his tiny upper lip twitching painfully. "Don't tell me what I have to do! " he shouted excitedly. "You ... you don't know a thing ... keep your advice to yourself! "

Several minutes later Kholin came in. He pushed the little plywood suitcase under the bunk, lowered himself onto the stool and began to smoke, inhaling avidly and deeply.

"Smoking all the time," the boy remarked with disapproval. He was admiring the knife, drawing it out of its sheath and shifting it from his right side to his left. "Smoking makes your lungs green."

"Green?" Kholin queried, smiling absently. "So what? Nobody sees 'em."

"I don't want you to smoke. My head will start aching! "

"All right, I'll go out."

Kholin stood up and looked at the boy with a smile. Noticing his flushed face he went up and put his hand to the boy's forehead. It was his turn now to say with disapproval:

"You've been playing about again? It's no good at all. Lie down and have a rest. Come on, lie down! "

The boy obediently lay down on the bunk. Kholin got out another cigarette, lit it from his fag end, then threw his coat over his shoulders and went out. I noticed that his hands were trembling slightly when he lit his cigarette. I may have had "ragged nerves", but he, too, felt nervous on the eve of the operation. I thought he looked sort of absent-minded and worried—observant though he was, he had not noticed the ink stain on the floor. Altogether he looked strange to me. It may have been my imagination, though.

After smoking outside for about ten minutes (obviously chain-smoking) he came back and said to me, "In about an hour and a half we'll be moving. Let's have some supper."

"Where's Katasonov?" the boy asked.

"He's been called out urgently to Divisional Commander. He's gone away."

"Gone away! " the boy sat up quickly. "Gone away without coming to see me, without wishing me good luck?"

"He couldn't. It was an urgent call—an alarm," Kholin explained. "I just can't imagine what's happened there. They know very well we need him."

"He could have dropped in for a minute. A friend, he calls himself," the boy said in a pained, agitated voice. He was genuinely upset.

He lay silent for about half a minute with his face turned towards the wall, then turned round and asked, "So only us two are going?"

"No, us three. He's going with us," Kholin said with a swift nod in my direction.

I stared at him blankly, then, deciding that he was joking, I smiled.

"You needn't grin and stare at me like a cow at a new gate. I'm talking seriously." He looked grave and even anxious.

I still refused to believe it, but said nothing.

"Didn't you want to go yourself? You asked to. And now you're funking?" he demanded. His hard contemptuous look was disconcerting.

Suddenly it dawned on me that he was not joking.

"I'm not funking! " I declared stoutly, trying to collect my wits. "It was so unexpected..." "Everything in life is unexpected," Kholin said musingly. "I wouldn't take you, believe me, but I can't help it. Katasonov has been called away urgently, you see. For the life of me I can't imagine what's happened there. We'll be back in about two hours," he assured me. "But you've got to make the decision yourself.

I don't want you to be throwing the blame on to me in case of anything. If they find out that you went across without permission we'll
both get it in the neck. So don't start whimpering afterwards: 'Kholin
said, Kholin asked me, Kholin put me up to it! ' Bear in mind, you
volunteered for the job yourself. Now you did, didn't you? In case of
anything I'll get beans, of course, but you won't get off scot-free
either. Who are you going to leave in your place?" he asked after a
short pause.

"My political assistant—Kolbasov," I said after a moment's reflection. "He's a go-ahead fellow."

"That may be. But I wouldn't have anything to do with him. Political assistants are such sticklers for principle. Before you know where
you are they'll slam you into political dispatches, and then may God
help you! " Kholin said with a grin, rolling up his eyes.

"Then Gushchin, Commander of the Fifth Company."

"You know best, decide yourself! " Kholin said. "But don't tell
him what it's all about. Only the outpost is to know that you're crossing over to the other side. Get me? Considering that the enemy is
on the defensive and no active operations on his part are to be expected, then what can happen? Nothing, really. Besides, you're leaving
someone behind, and you won't be gone for more than two hours.
Can't you go down to the village, say, if it comes to that? You're
only a man, dammit! We'll be back in two hours ... three at the most.
It's not worth talking about."

He did not have to tell me all this. Of course, it was a serious
matter, and if headquarters got to know about it there would be
ructions. But my mind was made up and I refused to think of the
consequences. I could think of nothing else but the job in hand.

I had never gone reconnoitring before. True, some three months
ago my company had carried out reconnaissance in force with no
little success. But what is reconnaissance in force? As a matter of fact,
it is an ordinary offensive action, only a brief one, conducted by
limited forces.

I had never gone reconnoitring, and naturally, the thought of it
was very exciting.

5

Supper was brought to the door. I went outside and collected
the mess-tins and teapot myself. I also put on the table an earthen-
ware pot of sour milk and a tin of cornbeef. We supped. The boy and

Kholin ate little, and I, too, was off my peck. The boy wore a pained, and somewhat sad expression. The fact that Katasonov had not come to wish him luck seemed to have hurt his feelings pretty strongly. The meal over, he went back to his bunk again.

When the table was cleared Kholin spread out his map and acquainted me with his plans.

The three of us were to cross to the other side, and, leaving the boat in the bushes, move upstream along the water's edge for about six hundred yards until we got to the ravine. Kholin pointed all this out on the map.

"It would be better, of course, to steer straight for the spot, but it's bare bank there and there's nowhere to hide the boat," he explained.

The boy was to slip through the enemy's forward line of defences by way of this ravine, which faced the positions of the Third Battalion.

In the event of his being spotted, Kholin and I, at the water's edge, were to disclose ourselves by sending up red flares—a signal to our artillery to open up—and to divert the enemy, "at all costs" covering the boy's retreat towards the boat. The last to withdraw was to be Kholin.

In the event of the boy being spotted, the "supporting weapons"— two 76-mm gun batteries, a 120-mm mortar battery, two mortar and one machine-gun companies, at our signal, were to blind and stun the enemy by an intense bombardment, laying down a barrage to keep the Germans pinned to the ground in their trenches on both sides of the ravine and farther left and to make safe our retreat towards the boat.

Kholin told me the signals for co-operation with the left bank, went over the details again, then asked: "Everything clear?"

"I think so."

After a pause I spoke to him about what was worrying me. Wouldn't the boy lose his bearings after the crossing, when left alone in the dark, and wasn't he likely to suffer in case of bombardment?

Kholin explained that "he"—a nod in the boy's direction—together with Katasonov had been studying the enemy bank at the crossing point for several hours from the positions of the Third Battalion and knew every bush, every inch of ground there. As for the bombardment, our artillery had the targets bracketed and would leave a "lane" open up to eighty yards wide.

I was thinking how many unforeseen accidents there might be, but I did not say anything. The boy lay staring wistfully at the ceiling. There was a look of distress in his face, and our conversation might not have concerned him for all the interest he took in it.

I examined the blue lines on the map—the German defences eche-loned in depth—and imagining what they looked like in reality, I asked quietly:

"Are you sure you've chosen the best crossing point? Isn't there any sector along the army's front where the enemy's defences are not so dense? Do you mean to say there are no weak spots or gaps in it, say, at the joints?"

Kholin regarded me mockingly with narrowed eyes.

"You fellows in the combat teams don't see an inch beyond your nose. You always think you have the enemy's main forces facing you, while other sectors have only a weak screen just for appearances' sake. Do you think we didn't make our choice carefully or under-stand less than you do? If you'd like to know, the whole front is oozing with Germans—there isn't room here to swing a cat. As for the joints, they're wide awake, those Germans, they're nobody's fools. There are no more fools left these days. A solid wall of defence for dozens of miles," Kholin added with a sigh. "Why, man alive, we've been over this dozens of times. These things are not decided off-hand, you can take it from me."

He got up, sat down on the bunk beside the boy and in a low voice began instructing him—not for the first time, I suspected.

"In the ravine keep close to the edge. Don't forget, the whole bottom is mined. Stop often and listen. Stop dead! The trenches are patrolled, so you creep up and wait. As soon as the patrol passes, slip across the trench and keep moving."

I rang up Gushchin, the commander of the Fifth Company, told him that I was leaving him in charge and issued the necessary orders. I hung up and heard Kholin's low voice again:

"You'll wait in Fedorovka. Don't stick your neck out. Be careful whatever you do! "

"It's easier said than done—be careful! " the boy said and there was a note of grimness in his voice.

"I know. But you've got to be. And remember always—you're not alone. Remember, no matter where you may be, I'm thinking of you all the time. And so's the Lieutenant-Colonel."

"And Katasonov went off without seeing me," the boy complained again with childish inconsistency.

"But I told you he couldn't. He was called out urgently. You know very well that he loves you. You know that he has nobody else in the world. You know it, don't you?"

"I know," the boy mumbled, and there was a catch in his voice.

"Still, he could have dropped in..."

Kholin lay down beside him, stroked his soft flaxen hair and whispered something to him. I tried not to listen. I discovered that I had lots of things to attend to and became fussily busy with little result. Then I gave it up and sat down to write a letter to my mother. I knew that all scouts, before going out on an assignment, wrote letters to their near ones. But I felt nervous and could not put my mind to it. After writing half a page with a pencil I tore it up and threw it into the fire.

"Time," Kholin said to me, glancing at his watch and getting up. He put the German suitcase on the bench, pulled the bundle out from under the bunk and undid it, and he and I began to dress.

Over his cotton underwear he put on fine woolen pants and a sweater, then a winter tunic and trousers, and on top of it all a green camouflage cloak. I followed his example. Katasonov's woolen pants were too small for me, and they ripped in the groin. I looked at Kholin irresolutely.

"Never mind! " he said encouragingly. "Go ahead! If you tear them we'll get a new pair."

The camouflage cloak was a near fit, though the trousers were a bit too short. We put on hobnailed German jackboots. I found them rather heavy, but Kholin explained that this was a precaution against leaving telltale footprints on the other side. He tied the cloak strings for me.

Presently we were all ready, with commando knives and F-1 grenades slung from our belts (Kholin also took a heavy antitank grenade, RPG-40), with loaded pistols stuck inside the belts, and with compasses and luminous dial watches hidden up the sleeves of the camouflage cloaks. The flare guns had been examined and Kholin checked the tommy-gun pans.

We were ready, but the boy was still lying with his hands under his head and his head and his eyes turned away from us.

A shabby, padded boy's jacket of a faded brownish hue, a pair of patched dark-grey trousers, a shabby fur cap with earflaps and a pair of broken-down high-boots had been extracted from the large suitcase. Linen underwear, an old jersey and socks—all darned and patched, a bedraggled little knapsack, foot-wraps and other rags were laid out on the edge of the bunk.

Kholin wrapped the boy's food up in a piece of homespun cloth. There was half a kilogram of sausage, two pieces of salted pork fat, a chunk of rye bread and several crusts of white bread. The sausage was home-made, and the pork was not our army supply, but thin, meagre-looking stuff grey from the dirty salt, and the bread, too, was home-made, baked in the hearth.

I could not help thinking how carefully every little detail had been thought out.

The food had been packed away in the knapsack, but the boy still lay there without stirring. Kholin stole glances at him, and without saying a word, began to examine the flare gun and check the pan fastenings again.

At last the boy sat up on the bunk and with slow unhurried movements began to take off his army uniform. The dark-blue breeches were soiled on the knees and the seat.

"Gum," he said. "Have them cleaned."

"How about sending them to the store and getting a new pair instead?" suggested Kholin.

"No, let them clean this pair."

The boy leisurely put on the civilian clothes. Kholin helped him, then inspected him from all sides. He looked, for all the world, like a homeless ragamuffin, a boy refugee, of whom plenty could be met along the path of the army's offensives.

The boy put away in his pocket a home-made penknife and sixty or seventy German occupation marks in crumpled notes. And nothing more.

"Let's jump," Kholin said to me.

We went through the sound test, jumping up and down several times. The boy jumped, too, although he had nothing on him that could make a noise.

Following an old Russian custom, we sat down before going. We sat for a while in silence. The boy's face had assumed its old expression of unchildlike concentration and inner tension. It was the face I had seen six days ago, when he first came into my dug-out.

* * *

After shining the red light of our signalling torches into our eyes to be able to see in the dark better, we made for the boat, I in the lead, and the boy some fifteen paces behind me, with Kholin bringing up the rear.

I was to hail everybody we met on the path and engage him in conversation to enable the boy to hide himself. Nobody else but us was to see him now—Kholin warned me about that in the most forceful terms.

On the right, out of the darkness, came quiet words of command:

"Gun crews in position! Action stations! " We could hear twigs
snapping among the bushes and men swearing softly as the crews
took up their stations at the guns and mortars scattered in the underbrush where my battalion and the Third Battalion were entrenched.

About two hundred men, besides ourselves, were taking part in
this operation. They were ready at any moment to screen us by raking
the German positions with a deadly hail of gunfire. And none of them
suspected that this was anything but a trench raid, as Kholin had been
obliged to tell the commanding officers of the supporting units.

The boat was near the outpost. It was a double sentry post, but
on Kholin's instructions I had ordered the outpost commander to
leave only one man in the trench—a middle-aged intelligent lance
corporal by the name of Dyomin. When we approached the bank
Kholin sent me forward to engage the man in conversation while he
and the boy slipped past. All these precautions seemed to me unnecessary, but Kholin's secrecy did not surprise me. I knew that all scouts
were like that.

"Mind, no comment! " Kholin warned me in a vehement whisper
as I walked ahead.

All these warnings at every step annoyed me. After all, I wasn't
a boy and had my own wits about me.

Dyomin challenged me from a distance in proper regulation style
and I answered back, walking up to the trench. I jumped down and
stood in it so that in talking to me he would have his back to the path.

"Have a smoke," I said, offering my cigarettes. He took one.

We squatted, and he began to strike damp matches until he got one
burning at last. He offered it me first, then lighted up himself. In the
glow of the match I saw someone sleeping on some hay in the shelter
recess. The trench cap looked oddly familiar. Inhaling deeply, I
switched on my torch without saying a word and saw that the man in
the recess was Katasonov. He was lying on his back, his face covered
with his cap. Still uncomprehending, I lifted it. An ashen face, gentle
as a rabbit's. Over the left eye a neat little hole drilled by a bullet.

"It was such a stupid accident," Dyomin muttered and his voice
came to me from far away. "They fixed the boat, and then sat with
me, smoking. The Captain stood here, talking to me, when the man
started to climb out. He no sooner got up than he slid slowly back
into the trench, I don't think we even heard any shooting. The Captain rushed up to him and shook him, 'Katasonov! Katasonov! ' We
looked, and he was dead, killed on the spot. The Captain said we were
not to breathe a word about it."

Now I understood why Kholin had struck me as looking rather

strange after his return from the river.

"Keep this to yourself! " I could hear his peremptory whisper from the direction of the river.

It was clear to me now. On no account was the boy to be upset now, when he was going out on his assignment. He was not to know anything.

I clambered out of the trench and slowly descended to the river bank.

The boy was already in the boat, and I got in beside him in the stern with my tommy-gun at the ready.

"Sit evenly," Kholin whispered as he covered us up with a cape. "See the boat doesn't list."

He pushed off, jumped in and took the oars. Glancing at his watch, he waited a little longer, then whistled softly. This was the signal for starting the operation.

The signal was answered immediately by the crack of a rifle in the darkness coming from the big machine-gun trench on the right where the commanders of the supporting units and the artillery observers were.

Kholin swung the boat round and started rowing. The bank disappeared immediately. Cold night wrapped its murky cloak about us.

6

I could feel Kholin's hot measured breathing in my face. He was driving the boat forward with powerful strokes, and soft splashes could be heard as the oars hit the water. The boy sat beside me without stirring, hidden by the cape.

On the right bank ahead of us the Germans, as usual, were sweeping their front-line area with desultory fire and sending up flares to illuminate the terrain. The flashes were not very bright owing to the rain. The wind, too, was blowing against us. So far the weather was favourable.

A burst of tracer bullets rose over the river from our side. The Third Battalion on the left flank was to give such tracer streaks every five to seven minutes to help us take our bearings on the way back.

"Sugar! " whispered Kholin.

We each put two lumps of sugar into our mouths and sucked away at them. This was supposed to sharpen our keenness of sight and hearing.

We must have been in midstream when a machine-gun started chattering in front of us. The bullets whizzed close around us, smacking the water and sending up a hissing spray.

"MG-34," the boy whispered unerringly, snuggling up to me. "Scared?"

"A bit," he confessed in a barely audible voice. "I can't get used to it. Nerves, I suppose. Begging, too—I just can't get used to it. It's sickening! "

I could easily imagine how humiliating it was to this proud touchy boy to have to go about begging.

"By the way," I whispered, recollecting, "we have a Bondarev in our battalion. A Gomel man, too. He isn't a relative of yours by any chance, is he?"

"No, I have no relatives. Only my mother. And I don't know where she is either." His voice shook. "And my name is really Buslov, not Bondarev at all."

"And your first name isn't Ivan?"

"It is. That's my right name."

"Sh! "

Kholin began to row more slowly. Apparently we were nearing the bank. I peered into the darkness until my eyes ached, but all I could make out through the mist of rain were the dull flashes of the flares.

We were barely moving along. In a moment the boat scraped on the sand. Kholin, with swift agile movements, boated the oars, stepped into the water and pulled the boat round stern-on to the bank.

For a couple of minutes we strained our ears, listening. I could hear the raindrops pattering on the water, on the ground and the now sodden cape. I could hear Kholin's regular breathing and the beating of my own heart. But not a single suspicious sound did we catch. Kholin whispered into my ear.

"Ivan stays where he is. Get out and hold the boat."

He vanished in the darkness. Cautiously, I crawled out from under the cape, stepped into the water onto the sandy bank, readjusted my submachine-gun, and took hold of the boat at the stern end. I could feel the boy stand up in the boat beside me.

"Sit down. I'll cover you with the cape," I whispered, groping for his hand.

"It doesn't matter now," he answered in a low voice.

Kholin suddenly reappeared and coming close up, said in a joyful whisper:

"Okay! The coast is clear! "

It appeared that the bushes at the water's edge where we were to leave the boat were only about thirty paces downstream.

A few minutes later the boat was hidden and we crept along the bank, stooping low and halting from time to time to listen. When a flare shot up nearby we dropped onto the sand under the projecting ledge and lay motionless like dead men. Out of the corner of my eye I could see the boy, his clothes dark with the rain. Kholin and I would return and change, but he...

Suddenly Kholin slackened his pace and taking the boy's hand drew him back into the water. Ahead of us on the sand light shapes appeared. "The bodies of our scouts," I guessed.

"What's that?" the boy asked.

"Jerries," Kholin whispered quickly, hurrying forward with the boy. "A sniper from our side got 'em."

"The dirty skunks! They even strip their own men! " the boy muttered with hatred, glancing back over his shoulder.

It seemed to me as if we had been moving an eternity and that we should have reached the spot long ago. I reminded myself, however, that it was about four hundred yards from the bushes where the boat was hidden to where these bodies lay. And we were still about the same distance from the ravine.

Presently we passed another corpse. It was in an advanced stage of decay and gave off a sickly smell from a distance. A tracer streak pierced the pall of rain behind us. The ravine was somewhere close at hand, but we could not see it. They did not use flares there probably because the whole bottom was mined, and the brow of the ravine was honeycombed with trenches and patrolled. The Germans, apparently, were sure that nobody would poke his nose in here.

This ravine was a good trap to anyone spotted in it, and our plan was based on the boy being able to slip through unobserved.

At last Kholin stopped, and motioning to us to sit down, he went on ahead.

Soon he reappeared and commanded in a whisper, "Follow me! "

We moved on about another thirty paces and squatted on our heels beyond the projecting bank.

"The ravine is straight ahead of us," Kholin said. He turned back the sleeve of his camouflage cloak and glanced at the luminous dial of his watch. "We have another four minutes. How are you feeling?" he whispered to the boy.

"O'kay! "

For a time we sat listening, straining our ears in the darkness. There was a smell of decay and dampness. One of the corpses—it was visible in the sand some three yards to our right—evidently served Kholin as a guiding landmark.

"Well, I'll be going," the boy whispered.

"I'll see you off a bit," Kholin suddenly whispered. "Through the ravine. Just a bit."

This was not according to plan at all.

"No! " said the boy. "I'm going alone. You're too big, they'll get you."

"What about me going?" I offered irresolutely.

"Let me see you through the ravine at least," Kholin almost pleaded. "It's clayey there, you'll leave footprints. I'll carry you through."

"I told you, no! " the boy declared obstinately and angrily. "I'm going alone! "

He stood beside me, a thin, pathetic little figure, trembling all over, as it seemed to me, in his shabby old clothes. Or was it just my imagination?

"So long," he said to Kholin after a pause.

"So long! " (I could feel them embracing, and Kholin kissed him.) "Be careful whatever you do! Look after yourself. Wait for us at Fedorovka."

"So long! " the boy turned to me this time.

"So long! " I whispered with deep emotion, finding the boy's slim little hand in the darkness and squeezing it hard.

I wanted to kiss him, but hesitated for a moment. I was terribly agitated, and had been repeating to myself at least a dozen times "So long! " to keep from blurting out "Good-bye" as I had done six days ago.

Before I could make up my mind to kiss him he had vanished noiselessly in the darkness.

7

Kholin and I crouched close against the bank, the projecting ledge of which hung over our heads, and listened intently. The rain came down in a slow steady patter, a cold autumn rain that seemed as if it would never end. A chilling dampness drew from the river.

Four minutes had passed since we were left alone, and from the direction in which the boy had gone we caught the sound of footsteps and a muffled conversation in guttural tones.

"Germans?"

Kholin gripped my shoulder, but the warning was unnecessary. I had caught the sounds before he had, and slipped off the safety catch of my tommy-gun. I froze into silence with a grenade clutched in my hand.

The footfalls drew nearer. The mud could now be heard squelching under the feet of several men. My mouth went dry and my heart hammered wildly.

*"Verfluchtes Weter! Hohl es der Teufel..."**
*"Halte's Maul, Otto! Links halten! "***

They passed so close to us that splashes of cold mud fell upon my face. A moment later, in the light of a flare, we could make out their figures through the mist of rain—tall figures (or so they seemed to me, looking upwards) in helmets over cap comforters, and heavy jackboots similar to those Kholin and I were wearing. Three of them wore ground-sheets, and the fourth a long raincoat glistening with rain and with a belt and holster drawn round the middle. They had tommy-guns slung from their shoulders.

There were four of them—the outpost patrol of an SS regiment, a combat patrol of the German army, past whom had just slipped Ivan Buslov, the twelve-year-old boy from Gomel, who went under the name of "Bondarev" in our intelligence files.

When we saw them in the flickering light of the flare they were on the point of descending to the water's edge within ten paces of us. In the darkness we could hear them jumping down onto the sand, then moving on towards the bushes where our boat lay hidden.

I was finding it harder than Kholin. I was not a scout, and had been fighting since the first months of the war. At the sight of the enemy, a live enemy with a gun, I was seized instantly with that excitement of the trigger-happy fighting man that I had so often experienced before. My first impulse, my first burning, irresistible desire, was to kill that enemy there and then. I'll kill them, I'll lay out the whole bunch with a single burst of my gun—I must have been thinking of nothing else but this as I swung my gun round. But Kholin had been thinking for me. Sensing my movement in the dark he gripped my arm in a vice. Collecting myself, I lowered my tommy-gun.

"They'll spot the boat! " I whispered, rubbing my arm, as soon as their footsteps receded.

Kholin was silent.

"We must do something," I whispered again anxiously after a short pause. "If they find that boat..."

"If! " Kholin breathed into my face in a fury. I felt he could have

*"Accursed weather! What the devil..." (*German*)—*Auth*.
**"Hold your tongue, Otto. Keep to the left." (*German*)—*Auth*.

strangled me. "And if they get the boy! What d'you think, we're going to leave him in the lurch? What are you, a cad, a swine or simply a fool?"

"A fool," I whispered after a pause.

"Probably a neurasthenic," Kholin muttered half-musingly. "When the war's over you'll have to take a cure."

I listened tensely, expecting every moment to hear the exclamations of the Germans on discovering the boat. On our left a machine-gun chattered, followed by another directly overhead. In the ensuing silence we could hear the steady patter of the rain. Flares shot up here and there at intervals along the whole line of the bank. They blazed, hissed and faded before they reached the ground.

The sickening smell of putrefaction for some reason grew stronger. I spat and tried to breathe through my mouth, but it didn't help much.

I was dying for a smoke. Never in my life had I yearned so much for one. But all I could do was to pull out a cigarette and smell it by crushing it between my fingers.

Before long we were drenched wet and shivering from the cold, but the rain did not stop for a moment.

"The ground's clayey in the ravine, damn it! " Kholin suddenly whispered. "A good downpour would wash away the footprints."

In thought he was with the boy all the time, and the clayey soil in the ravine, which would preserve the tracks, worried him. He had good reason to worry, I realised. If the Germans discovered those fresh and strikingly small footprints running from the bank through their forward positions they would certainly hunt Ivan down. Maybe with dogs. Trust the SS regiments to have dogs specially trained for hunting people.

I was now chewing the cigarette. It was anything but pleasant, but I went on chewing. Kholin must have heard me, because he asked, "What are you doing?"

"I'm dying for a smoke! " I sighed.

"Don't you want your mummy?" Kholin said sarcastically. "I wouldn't mind going home to mummy. Not bad, eh?"

We waited another twenty minutes or so, cold, wet and shivering. My shirt was like an icy compress on my back. The rain gradually turned to snow, and its soft wet flakes covered the sand with a white shroud that melted reluctantly.

"Well, I think he's made it," Kholin murmured in a tone of relief and stood up.

Bending low and keeping close to the projecting ledge we started off towards the boat, stopping every now and then to listen. I was almost positive that the Germans had discovered the boat and were lying in ambush there among the bushes, but I dare not tell Kholin this for fear of his ridicule.

We crept along the bank in the dark until we ran into the bodies of our scouts. We had moved no more than five paces from them when Kholin stopped, and pulling me towards him by my sleeve, he whispered into my ear:

"You stay here. I'll go and fetch the boat. There's no need for both of us to run risks. Hail me in German when you hear me coming. Very quietly, though. If I get into trouble, there'll be a racket—so swim across. If I don't come back in an hour, swim across anyway. You can swim there and back five times, can't you?" he said mockingly.

"I can," I confirmed in a trembling voice. "But say you're wounded?"

"Never mind about that. Cut the cackle."

"It would be better to get at the boat not from the bank but by swimming up to it from the river," I remarked rather uncertainly. "Let me do it."

"That's what I'll do, probably. In case of anything, don't you start butting in! If anything happens to you we'll get it hot. Get me?"

"Yes, but what if..."

"There are no 'ifs' about it! You're a good chap, Galtsev," he suddenly whispered, "but you're a neurasthenic. And in our line of business that's a terrible thing."

He vanished in the dark, and I was left waiting. I don't know how long I waited—it seemed an eternity. I was freezing and felt so nervous that it did not even occur to me to glance at my watch. Taking care not to make the slightest noise, I worked my arms vigorously and flexed my knees in an attempt to keep warm. Every now and then I stopped to listen.

At last I caught a faint splash, and cupping my hands over my mouth, whispered in German, "Halt. Halt."

"Shut up! Come over here."

Treading gingerly, I took several steps, and the cold water ran into my boots, enfolding my feet in an icy embrace.

"How are things at the ravine—quiet?" was Kholin's first question.

"Yes."

"There, you see. And you were scared," he whispered, pleased. "Get in at the stern end," he commanded, taking my gun from me, and as soon as I got into the boat he started rowing, pulling against the stream.

Seated in the stern, I pulled off my boots and poured the water out of them.

It was snowing heavily, thick snowflakes that melted as soon as they touched the river. From the left bank came another tracer streak. It passed directly overhead. We had to turn round, but Kholin continued to drive the boat upstream.

"Where are you going?" I asked.

He pulled hard without answering. I repeated my question.

"Here, take a swig," he said, handing me a small flat flask.

With difficulty I unscrewed the top with freezing fingers and swallowed some of the vodka. It left a pleasant burning sensation in my throat and I felt warm inside, but I could not stop shivering.

"Knock it all back! " Kholin whispered, barely plying the oars.

"What about you?"

"I'll have a drink when we get back. Will you treat me?"

I took another swig, and finding, to my regret, that the flask was empty, I thrust it into my pocket.

"What if he hasn't gone through yet?" Kholin suddenly said. "What if he's lying there, waiting. I wish I could be with him there now! "

I realised then why we were dawdling. We were opposite the ravine so as to be able, "in case of anything", to land on the enemy bank and come to the boy's rescue. From there, out of the darkness, long bursts of machine-gun fire swept the river at regular intervals. Every time the whistling bullets smacked the water alongside the boat I flinched. It was probably impossible to spot us in this darkness, through the pall of wet snow, but it was a nonetheless damnably unpleasant experience to find oneself exposed to the enemy's fire on an open patch of water where one could not dig in or seek shelter. Kholin tried to cheer me up, whispering:

"Only a fool or a coward can stop crazy bullets like these. Bear that in mind! "

Katasonov had been no fool, nor coward—I was sure of that, but I did not say anything.

"That M.O. of yours is a peach! " he resumed after a while, evidently wishing to distract me.

"N-n-not bad," I concurred through chattering teeth, least of all thinking of that medical officer. If I was thinking of anything it was the aid post's warm dug-out and the stove. That lovely iron stove!

Three more tracers were given on the left bank, that desirable bank, which spelt safety and warmth. They were signalling to us to return, but we were still lingering on the water closer to the right bank.

"I daresay he's made it," Kholin said at last, swinging the boat round with vigorous strokes.

He took his bearings and steered with remarkable accuracy in the darkness. We made for the vicinity of the large machine-gun trench on the right flank of my battalion, where the outpost platoon commander was.

They were waiting for us, and challenged us quietly but commandingly: "Halt! Who goes there?" I gave the password. They recognised my voice, and in a moment we stepped ashore.

I was completely done up, and although I drank a full tumbler of vodka I was still shivering and could barely drag my freezing feet. Trying to keep my teeth from chattering, I gave orders for the boat to be pulled in and camouflaged, and we started down the bank, accompanied by squad commander Sergeant Zuyev, my favourite, happy-go-lucky man of reckless bravery. He was walking in the lead.

"But where's the prisoner, Comrade Senior Lieutenant?" he suddenly asked, turning round.

"What prisoner?"

"They said you were going out to get a prisoner."

Kholin, who was walking behind, pushed me aside and strode up to Zuyev.

"You'd better keep your tongue about prisoner! Get me?" he said grimly, clipping his words. I even thought he clapped his heavy hand down on Zuyev's shoulder or maybe gripped his collar. Kholin was like that—he was much too blunt and quick-tempered. "Keep your tongue between your teeth! " he repeated threateningly. "You'll find it healthier! And now go back to your post! "

Zuyev was still well within earshot when Kholin said in a deliberately loud stern voice:

"You've got too many tongue-waggers in your battalion, Galtsev! In our line of business that's a terrible thing."

He slipped his arm through mine in the darkness, squeezed my elbow and whispered mockingly:

"You're a fine one, too! Fancy chucking your battalion to go sneaking off to capture a prisoner! "

* * *

Back in the dug-out we got the stove blazing with the aid of spare mortar charges, then stripped naked and rubbed ourselves down with towels.

Putting on dry underwear, Kholin slipped his coat over his shoulders and sat down at the table where he closely examined the map he had spread out on it. He seemed to have wilted the moment he came into the dug-out. He looked tired and worried.

I put some food on the table—a tin of cornbeef, pork fat, a billycan with pickled cucumbers, bread, sour milk and a flask of vodka.

"Oh, I wish I knew how he's getting on there! " Kholin suddenly exclaimed, getting up. "I wonder what's the matter?"

"Why?"

"That patrol—on the other side—it was due to pass half an hour later. Understand? That means, either the Germans have changed their outpost routine, or else we've made a mess of it. In either case the kid may pay for it with his life. I can't understand—we had it all worked out to the minute."

"But he's made it. We were waiting so long—close on an hour—but everything was quiet."

"Made what?" Kholin said irritably. "If you'd like to know he's got to cover over thirty miles. About thirteen of them he has to make before sunrise. At every step he may run into the Germans. And how many unforeseen things may happen! Ah, well, talking about it won't help! " He removed the map from the table. "Come on! "

I poured vodka into two mugs.

"No clinking, please," Kholin warned me, taking one of the mugs. We sat for several moments in silence with raised mugs.

"Ah, Katasonov, Katasonov! " sighed Kholin, scowling at me and adding with a catch in his voice, "He's nothing to you! But he saved my life, he did."

He tossed off the vodka at a single gulp, took a sniff at a piece of black bread and demanded, "Some more! "

I drank my own, and refilled the mugs—his full to the brim and mine just a little. Picking up his mug he turned towards the bunk on which lay the suitcase with the boy's things in it, and uttered quietly:

"Here's to your coming back and never going out again. Here's to your future! "

We drained the mugs and started on the snacks. Unquestionably, we were both thinking of the boy at that moment. The sides and top of the stove were red-hot. We had come back and were sitting here warm and safe, while he was out there, in the enemy's lines, crawling through the snow and murk with death lurking at every step.

I had never had any special love for children, but this boy—though I had met him only twice—had grown so near and dear to me that I could not think of him without a pang.

I did not drink any more. But Kholin drained his third mug in utter silence. Soon he got tipsy, and sat with a brooding air, glancing at me gloomily with inflamed eyes.

"Been fighting over two years, you say?" he muttered, lighting a cigarette. "So have I. But we haven't looked death in the face, at least not the way Ivan has! You have a battalion, a regiment, a whole army behind you. But he's all on his own! " Kholin shouted this out in a flash of anger. "A child! And you grudged him that lousy knife! "

8

"Grudged him! " No, I couldn't, I had no right to give that knife to anyone. It was a keepsake, the only memory of a dead friend.

I kept my word, however. There was a handyman, a fitter, working in the divisional ordnance workshop, an elderly sergeant from the industrial Urals. Last spring he had carved a handle for Kostya's knife, and I now asked him to make a similar one and set it on a brand-new commando knife which I gave him. I not only asked him, I brought a box of tools—a vice, drills, chisels of German make—spoils of war. I did not need them, and he was delighted as a child.

He made a splendid job of that handle, and the knife could be distinguished from Kostya's only by the absence of notches on the blade and the owner's initials "K.K." carved on the knob. I pictured to myself how pleased the boy would be to get a real commando knife with such a fine handle. I understood him. I was out of my teens myself not so very long ago.

I wore the knife on my belt, figuring on handing it over to Kholin or Lieutenant-Colonel Gryaznov as soon as I met them—I could hardly expect to meet Ivan myself. Where could he be now, I often wondered, thinking of him.

These were hectic days. The divisions of our army were forcing the Dnieper, and as the Informbureau communiques reported, "were waging successful battles to widen the bridgehead on the right bank".

I hardly made any use of the knife, not counting the hand-to-hand fight when I used it on that burly corporal from Hamburg who would otherwise have cracked my head open with his spade.

The Germans put up a desperate resistance. After eight days of heavy offensive battles we received orders to take up a defensive position. It was then, on a bright cold day early in November, just on the eve of the revolutionary holiday, that I met Lieutenant-Colonel Gryaznov.

A man of medium height with a large head on a thickset body, wearing a greatcoat and fur cap with earflaps, he walked up and down the roadside slightly dragging his right leg, which had been wounded in the Finnish campaign. I recognised him from afar as soon as I came out on the edge of the wood where the remnants of my battalion stood. I could say "my" battalion now with full right, as I had been confirmed in my appointment as battalion commander on the eve of the forcing.

It was quiet in the wood. The ground was covered with hoarfrosted leaves, and the place smelt of horse dung and urine. A Cossack corps had taken part in the break-through on this section, and the wood had been their bivouac site. The smell of horses and cows was associated in my mind since childhood with that of new milk and hot bread fresh from the oven. It brought back memories of the country, where, as a child, I used to spend every summer with my grandmother, a dried-up little old lady who simply doted on me. It was not long ago, really, but it seemed so far away now, far away and never-to-be-repeated, like everything pre-war.

Childhood memories left me as soon as I emerged from the wood. The road was cluttered with German vehicles, burnt, wrecked or simply abandoned. The German dead lay strewn about the roadway and in the ditches in a variety of attitudes. Grey mounds of corpses could be seen everywhere in the trench-gashed field. In the roadway, some two hundred feet from where Lieutenant-Colonel Gryaznov stood, his driver and interpreter—the latter with the shoulder straps of a lieutenant—were busy doing something in the body of a German armoured carrier. Four others, whose ranks I could not make out, were searching among the trenches on the other side of the road. The Lieutenant-Colonel was shouting something to them, but I could not make out what it was owing to the wind.

As I approached, Gryaznov turned to me a swarthy, pock-marked, fleshy face and cried out in a gruff voice that sounded surprised or pleased, "Hullo Galtsev, you're alive?"

•"Alive and kicking, as you see! " I smiled. "How do you do?"

"How do you do? Glad to see you! "

I shook his proffered hand, then looking round to make sure there was no one else about, I asked:

"Comrade Lieutenant-Colonel, may I ask a question—has Ivan come back?"

"Ivan? Ivan who?"

"That boy, Bondarev."

"What's it to you whether he's back or not?" Gryaznov said with a frown, studying me with black shrewd eyes.

"Well, considering that I helped him across..."

"What's that got to do with it! Everyone knows what he's supposed to know. That's law for the army, and especially for intelligence."

"But I'm not asking this officially. It's purely personal. Will you please do me a favour? I promised to give him this..." I undid my coat, took the knife off my belt, and handed it to Gryaznov. "Please give this to him. If you only knew how he wanted it! "

"I know, Galtsev, I know," the Lieutenant-Colonel sighed, taking the knife and examining it. "Not bad. But I've seen better ones. He has about a dozen of these knives, if not more. He's collected a box-ful. Has a passion for them, you know. He's at that age. A kid, what can you expect! All right, I'll give it to him when I see him."

"Then ... he hasn't come back?" I said agitatedly.

"He came back, and went away again. Went away himself."

"What do you mean?"

Gryaznov frowned and stared into the distance in silence. Then in a deep, husky voice he said quietly:

"We were sending him to school and he seemed to agree. In the morning we were to have his papers ready for him, but during the night he went away. I don't blame him. It's a long story and there's no need for you to know it." He turned his large pock-marked face to me. It was stern and thoughtful. "The hatred hasn't burnt out of him yet. He can't find any peace. Maybe he'll come back, but most likely he'll join the partisans. I advise you to forget about him, and remember this in future—never ask questions about our men behind the lines. The less said about them and the less people there are in the know, the longer they live. You met him just by chance, and—forgive my saying it—you're not supposed to know anything about him. So please remember in future—you know no Bondarev, there is no such person, and you've never seen or heard anything. And you've helped no one across! So there are no questions to ask. Get me?"

And I asked no more questions. There was no one to ask them of, for that matter. Kholin was killed shortly afterwards during a scout mission. His party ran into a German ambush in the gloom of a grey pre-dawn and Kholin was hit in both legs by a machine-gun burst. He ordered all his men to withdraw and kept the enemy at bay till the last. And when he was captured he exploded an antitank grenade. As for Lieutenant-Colonel Gryaznov, he was transferred to another army and I never met him again.

But naturally, I could not forget about Ivan, as the Lieutenant-Colonel had advised me. I often thought of the little scout, but never thought I would ever meet him or learn something about his fate.

9

During the fighting at Kovel I was badly wounded and became a "limited service man", allowed to be employed only as a noncombatant in unit staffs or rearward services. I had to say good-bye to my battalion and my division. During the last six months of the war I worked as interpreter in Corps Intelligence on the same First Byelorussian Front but in another army.

When the battle for Berlin started I and two other officers were detailed to one of the operational groups that had been specially organised for the seizure of German archives and documents.

Berlin surrendered on May 2 at 3 p.m. Those historic minutes found our group in the centre of the city, in a half-demolished building in Prince Albrechtstrasse, only recently the headquarters of Gestapo, the German secret police.

As was to be expected, most of the documents had been removed or destroyed. Only on the third, top, floor did our men discover filing cabinets and a huge card-index with their contents intact. This find was announced with a joyous shout from the window by the tommy-gunners who were the first to enter the building.

"Comrade Captain, there's a truckload of papers out there in the yard! " a broad-shouldered dumpy little soldier reported running up breathless.

The vast yard of the Gestapo, now littered with stones and debris, had been used as a garage for dozens or maybe hundreds of cars and lorries. A few of these remained, wrecked by explosions. I glanced around: a dug-out shelter, dead bodies, bomb holes, in a corner of the yard sappers with a mine-detector.

Near the gate stood a tall lorry with gas-generators. The tail-board was down, and inside, covered with a tarpaulin, was the body of an officer in the black uniform of the SS and thick files and dossiers tied up in packages.

The soldier clambered into the lorry and dragged the packages to the edge. I cut the ersatz-strings with my commando knife.

There were documents of the S.F.P.—the Secret Field Police—of the Army Group Centre, dating to 1943/44. Reports on punitive "actions", agents' messages, search orders, identification records, copies of various dispatches and secret reports, all telling their story of heroism and cowardice, of people shot and of people who had avenged them, of people who had been caught and people who had not. To me these documents were of special interest. Mozir and Petrikov, Rechitsa and Pinsk—before me rose all those familiar places in the Gomel and Polesye districts through which our front line had passed.

The files contained no few registration forms with brief information concerning the people whom the secret police were searching for, or had hunted down. Some of these forms had photographs attached to them.

"Who is this?" The soldier standing in the lorry poked a stubby finger at the different forms, asking me: "Comrade Captain, who is this?"

Without answering him, in a sort of daze, I turned over sheet after sheet, going through one file after another, oblivious of the rain that was wetting us. Yes, on that glorious day of our victory it was raining in Berlin, a thin, cold drizzle from a grey sky. The weather did not break until late in the afternoon, when the sun peeped out through the smoke and mist.

After the shattering noise of ten days' furious fighting silence now reigned, broken here and there by tommy-gun bursts. Fires raged in the centre of the city, and whereas, in the suburbs, where there were many gardens, the scent of the riotous lilac overpowered all other smells, here there was a strong smell of burning and black smoke drifted over the ruins.

"Carry it all into the building! " I said at last, pointing to the packages, while I automatically opened the file I was holding in my hand. I glanced at it, and my heart stood still. Looking at me from the photograph pasted to the form was Ivan Buslov.

I recognised him at once by those high cheekbones and the grey wide-set eyes—I had never seen eyes set so wide apart.

He wore a scowl, as he did that time I first met him in the dug-out on the Dnieper. A bruise made a dark patch on his left cheek.

The form with the photograph on it had not been filled in. With a sinking heart I turned it over—pinned to the bottom was a sheet of paper with a typewritten text, the copy of a special report from the Chief of the Secret Field Police of the Second German Army. Here it is:

"Town of Luninets. 26.12.43. Secret.

"To the Chief of Field Police, Army Group Centre.

"On December 21, 1943, Yefim Titkov of the auxiliary police detected, and, after two hours' observation, detained a Russian schoolboy of 10 or 12 in the restricted area of our 23rd Army Corps near the railway line, who was lying in the snow and watching the movements of military trains on the Kalinkovichi-Klinsk section.

"The unknown detainee (it was later established that he had given his name as 'Ivan' to a local inhabitant Maria Semina) offered a fierce resistance, biting Titkov's hand, and it was only with the assistance of Corporal Wintz, who happened upon the scene, that the boy was taken to the field police...

"...it has been established that 'Ivan' spent several days and nights in the lines of the 23rd Corps ... went about begging ... slept in an abandoned threshing-barn and in sheds. His fingers and toes were frostbitten and partially affected by gangrene...

"On being searched 'Ivan' was found to have in his pockets a handkerchief and 110 (one hundred and ten) occupation marks. No material evidence was found that he belonged to the partisans or engaged in spying... Distinctive marks: a large birthmark down the middle of the spine, and a scar over the left shoulderblade—the result of a bullet wound.

"Interrogated with all thoroughness and strictness in the course of four days and nights by Major von Bissing, Ober-Leutnant Klammt and Sergeant-Major Stammer, 'Ivan' gave no evidence that would have helped to establish his identity or ascertain what reasons he had for being in the restricted area and in the lines of the 23rd Army Corps.

"During the interrogations he bore himself in a defiant manner, and did not conceal his hostile attitude towards the German army and the German empire.

"In accordance with the Instructions of the Supreme Commander-in-Chief dated November 11, 1942, the detainee was shot on 25.12.43 at 6.55. a.m.

"...a reward of 100 (one hundred) marks was issued to Titkov, as per receipt attached..."

Translated by Bernard Isaaks

Vitaly Zakrutkin
(1908-1984)

Zakrutkin began his career in the 1930s as a philologist and author of many scholarly papers on Russian literature.

During the Great Patriotic War he was a war correspondent and fought along many fronts. His novella, *Maria, Mother of Man* (1968), which won him the State Prize, is about the wartime heroism of Soviet people and about Russian women.

According to a press review, "no one except a people's writer could have produced such a book. It is, as it were, a reply to Maxim Gorky's appeal 'Let us glorify Woman-Mother, to whom death itself humbly resigns' ".

Zakrutkin is also the author of the novels *The Floating Stanitsa* and *Creation of the World*, and a documentary novel *Caucasian Notes.*

Maria, Mother of Man *

She was a woman I could not, had no right to forget. Her story, her pure heart, integrity and kindness, and those terrible months of utter solitude, which were such a grim test of her moral and physical strength, were well known to me, and I did not forget her. But then, the gory battles of the last years of the war, the difficult campaigns through foreign lands, the weeks I spent in hospital recovering from my wound, the return to my home village, devastated by the enemy, and the loss of my dear and near ones, blurred the image of this woman in my memory, and I could no longer remember her face clearly. Her features appeared to me as through the milky haze of an early morning mist above a river, chilled in the autumn night.

Years passed. And then, one day, in an old Carpathian town where I was staying on the invitation of an old front-line friend of mine, I suddenly remembered everything I knew about this woman whom I dared not forget.

This is how it came about. Every morning I got up before sunrise and went for a walk in the old deserted park, and then slowly ascended the steep slope of the tall hill which the local people called Prince's Hill. There, sitting on an iron bench, from the top of the hill I admired the panorama of the old town, illumined by the roseate light of the sun and veiled with a gauzy film. The town presented a tableau of life over a period of seven centuries: there were the ruins of ancient castles, crumbling monastery walls, gilt-decorated churches of the Jesuits, Bernadines and Dominicans, ancient wooden churches and sombre cathedrals; there were dwelling houses with the tall tapering roofs covered with red tiles, and remains of powder towers, touched with a mossy green; there were narrow, crooked little streets and wide concourses, bronze statues on granite pedestals, fountains, parks, and cemeteries—memorials left by many generations of people, which invited silent reflection and thoughts about the irrevocable passage of time...

Not far from the bench on which I usually sat grew a spreading maple tree and beside it there was a niche of white porous stone, bored away by the rains. In the niche stood a statue of the Madonna with Child. Her dark-haired head was adorned with a wreath of waxen

*English translation © Raduga Publishers 1985

flowers, grey with dust, and on the stone ledge at her feet there were always fresh flowers, sprinkled with water—white and red gladioli, mauve phloxes, and green ferns.

The flowers were brought by an ancient couple, a man and wife. They appeared on the top of Prince's Hill before I did, laid the flowers at the feet of the Madonna and stood there for a long time in silence, clinging to each other. More often than not I saw only their bent backs and their drooping grey heads. What sorrow was weighing down on those two poorly dressed people, for what were they praying the Madonna—who knows! Had they lost the son they loved, or was their only daughter dying of an incurable disease? Or perhaps, someone had treated the defenceless old couple cruelly, and they were left without a roof over their heads, without a crust of bread, unwanted, and with no one to care for them. Wide and deep as the sea is human grief, and mostly it remains mute...

Having offered up their wordless prayer, the old couple walked past my bench every day, never once giving me so much as a glance. When they had gone I stayed looking at the Virgin Mary for a long time. And the memory of the woman whom I dared not, had no right to forget, suddenly came back to me. Once, during the war, our paths crossed by chance, and now all these years later I feel I simply must tell people about her.

* * *

That September night the sky shuddered and shivered and glowed red from the reflection of the fires raging down below, and neither the moon nor any stars could be seen in it. Over the hollowly droning earth roared near and far artillery volleys. Everything around Maria was flooded with an eerie copper-red light, an ominous rumbling was heard all the time, and indistinct, blood-chilling noises came creeping from here, there and everywhere.

Maria lay hugging the ground in a deep furrow. Above her, a thick stand of maize, all but indistinguishable in the semi-darkness, rustled its dried tasselled ears. Biting her lips from fear and covering her ears with her hands, Maria stretched out in the furrow. She wanted to dig herself into the upturned but since caked and grass-grown earth and cover herself with it so she could not see or hear what was happening in the village.

She lay down on her stomach and thrust her face into the dry grass. But the next moment she remembered that she was pregnant, turned on her side, lay like that for a little, and then stretched out on her back. In the sky above streaked mortar-launched missiles, humming and whistling and leaving a fiery trace, and tracer bullets pierced the dark like green and red arrows. From the village down below came a nauseating, suffocating stench of burning.

"O Lord, let me die, O Lord," Maria whispered, sobbing. "I have no more strength... I can't ... let me die, please, let me die, please..."

She rose to her knees, and listened hard. "Come what may, better to die there, with all the others," she told herself in despair. Glancing about her warily like a trapped she-wolf, and seeing nothing in the crimson shifting murk, Maria crawled to the edge of the maize field. The village was seen perfectly from here, from the top of the gentle rise. It was about a kilometre and a half to the village, no more, and what Maria saw froze her blood.

All the thirty houses were burning. Swayed by the wind, the slanting tongues of fire tore through the black clouds of smoke and shot thick sprays of burning sparks into the troubled sky. German soldiers with long flaming torches in their hands unhurriedly walked up and down the only village street, lit by the glow of the fires. They poked these torches at the eaves of the straw or rush roofs, they overlooked nothing, not a barn or a chicken coop, not the wretchedest shed, not a dog kennel, and new bursts of fire marked their passing.

Suddenly, the very air shuddered from two explosions coming one after the other in the western part of the village, and Maria guessed that the Germans had blasted the new brick cow-shed, built by the collective farm just before the war.

The Germans had chased all the surviving villagers, about a hundred men, women and children in all, out of the houses and assembled them in the open space behind the village, where grain was threshed in the summer. A barn lantern swung from the top of a tall pole. Its faint, winking light was barely noticeable. Maria knew this spot well. The year before, soon after the outbreak of the war, she had raked the grain there together with the other women on her team. Many of them cried as they worked, thinking about their husbands, brothers or sons who had gone to the front. But the war seemed far away then, they could not know at the time that it would come rolling in a bloody wave to their small inconspicuous village nestling in the hilly steppe. And here, on this terrible September night, their home village was burning down before their very eyes, and they themselves stood surrounded by enemy soldiers armed with tommy guns, and did not know what lay in store for them...

Maria's heart hammered, her hands trembled. She sprang to her feet, ready to rush down to the threshing floor, but fear held her back.

She dropped on her knees, then hugged the earth again, and bit hard on her hand to stifle the shriek bursting from her throat. She lay like that for a long time, whimpering like a child and choking with the acrid smoke drifting up from he village.

The fire was burning its last. The roar of artillery fire was subsiding. From above came the low hum of heavy bombers flying somewhere. Maria heard the heart-breaking sobbing of women and the curt, angry shouts of the Germans. Now the straggling crowd of villagers, prodded on by the soldiers, started moving slowly down the country road. This road ran alongside the maize field, no more than forty metres from where Maria was.

She clung to the ground, hardly breathing. "Where are they taking them? Surely not to shoot them? There are little children there, and innocent women! " The frightening thought beat in her fevered brain. She stared at the road with wide-open eyes. The crowd trudged past her. Three of the women were carrying babies. Maria recognised them. Two of them were her neighbours, young wives whose soldier husbands went off to the front just before the Germans descended upon the village. The third woman, a schoolteacher, was an evacuee, and it was already here, in the village, that her baby daughter had been born. The older children trotted along the road, keeping a tight hold on their mothers' skirts. Maria recognised the mothers and the children. Behind them came Uncle Kornei, hobbling on his home-made crutches. He had lost his leg in the first German war. Supporting each other came two ancient widowers, Kuzma and Nikita. Every summer the collective farm hired them to watch the melon-fields, and they had often treated Maria to a cool, sweet slice of water-melon. The villagers were walking in silence, and when one of the women broke into loud sobs, a German sprang at her at once and hit her with his tommy gun, knocking her down. The crowd stopped. The German then gripped the woman by the scruff of her neck, picked her up and ordered her to walk on, pointing ahead with his arm and babbling something quickly and angrily.

Peering into the strangely luminous dusk, Maria recognised nearly all the villagers. Carrying baskets, buckets or sacks slung on their shoulders, they shuffled on in obedience to the soldiers' curt shouts. No one spoke a word, the crowd was silent except for the crying of the children. And then when they got to the top of the hill and paused there for some reason, a shrill, heart-rending scream rang out:

"Bastards! Murderers! Nazi scum! I shan't go to your Germany! I'm not going to slave for you, vermin! "

Maria knew the voice. It belonged to Sanya Zimenkova, a fifteen-

year-old Komsomol member, daughter of the village tractor driver
who had gone to the front. Before the war Sanya lived in a boarding-
school in the far-away district centre, but when the school closed
down a year ago she returned home and remained in the village with
her mother.

"Sanya, hush, dear child! Stop it, daughter," her mother tearfully
begged her. "Please, please, keep quiet! They'll kill you, oh my darling, darling child! " But Sanya shouted still louder. "God damn the
bastards, let them kill me! "

A tommy-gun rattled briefly. Women burst into a husky-voiced
wail. The Germans barked something. The crowd moved on and
disappeared from view behind the hill.

A wave of cold, sleazy fear poured over Maria. "They've killed
Sanya." The realisation scorched her. She waited awhile listening
alertly. No voices could be heard, only the rapping of machine-guns
somewhere in the distance. Illuminating flares went up here and there
behind the copse, to the east of the village. They hung in the air
casting a dead yellowish light on the mangled earth, and in a minute
or two began to bleed drops of fire and die away. There, about three
kilometres east of the village, was the front line of the Germans'
defences, Maria had been there together with the other villagers when
the Germans rounded them all up to dig trenches and connecting
passages for them. The trenches meandered down the eastern slope of
the hill. For many months now the Germans had been firing these
flares at night to light up their defence line for fear they might not
notice in time the chains of attacking Soviet soldiers. The Soviet
machine-gunners for their part—and Maria had seen it many times
with her own eyes—blasted the enemy flares with tracer bullets and
they went out at once and fell on the ground. That's what was happening just then: from where the Soviet trenches were machine-guns
started up and green tracer bullets went for one rocket, then a second
one, a third one, and snuffed them out.

"Maybe Sanya is alive? Maybe they only wounded her and the
poor girl is lying there, bleeding to death?" Maria thought. She took
a look about her. No one anywhere. The village had burnt almost to
the ground, only here and there small flames still leapt up, and sparks
flickered over the smouldering remains. Keeping to the balk on the
edge of the maize field, Maria crawled to the spot where, she believed,
she had heard Sanya screaming and the tommy-gun firing. Crawling
was painful and difficult. The floor of the furrow was packed with
tumbleweed shrubs, driven there by the wind, and they prickled her
elbows and knees. Maria was barefoot and wore only an old print

dress, the way she was when she ran away from the village at dawn the
day before. Now she cursed herself for not taking her overcoat and
shawl, and not stopping to put on stockings and shoes.

She crawled slowly, more dead then alive. She stopped all the time,
listening hard to the cavernous rumble of guns in the distance, and
crawled on. Everything seemed to be droning—the ground and even
the sky—and this laboured, deathly droning was also going on continuously in the most inaccessible depths of the earth.

She found Sanya where she thought she would. The girl lay in the
ditch, her thin arms spread out and her left bare leg drawn up under
her awkwardly. Maria clung to her for a moment, feeling with her
cheek a sticky wetness on the girl's warm shoulder, and, pressing her
ear to the small, pointed breast, she heard the heart beating in fits and
starts. "She's alive! " Looking about her to make sure that there was
no one there, Maria picked up the girl and ran to the safety of the
maize. That short run felt endless: she stumbled, her breath came in
wheezy gasps, and she thought that she would drop Sanya, she'd
collapse and never get up again. Already past seeing or understanding
that she had already reached the safety of the metallically rustling dry
stalks of maize, she fell on her knees and fainted.

She was roused by Sanya's heartbreaking moans. The girl was lying
under her, choking with the blood that filled her mouth. The blood
had poured also over Maria's face. She sprang to her feet, rubbed at
her eyes with the hem of her dress, lay down close to Sanya, and
pressed her whole body to the girl's.

"Sanya, darling child, open your dear eyes, my poor little girl,"
Maria whispered, her throat clogged with tears. "Open your pretty
eyes, say something, if only one little word..."

With shaking hands Maria tore at the hem of her dress, ripped off a
piece, lifted Sanya's head and wiped her face and mouth. She touched
the girl with gentle care, kissing her forehead with its salty taste of
blood, her warm cheeks, and the thin fingers of her meek, lifeless
hands.

She could hear the wheezing and gurgling in Sanya's breast. As she
stroked her childish legs with the angular knees, she was horrified to
feel them turning cold.

"Wake up, darling child, please wake up," Maria beseeched her.
"Please don't die, Sanya... Don't leave me all alone... It's me, Auntie
Maria, who's here with you, can you hear me? There's just us left,
just we two, you and I..."

The maize rustled monotonously above them. There was no sound
of gunfire. The sky turned dark, and it was only somewhere far away,

behind the forest, that fires were reflected in it with a shuddering red glow. It was that pre-dawn hour when thousands of men who were killing each other—those who like a grey sand-storm surged to the east, and those who staunchly tried to hold it back—felt exhausted and tired of mangling the earth with mines and shells, and, dazed by the roar and the smoke, stopped their terrible work for a while to get their breath back, rest a bit in the trenches, and then resume their difficult, bloody reaping...

Sanya died at dawn. For all Maria's efforts to warm the mortally wounded girl by hugging her and pressing her hot breast to her body, it was no use. Sanya's hands and feet turned cold, the wheezing and gurgling in her throat stopped, and slowly she froze in death.

Maria closed Sanya's eyes, folded her stiffened hands on her breast—hands covered with scratches, blood, and ink spots on the fingers—and silently sat down beside the dead girl. In those moments Maria's own inconsolable grief—the death of her husband and little son, hanged by the Germans on an old poplar two days ago—seemed to recede into a fog and shrink in the face of this new death, and Maria realised, stabbed by this sudden thought, that her own grief was but a tiny drop, invisible to the world, in that frightening, wide river of human grief, a black river with the glow of fires on it which, flooding and destroying its banks, spread wider and wider and flowed ever faster to the east, and everything that had been her world in those not very long twenty-nine years of life drew farther and farther from her.

Morning was slow to come. The pale, washed-out dawn broke reluctantly. A flock of crows flew low over the maize field with their throaty cawing. The tasselled maize ears, damp from the cold dew, drooped limply, their rustling stilled. From where the trenches were came muffled rifle shots and occasional bursts of machine-gun fire.

Clasping her hands round her knees, Maria sat and looked at the dead girl. Her nose had sharpened already, and her forehead and cheeks were waxen. Dark spots of blood had congealed on her chin and left cheek. A strand of flaxen hair was stuck to her temple.

"I'll lay you out properly in a minute, you poor dear," Maria spoke very quietly. "I'll wash your pretty face, I'll braid your hair, and I'll close your mouth too. I don't know how I can dig a grave for you, my poor child, I've no shovel, nothing."

She was shaking with fever. Shivering and twitching her shoulders, she went on whispering things that simply came to her... Touching Sanya's waxen hand, she spoke to her as if she were alive:

"You've got ink on your fingers, child ... they've closed down your school, but you went on learning... A schoolteacher you wanted to be. It was not to be..."

Early-morning dew lay on the wilted witch grass growing in abundance between the rows of untended maize. Maria got up, washed her sticky, dirty hands with the dew, tore another strip from her dress, wetted it with dew and washed the blood off Sanya's frozen face. Very carefully she put the bit of cloth under the girl's chin to close the open mouth and tied the ends on top of her head. As she smoothed down her hair, she cried out from a sharp stab in her finger. She sucked out the drop of blood, and then, as she undid the tangled braid she came upon the badge with the unfastened pin in it.

Maria held it in her palm. A Komsomol badge with Lenin's profile on the red enamel.

"See, comrade Lenin" she whispered, choking with tears. "See what they've done to people, to poor Sanya here, to me... Where am I to go now, comrade Lenin? Tell me, answer me, comrade Lenin, teach me what to do... My father and my mother, my husband and my little son are all dead, and I've no one left in the whole wide world..."

Maria sobbed and wept for a long time, whimpering and intoning, and then she fell face down on the ground, and she felt as if she were hurtling into a black void. Attack planes flew low overhead with a sibilant wailing. Maria started up. She pinned the badge to Sanya's damp dress, walked away a few steps, dropped on her knees and started digging a grave.

There had been little rainfall that autumn, and the ploughland, overrun by weeds, had hardened. Maria dug in the manner of dogs, scraping at the dry, clumpish soil and raking it under her. Her fingers began to hurt, there were hang-nails, painful and bleeding. She sat down and wiped the sweat from her face. She thought for a moment, then tore another long strip from the bottom of her dress and ripped it into ten equal ribbons. Her print dress, discoloured through too many launderings, was now reduced to tatters. Helping with her teeth, Maria bandaged all her ten fingers tightly. She was dying for a drink of water. She chewed some dew-wet grass, spat out the bitter green blob with disgust, and went back to her digging. It occurred to her that she ought to know what length the grave should be, and so she went back to Sanya and measured her motionless body with her hand, the fingers fully spread out. She made it seven and a half hands, but she marked the length of the grave as nine. "She won't feel so cramped then," Maria thought and, going down on her knees again, resumed the digging.

An indistct hum came from the west somewhere. Maria lay down and pressed her ear to the ground. The low, deep sound was swelling rapidly. Maria understood what it was: German tanks were moving along the road past the village. She had seen them once, heavy heat-breathing monsters with black crosses and some foreign letters on their sides and towers. "They'll crush our people to death, they'll lie low in the forest, then they'll jump out and start squashing everybody," she thought with fear and anguish. No sooner had she thought this than guns started roaring suddenly and haphazardly from behind the forest. Shells flew past above her with a savage, piercing wail, and burst in the road from where came the sinister, grating roar of the tanks. Three of the shells burst somewhere close, right in the maize field, and the blast wave threw Maria and the dead girl to the very balk.

There was a terrible ringing in Maria's ears. Her eyes were full of dust. A grey cloud of dust hovered over the maize field, blocking out the sun. Sanya's stiff, motionless body lay near her. Evidently the volleys fired by the Soviet guns had been unable to arrest the advance of the German tanks because now she could hear them close to the very edge of the forest.

Maria waited a little, then went to Sanya, cleared away the shrubs of tumbleweed uprooted by the blasts and gathered round her, picked up the body and carried it to the unfinished grave. She went on digging until evening, on the alert for any sounds, but all she heard was the faraway rattle of machine-guns and now and then a gun firing or a shell exploding. Her tired hands ached terribly, her mouth was parched, but the morning dew had long dried up and there was no moisture anywhere to quench her thirst.

When the sun went down she dragged Sanya's body to the grave, lowered the bare legs into the hole, kissed the girl on the forehead, and then laid her down. Maria was now past weeping.

"Goodbye, darling child," she said huskily. "Rest in peace."

Maria's tattered dress was soaking from sweat. The sun had set, and there was a chill in the air. She began to shiver. With feverish haste, while there was still some light, she started tearing the dry, rustling leaves off the maize ears and heaping them in the furrow. Her hands had grown quite numb, but still she went on ripping the leaves in the hope that if she buried herself in them they'd give her some protection from the night's cold. She was very hungry, but there was nothing there except the maize which had over-ripened to the hardness of stone. She broke a long cob in two and with her teeth dug out the hard grains, masticating them with an effort, but they stuck in her throat, making her cough and throw up.

Feeling completely done in, she lay down on the heap of leaves and tried to dig herself in, stuffing an armful under her head and piling as much as she could over herself. At last, she curled up on her side, but she did not fall asleep at once. She lay whimpering and breathing in gasps, and then for a few minutes she fell into a semi-somnolent state, and rested. It must have been midnight when sound, healing sleep came to her at last. Her whole life flitted past in snatches in her dreams, now bitter, now sweet ones.

She dreamt that she was flying through the warm spring air over green fields and suddenly recognised their own field and her father standing there—his face not gaunt and bristling with a growth of reddish beard as when the Whites shot him, but looking young and handsome. The wind was playing with his curly hair, he waved to Maria, calling her, but she only smiled because she did not want to come down to earth, it was so nice to feel weightless and soar in the air like a bird, looking down on the blue ribbon of the little river, the weeping willows on the banks, the hayricks, and the white toy-like cottages...

Then there was a hiatus, dark and painful, and after that Maria saw fire. She moaned in her sleep, thinking that it was the village burning, but it turned out to be a Young Pioneers' campfire on the bank of the small river, with boys and girls wearing red Pioneer scarves dancing round it, and herself among them, a girl of twelve, also holding someone by the hand, singing a jolly song, and feeling so happy that she wanted to hug everyone—the teachers who stood under the willows, and Vanya, the tall, smart patrol leader, who became her husband six years later, and all the rosy-cheeked, neatly dressed village boys and girls. They were all dancing, singing and laughing, and suddenly they saw a radiant, crimson glow rising in the eastern sky beyond the river, beyond the green meadows. But it was not the sun at all, it was a huge, transparent badge, taking up half the sky, and against the crimson background there was Lenin—they all saw him—smiling down on them.

The cold awakened Maria. Opening her eyes, she stared up at the starry sky and could not at first understand where she was, but when the horror of what had happened came home to her, and she understood that there was no campfire, no teachers, no Ivan, nothing but the burnt-down village, killings and death, she buried her face in the cold husks and lay there, sobbing her heart out.

Maria did not know that in those two or three hours while she slept the enemy tanks had broken through the weak lines of Soviet

defences behind the river, had dislodged our soldiers from their
trenches, and surged eastward, accompanied by the infantry and the
self-propelled artillery. The sound of gunfire came from farther and
farther away, and there were no machine-guns or exploding shells to
be heard at all. It was perfectly quiet save for the barely distinguishable rumble of lorries driving along the highroad that ran fifteen
kilometres or so to the north of the village, and very rarely the zoom
of German night bombers, invisible in the dark sky. Maria did not
know and could not know that she had been left behind all alone in
this unharvested maize field, alone in the Germans' rear, that the front
was moving farther and farther to the east, that all the villages in the
vicinity had been razed to the ground on the orders of the German
command, and the inhabitants who had not been brutally executed
had been packed off to Germany. And that there was not a living
soul left here, in these backwoods, except her...

Afraid of the dark, Maria buried herself in the husks again and,
though the warmth they offered was little enough, her shuddering
sobs subsided and she fell asleep. And again in her dreams she saw
snatches of her life: her mother's funeral years ago; a moonlit night in
the forest in May and Ivan's ardent caresses: haymaking, the narrow
meadows along both banks of the river, the intoxicating smell of the
freshly cut grass; herself as an eighteen-year-old bride in a white dress,
and the thrill of her darling Ivan kissing her for the first time in public;
she heard the loud talk and quarrelling of the village men that memorable evening when a representative of the district Party Committee
came down to propose that they should all join the collective farm;
she was suffering miseries from the fierce cold, cursing the rotten old
cowshed and the collective-farm chairman who would not bother to
have the roof mended, and hating the milking from which her hands
became so swollen...

What awakened Maria was the chattering of magpies. She opened
her eyes and watched them, without making a stir. Two magpies were
swinging on maize stalks which bent slightly under their weight, and
chatting about something. The silence amazed Maria, and also these
live birds, for she had not seen any for three days. She heard the roar
of gunfire somewhere very far away. The sun shone down on the
maize. The weeds between the rows looked silver from the abundant
dew. Maria swept aside the husks and sat up. The magpies flew away
at once.

She was weak from hunger and thirst, and when she tried to stand
up she felt sick and dizzy. What was she to do? Go where? She
remembered the collective farmers planting late potatoes, beets and

cabbages next to the maize field. None of the vegetables had been gathered. "I'll go there, otherwise I'll die," she decided. She made her way slowly to the western end of the field, looking about her warily and trying not to touch the maize stalks lest the rustling of the dry leaves should give her away.

She plodded on with short, clumsy steps, a small, brown-eyed woman with a lightly freckled nose, her body barely covered by the tatters of her dress, crusted with blood. Her brown hair which had fallen loose bristled with maize husks and wormwood stems; her bare legs and small feet were covered with scratches and bruises.

When she came to the edge of the field, she looked round fearing an encounter with the Germans, dropped on her knees and crawled between the potato rows. Without lifting her head she started digging. Her lacerated fingers hurt unbearably, but still she dug out two potatoes, rubbed them in her palms to clean them of the lumps of dry soil, and ate them greedily. They did not appease her hunger and only gave her a sharp pain in her stomach.

She lay down in the furrow, pillowed her head in her hands and closed her eyes. Sick with misery she recalled everything that had been her life...

In the Civil War a punitive detachment of the Whites shot her father, a Communist. Maria was seven years old then, but she remembered how four elderly bearded Cossacks led her securely bound father to the neighbours' barn, stood him against the wall, shot him, threw his body into a cart, shovelled some manure on top, and drove the cart out into the fields. It was early spring, the manure which had become caked during the winter began to steam, and the scrawny horses had a long struggle pulling the cart out of the mud. When the Whites went away, the village men brought back her father's body and buried it in the cemetery. Maria was sixteen when her mother died. Their neighbours, Ivan's father and mother, looked after her. They fixed up her crumbling cottage for her, and helped her to put a wattle fence round the yard. Ivan was three years older than Maria. Both had only had four years of elementary school because the secondary school was too far to go and they had to work to procure their daily bread. Both were members of the Komsomol, and were among the first to join the collective farm. Ivan had long had an eye on this small, well-knit girl; they often went walking in the woods together, and spent the long summer evenings sitting on the bank of the river. Soon they got married, and a year later a son was born to them. They called him Vassya.

Big, tall Ivan adored his small wife. Out of sight and earshot of the villagers, he carried her about in his arms and called her his "tiny tot" and "freckly darling". With the years he became more and more attached to Maria, appreciating her gentle, placid temper, modesty, and her housewifliness. Maria's love was equal to his.

Both worked on the third team of the Lenin collective farm, he as a driver, and she as a milkmaid. Actually, this third team comprised the entire adult population of their small village, situated all of thirty kilometres from the central farm where the board had its offices. The team ploughed and sowed the land, raised cattle and pigs. The leader was Uncle Fyodor, a former shepherd, and a Party member of long standing. Ivan was the second Communist there.

Just before the war, with help from the collective farm, Ivan and Maria built themselves a new house and planted an orchard. The site they chose was on the edge of the village. They thought they'd live to the end of their days there. But it was not to be. On the very day the war broke out, Ivan, Uncle Fyodor, and eleven other men were summoned to the enlistment office and despatched to the fighting front. In the autumn Uncle Fyodor was killed in action, and a few months later Ivan returned home, a mere shadow of his old self, and with his left arm amputated above the elbow. Maria consoled him as best she could, happy to have him back, but this was no time for rejoicing. Like an irresistible avalanche the war came sweeping towards the village. The Germans had successfully launched their summer offensive in the south. The Soviet army was retreating to the Volga and the Caucasus.

Fistulas opened in Ivan's stump and he was running a fever. The collective farm chairman took him to the district hospital where Ivan was told that he had an inflammation of the marrow of the bone, something that was called osteomyelitis, that it required special treatment which could not be provided at the present as the entire staff was being evacuated.

The days following Ivan's return from the hospital were the darkest in the life of the family...

And now, lying amid the dry potato tops, Maria remembered those awful days, loaded with sorrow, tears, premonitions, and expectation of something inevitable and imminent like death. She remembered every word spoken then by Ivan and herself, she remembered how those words were spoken, what the face of her sick husband expressed, and how Vassya, their ten-year-old son, cried.

...On return from the hospital, Ivan lay down on the wide wooden bench that had been placed in the shade of the old apple tree, the only tree they did not uproot when planting their new orchard. This apple tree was planted in times of yore by Ivan's grandfather who had his homestead here, on the bank of the river. The homestead fell into decline when he died, and it was here, on the site of his grandfather's orchard, that Ivan built his new house, keeping the old tree.

It was a warm August day. The sunlight filtered through the leaves; the boughs stirred in the light breeze, and sun spots played on the ground. With his padded coat for a pillow, Ivan lay on his back with his eyes closed. Maria perched on the edge of the bench, holding his hot hand in hers. Vassya was squatting on the ground, weeding the onions in the patch he had just watered. It was somnolently quiet. A lone bee was buzzing in the young trees. Suddenly, Maria's ear caught a strange, drawn-out sound. It was like very distant thunder. She raised her head. The sky was perfectly clear, the sun was shining, and there was not a cloud in the blue. But the distant thunder, though barely audible, went on rumbling.

Ivan opened his eyes, listened for a moment, and looked at Maria.

"We must go away, it's them," he said.

"Who?" Maria did not understand.

"Germans."

"What are you saying, Vanya? What Germans?"

"Enemy Germans, who else. Seems they're going to be here soon."

Maria had never seen her husband like that: he was looking at her with anguished, inflamed eyes, his unshaved cheeks, sprouting a flaxen growth, had sunken in, there was an unhealthy flush on his cheekbones, and his dry, cracked lips were trembling.

"We must go before it's too late," he said.

"Where can you go in your condition?" Maria protested. "Look at yourself, you're burning in a fever, your hand is as hot as a heated iron!"

"We've got to go just the same. Can't you understand? We've got to go before those beasts come here. They spare no one, they kill old and young alike. You haven't seen their doings, but I have... There's nothing human in them. Understand? Nothing! They shoot young children ... they finish off the wounded ... they rob ... rape... We've got to go, we've got to go..."

His speech was becoming more and more jerky, more incoherent. He fainted for a minute or two and fell silent, then came to and again said the same thing over and over again: "We must go, we must go."

Maria burst into tears.

"But how can we go, dear? You're so ill, you were senseless only a minute ago. Where can we go, to whom? And, besides, for another thing ... you know that I'm pregnant, dearest," she dropped her voice and blushed. "Who knows where we'll be knocking about when my time comes..."

She laid her cheek on Ivan's chest. There was a long silence. And then, stroking his wife's hair, he whispered:

"Alright, alright, we'll think about it... Maybe I'll feel better tomorrow, I'll go to the chairman and talk it over with him. I'm a Communist, after all... There's much I can do... Never mind that I have only one hand. You can shoot with one hand too..."

"But what if someone informs against you, Vanya?" Maria asked, paling. "What if some skunk goes and tells the Germans that there is one Communist in the village, the only one, and a soldier besides? What will happen then?"

"It can't happen," Ivan replied. "We have no traitors here, and most of the villagers are our relatives." He fell silent, staring into space above Maria's head. "Still, I'd better go and see the chairman, and make a trip to the district Party Committee as well. Pity I've no strength, my legs won't hold me... I'll never get there if I go alone, I'll collapse on the way and die like a dog..." His lips twisted in a bitter, apologetic smile. "I'm sorry, I shouldn't have said that... Tomorrow I'll ask for a horse and cart and we'll go together ... and take Vassya along..."

But he was not fated to go anywhere. For nearly two hours he lay unconscious, thrashing about, ripping at the neck of his shirt, and raving. Vassya cried. Maria kept changing cold wet cloths on his burning forehead, kissing his hand, breaking into a wail, stifling her sobs, and starting all over again. Her wails brought the villagers running, they crowded under the apple tree, and gazed pityingly at Ivan's distorted face, covered with drops of sweat. When he came to and opened his eyes, two of the women helped him to sit up.

It was the quiet hour of approaching twilight on a summer's day. Hens were clucking in the yard. Vassya's pigeons were cooing on the roof of the house. A cool swampy smell wafted from the river. Somewhere behind the village a calf was lowing plaintively. Nothing seemed to portend disaster in that blessed hour of peace and quiet. And then a hum of motors, low and distant at first, was heard through the cooing of pigeons, the clucking of hens, and the various discrete sounds of a peaceful evening. The sound came from above somewhere, from that part of the sky where the crimson sun was setting on a long purple cloud. The low hum was coming nearer, and now the sound changed to a monotonous moaning as though someone up there was struggling under an unbearably heavy load.

People lifted their heads. Large transport planes with black crosses on the wings and escorted by fighters flew across the sky with a deafening roar. They made a semicircular turn to the north of the village, and when they were some distance from it they suddenly started dropping small dark dots and, as they fell, parachutes, coloured a pretty pink by the setting sun, opened above them.

"Well, that settles it," Iven said through set teeth. "They're German paratroopers. Evidently they want to cut off our troops' retreat..."

The crowd was silent and frightened. Some of the women burst out crying. The old men exchanged perplexed glances. Everyone looked at Ivan, waiting to hear what he would say.

"So we have guests coming too," he spoke after a pause. "There's only one thing we can do now: be all for one, and one for all, otherwise we're in for it. This is what we must do." Peering into the faces about him he said slowly, almost calmly: "Those of you who have provisions—flour or pork fat, sugar or anything else, hide everything safely, otherwise they'll clean you out. Slaughter your pigs, sheep and geese, salt the meat down and keep it in some good hiding place so you don't starve to death. Hide all the photographs of your men in uniform as well as all their letters from the front, and if you're asked say that your husband or son was killed at the very beginning of the war. If anyone has any pictures of Lenin and Stalin or their books keep them where the Nazi scum cannot find them..."

Ivan had known all the people gathered under the apple tree since his infancy, and so he addressed each one in turn now:

"You, Fenya, had concealed your wireless when the order was published to hand in all radio sets, so mind you keep it safe now, we'll need it... The same goes for Kornei and his double-barrelled gun. Bury it somewhere and let no one else know where. Now you, Aunt Varya, don't mind my telling you straight, but you have a very long tongue and you might do people a lot of harm with it, so better keep your mouth shut..." When he had said all he wanted to say to the different men and women, he addressed them all together: "The main thing is don't panic. Stick fast together. We're not going to live under the Germans forever, victory will be ours anyway and our Soviet armies will come back."

He fell silent, and then added:

"Not one German must find out that Aunt Marfa's late husband Uncle Fyodor was a Communist because they'll shoot her straight-away. You must also keep quiet about our schoolteacher, Nina Lvovna, that she's been evacuated here and that she's Jewish, otherwise the Germans will murder her together with her child. Well, it's the same about me. If you're asked about me you must all say the same thing that I was born and bred here in the village, that I never was a Communist, and that I lost my arm in a mowing-machine."

By this time the rest of the villagers had assembled to hear what Ivan was saying. The old men and women promised to do as he said and come to him for advice when in difficulty. The crowd dispersed in glum silence.

When darkness fell, the secretary of the district Party Committee came to see Ivan unexpectedly, driving an old battered car. He asked Maria to leave them, had a brief talk with Ivan, and drove off.

"What did he say?" Maria asked her husband.

"He said that if our village folk won't betray me to the Germans I'd better stay here, and our people will get in touch with me when the time comes."

"And what did you say?"

Ivan shrugged his shoulders.

"I'm a soldier. What could I say? I told him that I'd vouch for our villagers with my life, and if I must stay I must."

There was fighting that night far behind the village. Shell bursts and machine-gun fire could be heard. Just before light, scattered groups of Soviet soldiers who had broken out of enemy encirclement, came down the village street. Many of them were wounded. In the meantime, Red Army units, which until the reserves came, were formed from home-guard battalions, the militia and regular soldiers who had come out of encirclement, were already taking up defence positions beyond the river. They were hurriedly digging trenches and building shelters. The villagers helped them. Leaving her sick husband at home, Maria took a shovel and with everyone else dug from dawn till dark. At night, Soviet soldiers—singly or in small groups—who had escaped with their lives from encirclement, came straggling through the village. Holding up their wounded comrades these tired, grimy men rested in the village for an hour or two, voraciously ate whatever the kind-hearted women set before them, and on being told that Soviet troops had taken up a defence position beyond the river, went to join them.

The chairman of the district Executive Committee sent an order to the village team to evacuate all their cows, calves and pigs to the rear of the Soviet trenches and hand them over against a receipt to the commander of the unit. The order was brought by a messenger on a lathery horse. That same day nearly all the animals belonging to the collective farm were taken across the river and from there the soldiers drove them further behind their lines.

A week later, a large column of German lorries with helmeted soldiers sitting in them, arrived at the village. Guns were linked to the lorries. The Germans stopped for half an hour or so in the village street, then made for the river, skirted the village and stopped on the edge of the forest. Fire was opened on them from the left bank of the river. In the night the Germans rounded up all the adults in the village and ordered them to dig trenches on the right bank. Maria and Ivan also had to go. This went on for five nights. They dug the trenches for the Germans under the mortar fire of their own people. The Germans returned the fire lazily from the forest.

"There's no less than a battalion of the vermin here," Ivan said to Maria. "Their sappers are building shelters for the officers in the forest. But it's only their vanguard, judging by everything. They're planning to make a break-through somewhere..."

For the time being the Germans left the villagers alone and except for the men driving the lorries or riding their motorcycles through the village, the inhabitants hardly saw any Germans. This is how it went until that day when someone blasted the Germans' staff car at a remote elevator. It was Fenya, the busy body, who brought the news.

"A lot of hand grenades were thrown at the car, people say," Fenya told her fellow villagers in a flurry of excitement. "They killed all the German officers to the last man, took some important papers off them, and set fire to the car."

It was after this that the horror which no one expected happened, their village and two other, larger ones, were razed, and Maria found herself all alone in a world wreathed in black smoke, in a world breathing death and a stench of burning...

She lay in the potato field, her hands under her head. Above her was the clear, blue, autumnally cool, infinite sky. A silver spider web was stirring slightly on the tall weeds. A small flock of partridges were bathing in the dust very close to Maria, without noticing her lying motionlessly. The grey, rusty-speckled birds raked the dust with their feet, flopped on the side, stretched out their necks and chirped merrily with one another. A hedgehog came down the furrow with a busy air. All at once the partridges started up and, flapping their wings jerkily and quickly, flew low over the ground to the maize field. The hedgehog lifted its snout, followed them with a long look, snorted crossly and strode on, sniffing at the titilative scent left by the birds.

This was her home, so beloved and so intimately known since childhood, and everything appeared to be as usual: the September sun, never generous in warmth, was generous in light, the desiccated grasses and thirsty earth had the familiar, melancholy, heart-tugging smell, and as familiar were the cries of the magpies, partridges and crows, and of the starlings getting ready for their long journey. Everything was as usual, and yet everything had shifted, as it were, into that no man's land which separated Maria from the whole world and left her all alone with the horror which had befallen her and which no one in the whole world could deliver her from...

The German punitive detachment came to the village in the late afternoon. The morose soldiers got down from the lorries and stood about in the middle of the street, glancing indifferently at the frightened people shrinking against their fences. And then an elderly thin-lipped sergeant-major rode up to the soldiers on a motorcycle. He said something to them, and they scattered over the entire village, going into every yard and searching the houses, barns and sheds quickly and carelessly. They brought out quilts and pillows from some of the houses, and dumped them in the lorries. They shot and skinned some dozen pigs. But so far they did not molest any of the people.

Only Ivan. No one knew why it was Ivan they picked out. Maybe it was his rather young age that made the Germans suspicious or maybe they simply did not like his glum face and the lowering look he gave them from under his ginger eyebrows. The Germans grabbed him and took him to the team's small office which stood apart on the edge of the village. All the villagers were also herded there. Maria, in a frenzy of fear, and sobbing wildly, did not notice that Vassya had come running after the crowd of them.

It had already grown quite dark. The German soldiers beamed their flashlights over the villagers they surrounded. The thin-lipped sergeant-major, standing up in his motorcycle, said:

"For the dastardly assault on the officers of the great German army we are going to execute many Russians to teach them that German officers and German soldiers are inviolable." With a long bony finger he pointed at Ivan. "Among others we are now going to execute this man."

The crowd was numbed. Suddenly Fenya's scream rang out in the darkness:

"But he hasn't done anything! He never left the village! "

A soldier quickly beamed his flashlight on her face. The sergeant-major's pointing finger swerved to her.

"We are now going to execute this woman also."

... The blinding sun made Maria close her eyes. Lying in the potato field she heard the throaty chattering of magpies, the croaking of crows flying past overhead, the whispering rustle of the dry potato tops, she breathed the bitter smell of wormwood mixed with the smell of smoke and burning, and through all these sounds and smells which had become alien and extraneous she saw only that unbearable oppressive world which had narrowed down for her to one night, or rather to those fleeting moments which broke her life in two.

At first, this world rose before her closed eyes as a swaying shroud of brown murk. Now this brown murk paled, now it thickened, and amidst this strange, tiresome swaying floated the setting sun, blurred and waning. The sun became more and more blurred until it finally disappeared in the frightening darkness... And in this pitch blackness Maria again saw the beams of the flashlights in the hands of those German soldiers. The bluish beams slid over the faces of the shaken villagers, they picked out of the darkness the sergeant-major standing up on his motorcycle, the corner of the slate roof, and the tall, spreading poplar. Two of the soldiers grabbed Fenya and twisted her arms behind her back. Fenya screamed. Two other soldiers bound Ivan with a length of black field-telephone wire. Maria burst into wails, and, elbowing her way through the crowd, rushed to her husband. Some women clapped her mouth shut and pulled her back. Choking, Maria tried to struggle free, but the women held her fast and she had only a fleeting impression of the soldiers pushing Ivan and Fenya to the poplar, and of her son, her Vassya, screaming wildly and biting the soldiers' hands as he locked his arms round his father's neck. The sergeant-major said something to the soldiers in a loud voice... Jerking his body to push his son away, Ivan shouted huskily:

"Death to the Nazis! Long live Communism! "

The next moment, Ivan and Fenya swung from the thick branch of the tree, strangled by the black wire. A black wire noose, like his father's, also went round Vassya's thin neck. Writhing and twisting, he hung next to his father... The black snake of the wire swelled and grew, it crawled over Maria and stung her in the heart...

She came to her senses in Marfa's cottage. There were women standing round her, with eyes red and puffy from crying.

"Quickly run and hide in the maize," Marfa whispered, leaning close to Maria. "The Germans have been asking about you. Lie low for a day or two, until they go away, otherwise they'll hang you too..."

Maria lost consciousness again, and when she came to for brief spells she struggled to break free from the women's arms, she beat her head against the wall, bit her hands, and tried to get up and run to the poplar. After midnight, she quieted down, drained of strength by her struggling, and lay stretched out on her back, staring at the ceiling with unseeing eyes. And then the fear of death seized her. Shaking from fear, she jumped down from the bed. She fancied that someone was outside the door, that the Germans would come in, put a black wire noose round her neck and strangle her as they had strangled her husband and her son...

"Hide me," Maria begged. "Hide me, my dear, kind friends. I don't want to die... I don't want to die... I don't want to die..."

Before daybreak Marfa took her through the kitchen gardens to the edge of the village and stood there for a long time, keeping a look-out until Maria had disappeared in the thickets of the unharvested maize...

A puff of wind rustled the dry potato tops. No shots had reached her hearing for some time, but she still lay there with her eyes closed. Once, when she was a little girl, she saw the neighbour's dog attacking the horses pulling a heavy stone roller round and round over the barley sheaves spread out on the packed-earth threshing floor. The roller crushed the grain and ground the straw. Barking frenziedly, the small ginger dog tried to get its teeth into the hind leg of one of the horses, but it jumped short of the horse and was run over by the roller. Maria heard a squeal, and in the next second saw that the dog lay dead, sprinkled with straw. The neighbour swore, stopped the horses, kicked the dead dog aside, and went back to his work. Maria remembered how that small ginger dog died, and felt as if she herself had been crushed by a gigantic stone roller. Her arms and legs ached, her heart was beating faintly, and there was a steady, frightening, monotonous ringing in her ears. She thought that the end had come, that she was dying because no one could survive what she had gone through, and of course it was better to die than to live like that crushed dog, alone and needed by no one.

"I'll starve to death, and it'll be for the best," Maria thought. "People say that it's a painless death: at first you feel very hungry, you suffer for a while, but then you pass out and die... If only my end came soon... Who cares for me now? I've no one left in the world, and I don't want to go on living. I'll just lie here like this, and die..."

She felt sorry for her wrecked life. Again she saw her hanged husband and son, and although she had seen the Germans hanging them with her own eyes she still could not believe that this had really happened, perhaps she was sleeping and this was just a bad dream which would soon end, she would wake up and everything would be as before: her naughty Vassya would come running home laughing happily, she would scold him a bit for the scratches on his rosy cheek and the tear in his shirt, and after that Ivan would return, looking tired and covered with dust, his hands shining with grease and his overalls, long discoloured and saturated with oil, smelling of gasoline. Ivan would wash his hands and face, comb his reddish hair with a large comb which had some teeth missing, and only then would come to Maria, bend over a little, put his arm about her, kiss her hard on the lips, and as usual call her lovingly his "tiny tot" or "freckly darling" ... and she, so small in comparison, would stand on tiptoe to reach up to his mouth, and they'd stand like that for a long time, in a close embrace, while the red setting sun clearly printed the pattern of the curtain lace on the clean floor...

Maria was weeping quietly. Licking her lip, salty from her tears, she whispered:

"There'll be nothing any more ... no Ivan, no Vassya ... no one will ever again call me his 'freckly darling', and I'd better die..."

She did not believe in God, since a child she knew that there was no one up there, in the deep blue to hear her ardent prayer, no one to answer her, no one to help her, and yet now she fervently prayed for death.

"O Lord, I can't go on living, I don't want to live," she whispered, choking with tears. "Maybe you really are? Put me out of my misery, let me die. O Lord, if you are, you can see my grief. How can I live with it? They've taken everything from me, they strangled my darling Ivan, and my little son Vassya, an innocent child... They've burnt down our homes, nothing but ashes left. And beasts that they are they killed Sanya, such a good little girl. And they've driven all the people off somewhere, they left no one... I don't want to live, O Lord! Let me die! Take me into your heavenly abode from this earth! "

Thus prayed Maria to a god unknown, thus she cried out for death. But life called her imperiously, reminding her that she was not alone, that kindling in her was another life, as yet fused to its mother's weary body but already with a feeble existence of its own, that in her womb lived a tiny human clot, as yet without sight, hearing or voice, but steadily growing by day and by night.

This live human clot could not see how cruelly people tortured one another, how mercilessly they killed each other. The clot, growing in the dark warmth of its mother's womb, could not hear how angrily roared the weapons of death as they mutilated the earth, it could not feel how the earth quaked and shuddered, how agonisingly groaned the trees when they were torn out by their live roots... Voiceless, it could not say: "Come to your senses, people! Take pity on your own selves, don't destroy life on earth! Take pity on those who have not yet come but will come into the world! Take pity on those who have not yet been born, not yet conceived! Leave them the bright sun, the sky, the waters, and the earth! Because it's you, people, men and women who in your beautiful love, in your passionate love-making, in the jubilant merging of your live flesh, call into being a new human who comes into the world from non-existence to enjoy the life given him by you, and to be happy. What will you leave him, the one you have yourselves called into being? The crippled earth, smouldering homes, blood, a stench of putrefaction, and a black wasteland? But the one coming into the world deserves a better lot. He will have to till this land and toil in the sweat of his brow for his daily bread. Just like you, who gave him life, he will want to delight in the spring, in the singing of birds, in the fragrance of flowers, and in the cool shade of trees. And also like you he will want to find happiness in love, in the great and mysterious fusion of human flesh, in that ineffably beautiful oneness of a man and a woman which makes life ineradicable and conquers even death. Leave him all that, people! Don't kill him! He's coming into the world, he wants to live!"

Tears ran down Maria's grimy cheeks. The thought of the unborn child, the thought that she, the woman who had conceived him, had to keep safe the living being in her womb because it linked her with Ivan and Vassya, banished the wish to die from her mind. Obeying the imperious call of life, she rose to her feet, but collapsed at once from weakness and nausea. "It's from hunger," she told herself. "I must crawl to that field where the beets and carrots are growing."

It was not far to go, no more than two hundred metres from where she lay, but the sun was already setting and so she had to hurry. She stood up and looked about her. Not a soul in sight. Swaying and staggering she started for the beetroot field. The reddish sun already touched the horizon. Dusk was falling. Behind her Maria heard the snapping of dry maize stalks. Frightened, she swung round. Four cows were slowly coming after her. In front of them ran a large grey dog. Maria knew this dog, a ferocious animal whom Gerasim, the village shepherd, kept on a chain. Together with the other villagers Gerasim and his old woman had been taken off by the Germans, and the dog broke loose when the fires started and ran away. Maria remembered that the entire village went in fear of this ferocious dog, that many had been bitten by him and that old Gerasim called him "Chum".

It was too late to run. Maria stopped, her blood turning cold, and pressed her hands to her breast. The dog and the cows were coming straight at her. She took a step back.

"Chum, Chum!" she cried.

The dog stopped, gave her a hard look, and wagged his tail, encrusted with burs. He did not appear menacing at all. The cows had stopped as well but, unlike the dog, they frightened Maria with their lowered heads, their queer grunting, and the tense look in their eyes.

All the four cows were of the same red steppeland breed, but Maria recognised each one: this one belonged to Marfa, that one to Fenya, and the other two to the collective farm. Here they all stood before her, she could not understand what they wanted of her, and started backing away from them. Slowly, the cows and the dog came after her.

She turned round sharply and broke into a run. Behind her, she heard them thudding and lowing. A spasm of nausea brought Maria to a stop. Helplessly, she looked at her pursuers. The cows stood lowing huskily. Milk dripped on the ground from their hard, swollen udders. And only then did Maria understand what was wrong with those poor cows: their owners had gone, and their calves had been killed by the Germans when they set fire to the village. The poor unmilked cows had been wandering about miserably and had run for help to the first human being they saw.

Maria stroked the cow standing nearest to her, squatted and felt her hot, very taut udder. At first Maria milked the cow merely to relieve her, letting the milk fall on the ground, but then she started milking with her right hand and cupping her left hand to catch the milk, and so drank her fill. She felt better at once. She washed her grimy face and hands with the milk, and dried them with her dress.

"Chum, come here, good doggie," she called the dog softly. "Have some milk. You, too, must be hungry."

The dog came meekly, lapped up the milk from Maria's cupped hand, gratefully wagged his tail, and walked away. Maria quickly milked the three other cows, stroking and patting each one.

"You poor things, how awful it was for you! " she said, scratching their foreheads with both hands. "And how could you do without water all this time? I, at least, am no longer thirsty thanks to you. You know the way to the river, why don't you go there and drink? It all seems quiet now. Maybe there's no one there any longer..."

The sun had set long ago. Darkness was thickening. There was a coolness in the air. It was time to settle for the night, and Maria decided to bury herself in maize leaves again.

"Goodnight, dearies," she said to the cows. "It's time to go to sleep. Come here tomorrow, and I'll milk you."

She started back for the maize field. Once, she turned round. All the four cows and the dog were following her at a leisurely pace. In the tall thickets of maize Maria came upon some deep shell holes. There were three of them, close to one another. Evidently a Soviet gunner, repulsing the advance of enemy tanks, had been firing at one point and the shells had burst close together.

Maria made herself a bed of leaves in the shell hole, thinking she would be warmer there. She adjusted herself as comfortably as she could and covered herself with more leaves. The dog also came down into the shell hole, fidgeted and whimpered for a while, and then curled up against Maria's back.

"That's right, Chum, that's right," Maria told him. "We're both homeless now. Lie down. With you here I won't be so scared."

The cows shuffled about, and then lay down on the edge of the crater.

It was quite dark now. Stars shimmered in the vault of sky. Nothing disturbed the silence. Maria gazed into the starlit sky, and listened alertly to the silence. "Our troops must have retreated far from here because there's not a shot to be heard," she was thinking. "I'm all alone among the enemies, and what I must do now, how can I live, I do not know... But one thing I do know: I've nowhere to go from my village, and I won't go anywhere. My Ivan and Vassya have remained here. And the graves of my father and mother are also here."

In the darkness she heard the dog, grumbling sleepily, turn on his other side. Up there, near the edge of the shell hole the cows were chewing the cud. The closeness of these living creatures comforted Maria, telling her that she was no longer all alone in this frightening world.

In the middle of the night she heard a cock crowing somewhere. Maria had no idea how he had survived and where he was, but this barely audible, home-like sound gladdened her. "In the morning, if all is quiet, I'll go to the village," she decided. "Maybe not everything has burnt down there. Surely I'll find some nook to keep out of the cold? And I can't leave Ivan and Vassya hanging from that poplar... I'll carry them to the cemetery, dig a grave and bury them. I'll bury both in one grave, next to my father and mother, so they'll all be together."

She gazed at the stars through her tears, and these shimmering, tear-blurred stars, the infinite depth of the sky, the strange silence, the smell of the maize moistened by the dew, the warmth of the dog's body and the peaceful sound of the cows chewing the cud, stirred Maria profoundly, compelling her to realise that for the sake of the unborn child she must survive her inconsolable grief, reconcile herself to the thought that the happiness she had known was gone without recall, and go on living.

She fell asleep just before daybreak, and very soon was wakened by the lowing of the cows. She climbed out of the shell hole. Chum was already sitting up there and wagged his tail in welcome, as he used to welcome his former mistress. The cows were chewing the corn cobs, masticating the hard grains and dribbling white foam on to the ground. They turned their heads to Maria. The sun had only just risen, and the withered maize silk looked rosy in the light.

Maria stood there for a minute or two, trying to stifle her sickening fear. "What if there are Germans there?" she thought. "What then? I'll come there, they'll grab me and string me up on that tree ... they'll kill the child in me, and myself too..."

She hesitated a little longer, listening. No, not a sound disturbed the silence, only the champing of the cows behind her. "I'll go," she decided, and slowly headed for the village, keeping close to the maize field so she could hide among the thickets in case of danger. She turned round and saw the cows and the dog following her. When she stopped they, too, stopped at once and stood waiting for her to go on.

And now she saw what only two days ago had been her home village. At the foot of the rise spread a black waste with only the ruins of sooty adobe walls on it and some brick chimneys which had withstood the fire. Old trees were still smoking here and there. It was a windless morning, the smoke went straight up, swaying almost imperceptibly, to melt away and vanish in the cloudless sky. Not a cottage had survived, not a single live tree. Everything was black, dead, mute. The only spot of green were the acacias in the cemetery outside the village. An acrid smell of smoke and burning crept up the rise. Even the crows gave this dead place a wide berth, darting away with alarmed croaks and making for the forest. Only a small flock of domesticated pigeons circled in the sky, now flying low to peer timorously at the black waste where their cotes had been, now soaring up, confused and distressed, to look in vain for asylum in the cool blue.

Maria, small and defenseless in her loneliness, stood on the slope looking down on the burnt-down village in which she grew up, fell in love, worked, married and gave birth to a son, and thought that perhaps none of that had ever happened, that she had dreamed up her Ivan and Vassya, the villagers, her carefree childhood and girlhood, and that there had always been and always would be nothing but this black waste from which rose pale wisps of smoke, to dissolve at once in the autumnal air.

Maria started down the slope. The dog, its ears cocked alertly, walked beside her, and after them came the cows in single file. It appeared that there was not a living soul left in the village.

She stopped before the collective-farm cow-shed—the pride of the villagers. They had built it themselves and finished it just before the outbreak of the war. It was a day of jubilation: in place of the ancient adobe barn with a thatched roof and rotting supports which had once collapsed and crushed eleven cows, there now stood a solid, brick building with plenty of light and good ventilation. Even the secretary of the district Party Committee, who did not dispense praise very readily, thanked the village team, and the regional newspaper gave the names of the best builders and printed a snapshot of the new cow-shed. Maria's and Ivan's names were also there among the best.

And now the cow-shed looked as if it had been hacked in two. The roof had fallen in the middle. And in the door lay two dead calves, their blue tongues hanging, crushed by falling bricks.

The cows, sensing death, did not venture to go near the dead calves and, thronging together behind Maria, lowered their horned heads and pawed the ground. With dilated nostrils they noisily drew in the air smelling of burning, uttered brief lows, and their cries were so plaintive, so stirring with a mother's pain that Maria began to weep.

"Oh, my poor dears," she said to them through her tears. "People didn't spare you either ... there's nothing for it now. What has been done can never be undone... I'll look after you. After all, we're the only living creatures left..."

Glancing about her warily, she went to where the cottages had been, and the nearer she came the hotter grew the road under her bare feet. But she hardly felt it as, with beating heart, she walked on, peering at the black ruins of the burnt cottages. Since childhood she had known the inhabitants of each cottage, and she wanted to believe that they would be coming back any minute now. They'd first appear over there, on the top of the rise, on the edge of the maize field where she had spent those terrible days and nights, they'd remain standing there for a while, looking down on this black waste, and then they would surely come—to start life anew on this hot, ravaged land in which their fathers and forefathers were buried. Believing this, she actually turned to look at the top of the rise, but there was no one there, nothing but the yellow, unharvested maize.

The first cottage on her right belonged to Vera, a childless widow who lived all her life in utter loneliness and who, old though she was, had kept working on the collective farm. In the cottage on the left lived Ignat Vassilyevich, a combine operator, with his large family of five girls, his jolly, talkative wife and his mother-in-law. Vera's and Ignat Vassilyevich's neighbours were the Voinovs and the Goryushins. Once upon a time, that is. They no longer lived there, and there was no knowing where they were. The Germans had marched them off somewhere, and all trace of them was lost. And all that remained of their homes were the rough-stone bases, wall ruins and black brick chimneys.

Maria was walking slowly down the street when a dog's heart-breaking, sobbing howl brought her up short. It was Chum. Recognising his burnt-down home, he had stopped, raised his shaggy head skyward, and broken into a loud, plaintive howl. He sat on the hot ground, stretching out his neck, gazing into the infinite blue and howled, saying goodbye forever to his old master and to his old home which, like the master, had strangely vanished. He had loyally watched this house for many years and now in his canine way he was mourning the passing of what had been his life.

Shaken by his grief, Maria went and put her hand on the dog's head.

"Enough, Chum, there's grief all round here," she spoke to him. "Stop it, please stop. There might be Germans near, if they hear you they'll kill both you and me."

She walked on. With hanging head Chum trotted beside her, while the cows followed them at a distance, afraid of losing the only human being there was.

Here were the ruins of the team office and the poplar. The poplar...

She stopped, and stood stock-still. The poplar was as black and scorched as everything else around it. The thin twigs had burnt away, and it looked like a charred skeleton. There were no bodies hanging from the poplar or lying anywhere near it. The timber, brick-faced team office had been razed to the ground, save for one wall which towered over a heap of ashes.

Maria put her arms round the still warm poplar and pressed her cheek to the trunk. She remained thus for a long time, seeing neither the sun, nor the clear blue of the sky. In those moments she was aware only of the rough, warm bark of the charred tree on which her husband and her son had died. There was no one she could tell about her grief. No one to tell her where the enemies had taken the bodies of the people they had executed, no one to show her where their remains lay. Would she find them, to weep over the two people who were dearest to her in the world, carry them to the cemetery, as honour and decency required, and bury them in the earth where their ancestors who had lived out their span now rested in peace?

Chum came up to Maria, rubbed his head against her knees, and raised his clear nut-brown eyes to her imploringly, as if he wanted to say: "Come, woman. Crying won't help. The living must live."

She patted the dog, and with drooping head walked away from the poplar. In the middle of the road she saw the red tin sign that had been torn off the team office door. It was Ivan who about a year and a half ago had done the lettering in white on the red ground: "TEAM THREE OF THE LENIN COLLECTIVE FARM". She remembered that day so well: Vassya stood at his elbow, watching his father raptly, handing him now a pot of paint, now a ruler, now some nails, and then washed the brushes in kerosene. Bees were humming in the crowns of the blossoming cherry trees. The team was preparing to celebrate May Day, and everyone was happy and gay. Maria was busy making pies and turning out the house, but she took a minute off to scold Vassya for smearing his brand new shirt with paint. After dinner Ivan and Vassya took the sign to the team's office, nailed it to the front door, and then Uncle Fyodor, the team leader, fixed a red flag with a silver-painted pole above the sign. When they came from work that evening, the villagers admired the sign and the flag, praised Ivan and teased Vassya about getting all that paint over him.

And now the sign was lying in the middle of the road. A German lorry had driven over it, smashing the wooden frame and squashing the rectangle of red tin into the ground. Beside it lay a pitchfork, the wooden handle only scorched on one side. It was hers, Maria recognised it at once and remembered how on that terrible night when the Germans seized Ivan she had been fixing the small rick of hay in her yard which the neighbours' calf had ravaged, and how, still holding the pitchfork, she had run after the crowd to the team office. She must have dropped the pitchfork when she fainted, and no one had picked it up. She also remembered how Ivan had puttered with that pitchfork, tempering the prongs in the smithy, sharpening each one with a file, and then working on the willow handle to give it a bend for a good grip and easy wielding.

Maria felt sorry for the squashed sign. She picked it up together with the pitchfork, and went down the road to where her home had once stood. Passing Uncle Kornei's place she saw an overturned cart, a dead German soldier and a dead horse. The German was elderly and fat, his puffy cheeks bristling with a dark growth. His head had been split in two. The reddish-brown horse, a huge animal the size of an elephant, had been killed with a shell splinter in the belly. Beside the overturned cart lay two enormous thermos flasks. One of them had lost its aluminium cap and inside Maria saw some remains of coffee. She was miserable with hunger. She unscrewed the cap on the other thermos flask: it was full of mashed potatoes with tiny pieces of smoked sausage. She ate a little, scooping the cold mashed potatoes with her hands, and then fed Chum, who pounced on the food greedily. She was dying of thirst now. She took a gulp of the bitter coffee, and then went to the well, to drink her fill of water and give some to the dog and the cows who followed hard on her heels.

The well was the only one in the village, it was just off the road, between the two rows of cottages. The timber frame, bound with metal hoops, the oakwood windlass and the iron chain were undamaged. Even the pail stood there. Maria ran to it, took one look into the well, and recoiled. The swollen bodies of cats and dogs were floating on the water. Luckily there was some water left in the pail. Maria quenched her thirst, gave a little to the dog, and then to each of the four cows—a mere drop. They must have gone without water for a long time. She could not tear them away from the pail, they clamoured for more, knocking their horns on the empty bottom.

"Bear it a little longer," Maria comforted them. "If everything's quiet, I'll drive you to the river tomorrow and you'll drink your fill..."

She turned round, glanced at the dead German soldier and the horse, and thought: "They should be buried. If only I could find a shovel. I've still strength enough to bury the man, but what am I to do with that huge dead horse? Maybe the ravens will pick it clean." She walked on, with the sign and the pitchfork in her hands. She walked slowly, haunted by fear which she tried to suppress. What if a German with a tommy-gun suddenly leapt out from behind a chimney and killed her together with her unborn child? But there was not a living soul about, and the silence was as oppressive and eerie as in an old neglected graveyard.

Before Maria's eyes there were only grey ashes and black soot. Ashes and soot. And a sharp smell of burning that choked her and made her cough. "If only one house had been left whole, just a roof over my head... Where am I to live? It will turn cold soon, there'll be rain, snow and frost, and there's not a board left here, not a nail, not a piece of glass. They destroyed and burnt everything, the beasts."

Every household had an orchard once. It was on Uncle Fyodor's initiative that the trees had been planted. For years he had reproached the villagers for letting their yards grow over with nettles, burdocks and weeds, he reasoned and pleaded, and finally deciding that he was wasting breath he asked the chairman to let him have a lorry, went to a nursery many miles away, brought back six hundred excellent saplings—apple, pear, cherry and plum—and that same day distributed them among the villagers at cost. Each household received twenty saplings. And people tended and mothered them, watering and fertilising them regularly, sprinkling them with insecticide and white-washing the young trunks. Just before the war, the trees began to bear fruit. The village became unrecognisable with the cottages nestling amid the lush orchards.

As Maria walked down the street she could not see for tears. Nearly all the orchards were gone. Nothing but charred sticks remained of the trees planted nearest the houses; a bit further away the charred apple, pear and plum trees were still smoking faintly, and only at the very rear of the orchards there were a few solitary cherry trees whose leaves, only licked by fire, remained green.

Maria turned to the right in the hope of finding some fallen apples. She could walk through anyone's yard: there were no fences, no gates left. The ground in the yards was hotter than in the road, it hadn't cooled yet. In the yard of Frossya, her cousin, Maria found a tin pail, a shovel and a rake lying beside a patch of onions. Frossya must have been about to dig up the onions on that fateful evening. She had been married to Lukyan for nine years, but no children were born to them. When the war was in its second year, Frossya received a notification that her husband was among the missing. "There's no Lukyan and no Frossya any more," Maria thought. "Everything has perished—trees and people..."

Finding no fallen apples, Maria went on dragging feet to where her house had stood only a few days ago. Her heart was hammering, her hands were shaking. With an effort she mastered her desire to turn and run, run anywhere only so she would not see this heap of dead ashes and the dead trees, but her tired legs drew her on to the place where she had known the joy of a wife and a mother, the happiness that a person is granted only once in his lifetime and which can never be repeated.

Here were the two iron angle bars on which Ivan had once hung the gate. Nothing remained but these two angle bars and the narrow path, paved with broken brick, running from the gate to the front porch. The path ran nowhere now and ended in a black void. And it seemed to Maria that everything had turned black—the sky, the fields, the hills. She fell down, and no longer fearing anything and lost to the world gave vent to her shuddering sobs, wailing at the top of her voice and clawing at the hot ground with her lacerated fingers.

Chum also began to howl. His deep, husky howl now subsided to a barely audible whimper, now it rose higher and higher, throbbing with a savage lament for the people who were gone and the village that lay dead.

The howl brought Maria to her senses. Supposing the enemies

heard her wailing amid these black ruins? She got up and gulping her tears walked to the ruins of her home. Leaning on the pitchfork and holding the sign in her left hand, she stood before the rough-stone foundation. She did not consciously will the thoughts that flickered across her mind: the kitchen was over there, the parlour here, and there the bedroom... Vassya slept on the couch in the parlour ... in this corner here stood her mother's rubber plant on a stool, and in the space between the windows the small cupboard where she kept her crockery, and on that wall hung an enlarged photograph of her father...

She stood there with drooping head. For a moment she believed again that it was only a bad dream, that she would come awake and see before her the clean blue walls of her little house, the freshly painted carved window surrounds, with a touch of blue added to the white paint, and her front porch on which lay a floor-mat cleverly woven from fine wire. However, the lowing of the cows, the soft whimpering of the dog and, above all, the nauseating smell of burning and smoke brought Maria down to earth again and, stifling a rising shriek of despair, she told herself that the burnt-down cottages, the death of her husband and son, Sanya's grave in the maize field, the dead German and the dead horse in the village street were the reality from which there was no escape.

Looking about her at her yard she suddenly remembered their cellar. She could hide there from the rain and the snow, from frost and enemy bullets, she could live there, in the cellar.

It was shortly before the war that Ivan and Maria had dug out this cellar a little way from the house. It was very deep and roomy, the properly levelled walls and floor were plastered with clay mixed with horse dung. In one of the walls Ivan made a tunnel for storing potatoes in winter. That autumn, their team had been putting the finishing touches to the new cow-shed, and Uncle Fyodor let Ivan take a dozen of the discarded concrete beams. Ivan trimmed them to a length and roofed the cellar with them, after which he and Maria heaped a lot of earth on top, about a metre high, and rammed it compactly. A length of pipe with a flue was fitted into the roof to give an outlet to the stagnant air in the cellar and keep the vegetables from rotting.

Beside the cellar grew the Grandfather's old apple tree. In the summer its spreading branches cast a protective shade and it was cool inside the cellar even in the sultriest days of July. Ivan's father had long ago placed a flat slab of rough stone under the tree and, sitting on it, he would mend the harness, do some carpentering, or just doze in the shade.

"I'll live in the cellar, fire couldn't have touched it," Maria decided. It looked undamaged, even the wooden trap door was not scorched. She reached for the handle to raise the heavy trap, but pulled it back, frightened by the behaviour of the dog. He was running in circles, sniffing the ground, and then suddenly froze to a standstill. The fur on his back stood up on end. Baring his sharp fangs, he snarled menacingly.

Clutching the pitchfork, Maria opened the trap, and sprang back: sitting on the floor of the cellar, leaning against a tub, was a live German soldier. He stared at her with unblinking eyes. He had a haggard, exhausted look, a thin boyish neck, and was wounded: his grey army jacket was unbuttoned and there was dark red blood on his undershirt. In that fleeting moment Maria saw that the German was afraid of her, and realised that he was unarmed.

Leaning over, she looked at him in silence. His light blue eyes, dilated with horror, never left her face. His lips trembled and twitched in a pathetic parody of a smile, but he was too numb with fear to utter a word. He looked no more than seventeen. The curly fair hair, matted on his sweating brow, the thin, dirty hands flung out so helplessly, the thin white neck, and the fluff on his cheeks and upper lip, betrayed in this wounded German soldier a lop-eared pup, a terrified kid.

Hatred and a wave of hot, blind anger swept over Maria, constricting her heart and bringing a lump of nausea into her throat. A red mist filmed her eyes, and in that flimsy mist she saw the silent crowd of villagers, Ivan swinging from the poplar, Fenya's bare feet, the black noose on Vassya's childish neck, and the executioners dressed in grey uniforms with a black band on the sleeve. And here, in her cellar, lay one of them, a half-squashed Nazi slug, dressed in that same grey uniform with a black band on his left sleeve with the same foreign letters on it in silver.

Maria leaned lower into the cellar. She gripped the pitchfork so tight that her knuckles turned white. In a hoarse voice she couldn't know for her own she said:

"So what do we do now? You tell me one thing: where is my husband Ivan, and where is my son Vassya? And one more thing: What did you strangle Fenya for, and kill Sanya? You won't talk? Alright, don't talk..."

She let her feet down into the cellar, and stood on the first rung of the ladder. Then she went down and stood for a minute on the second rung, clutching the pitchfork, never taking her eyes off the German.

"So you won't talk?" she repeated. "You know nothing and you can say nothing, is that it? And you don't know who marched our people off into salvery... You don't know who burnt down our village and shot our animals either... You're lying, you louse. You know everything and just now you're going to answer for everything."

Maria descended slowly into the cellar, stopping on every rung, remembering that each rung—there were nine in all—was bringing her ever closer to that inevitable deed which she had to accomplish in the name of supreme justice and which in her fevered mind was justified by the words of a prayer she had heard from her old grandmother when she was a little girl: "Christ has risen from the dead, defeating death with death". True, she had interpreted these words in her own way, and now they seemed to demand: kill the killer!

Here was the last rung. Maria stopped, then put her foot down on the floor. The German stirred. He wanted to move back, crawl behind the tub into the corner, but fear had paralyzed his weakened body. Already from the first, when Maria's head appeared in the open trap, he had known from the look on her face that he was to die. Death was approaching him, and death was this small, brown-eyed woman who planted her strong bare feet so firmly on the ground. With every second the three sharp prongs were bringing his end nearer, and nearer.

Maria raised her pitchfork high, averted her face a little so as not to see the frightening deed she had to perpetrate, and in that moment heard a small, choking cry which to her sounded like a thunder bolt:

"Mama! Mama! "

She felt stabbed in her breast by countless red-hot daggers, the faint cry pierced her heart, and the word "mama" made her wince from unbearable pain. She dropped the pitchfork, and her legs gave way. She fell on her knees and in that instant before she fainted saw a pair of boyish eyes, light blue and filled with tears, very very close...

The touch of damp hands aroused her. Gasping with sobs, the German was stroking her hand and saying something in his language which Maria did not know. But from the expression on his face and his gesturing hands Maria understood that he was telling her about himself. He had never killed anyone, his mother was a peasant woman like herself, his father had been killed at Smolensk, he himself had been mobilised and despatched to the front no sooner had he finished school, he had not been in any battles yet and only delivered food to the soldiers. Three days ago he had been driving in the cart with that fat, elderly German, whose body now lay in the street, a Soviet plane had dropped a bomb on them, killing his elder comrade and the horse, and wounding him in the chest, after which he had crawled here and hidden in the cellar.

Maria wept in silence. The death of her husband and son, the burning of the village, seeing all their people being taken off somewhere, and then those agonising days and nights all alone in the maize field, had overtaxed her strength, and she wanted to weep out her sorrow, to tell someone about it, to this first living person she had come upon. To be sure, he wore the hateful grey uniform of the enemy, but he was gravely wounded and, besides, he was a mere youngster and obviously could not be a murderer. The thought horrified Maria that only a few minutes ago, blindly obeying the impulse of violence and vengeance, she might have murdered him. It had only been the sacred word "Mama", the plea which the poor boy had put into his faint, sobbing cry that had saved him.

Gingerly she unbuttoned the neck of his blood-stained shirt, ripped it open a little more and bared his narrow chest. On the right side there were two wounds, crusted with blood. As carefully she pulled off his jacket, turned the boy over on his side, and examined his back. There was only one wound there, and Maria guessed that the second splinter was embedded somewhere in his chest.

The German watched the woman bending over him in silence, controlling his moans, and then crossed two fingers on his chest and asked quietly:

"Kaput?"

"Why kaput?" Maria said, averting her eyes. "You'll live."

Cupping her hands as though she were holding a glass and raising them to her lips, she asked:

"You're thirsty, I guess?"

He nodded.

"Wait a bit, I'll milk one of the cows and give you some milk. There's no water in the village."

In a dark corner of the cell she found a clay bowl, and climbed out of the cellar. Chum and the cows were waiting for her under the apple tree. Clutching the bowl between her knees she milked first one cow, then the next one, thinking meanwhile: "He won't pull through, he'll die, and I won't be able to save him." She felt sorry for that youngster, and for herself too, because she'd be all alone again with no one to talk to. Even though she did not know German and he did not know Russian, they could anyway speak to each other like deaf mutes with their hands, eyes and heads. She did understand, didn't she, when he tried to tell her that his father and mother had done farm work, and that he himself had not killed anyone and had never been in battle yet?

Stepping carefully, so as not to spill the milk, Maria went down into the cellar. She squatted beside the German, and supporting his hot head with a hand gave him a drink of milk. Clutching her hand, he gave a whimper, closed his eyes and dozed off. Maria sat beside him for a long time, looking at his pallid face. The shadow cast on his cheeks by his reddish eyelashes made his face seem all the more waxen; his bloodless, swollen lips twitched.

"No, you're not long for this world," she was thinking with pain and pity. "And what are you in this blazing hell for anyway? A tiny speck no one gives a hang for. Did you need this war, did you want to fight? You did not, I'm pretty sure. You didn't know our country, our village or me. You lived in that Germany of yours and worked on the farm with your father and mother. You went to school, got bad marks sometimes I'll bet, and came home with a tear in your pants, just like my Vassya... And then they went and stuck you into this mincing machine, and on that ended your life which you hadn't even begun to live... And here you'll die, you poor thing, in our village, and I'll have to bury you. And there, in your Germany, your poor mother will weep her eyes out for years and years, mourning her son, and no one will tell her and she'll never know why you had to die in a foreign land..."

Gently she freed her hand, and started tidying up the cellar, moving as quietly as she could. She carried out the old tub, and whatever rubbish there was. She remembered that a few small hayricks had been left standing on the meadow at the edge of the forest, and decided to go there and fetch an armful for the dying German to lie on. She made her way timorously, on the alert for Germans. Maria could not know that the line of fighting had moved a long way eastward. There was not a sound to be heard. The sun was going down on a gentle, windless day. When Maria reached the hayricks, she sat down to rest against one, and suddenly noticed a mound, sprinkled with leaves, on the edge of the wood. That mound had not been there before. Glancing about her warily, she went there and discovered that it was an abandoned German dug-out. She entered it and when she had found her bearings in the semi-darkness she discovered some rolls of gauze, two mess-tins, and under the low plank-bed nailed together from unplaned boards—a broken mirror and a cloth-covered flask with a plastic screw-on cap to drink from. She collected all these things and decided she'd come back to dismantle the plank-bed and take the boards to her cellar.

A little distance away there was another, similar dug-out. A knife bayonet was stuck into a tree beside it, and Maria took it along. "Everything will come in handy now," she was thinking, as she picked up a pair of brown socks, stiff from sweat, a half-filled writing pad with a pencil stub, a field lantern with a melted stearin candle in it, a soap dish with a cake of pink soap, and a ball of telephone wire. She put all this stuff in the mess-tins.

But her happiest find was a small, solidly made iron stove, complete with a sectional pipe, a ring, doors and an ash-pit. The stove was what she needed most. October was coming with its usual icy rains, and in the stove she saw her salvation. "I'll come back for it this very evening," she decided. She tied the hay with wire, hoisted it on her back, and clutching the mess-tins, the flask and everything else she had found in the dug-outs, started back to her cellar. The German was no longer asleep, he welcomed her with a feeble smile, pointed a finger at himself, then Maria, then the entrance to the cellar, and waved goodbye.

Maria understood what he wanted to say:

"I thought you had left me for good."

She shook her head, and said:

"Oh no. Here I've brought some hay to make a bed for you so you won't have to lie on the bare floor. And I've found something for myself too, I've got to get ready for winter, or we'll perish in the cold."

With quick, deft hands she spread out and smoothed the hay, shifted the wounded man on to it, and put under his head his grey uniform jacket, stiff from blood. Gesticulating to make her meaning clearer, she told him:

"I'll leave you for a little while, I must go back to the forest and bring the stove. That's one thing I can't do without. There's no one there now, no Germans, no Russians. And there's no firing anywhere, the fighting must have moved on somewhere far..."

The stove and the pipe turned out to be pretty heavy. Every so often Maria had to take a rest, sitting on the stove laid on its side. Dropping her tired hands on her knees she gazed at the little river, pink in the sunset, and at the valley on the other side, along which barely distinguishable country roads ran away into the distance. She could clearly see the meandering lines of the trenches, the breastwork with no grass sprouting on the dark earth as yet, a tank which had been put out of action standing behind the yellowish brush of reeds, and a little further away—two lorries, one of them lying on its side, and the other standing beside it like a silent sentinel. The whole of that recent battlefield, pitted with black shell holes stuffed with corpses, and humping with the brown mounds over the abandoned dug-outs, was so strangely quiet and desolate as if no machine-gun bullets had ever danced on it crazily, no heavy shells had exploded, and no soldiers had died on it, screaming and wheezing in agony.

Maria's heart ached at the sight. It seemed only the other day that this mutilated land had looked so beautiful and green with the neat fields of winter wheat, rye and barley, the vegetable gardens, and the pastures covered with couch-grass. Year after year, like the other villagers, Maria had waded across the small, shallow river to plant tomatoes, cucumbers and cabbages. In those first years as a member of the collective farm she had walked behind the reaper, bound sheaves, weeded the fields, shepherded pigs and cows, and later, just before the war, had become a milkmaid. In short, she had done her share of all the hard, never-ending work which farming had enough of for everyone. It was gruelling work, and at the time it seemed too trying, but what she remembered now were the clear and peaceful skies above, the nightingales singing at sunrise and sundown in the riverside poplars, she remembered coming home from work to her lovely new house, lighting the white-washed brick stove Ivan had built in the yard, warming up the supper, giving Vassya a scolding for getting into some mischief or other, and then, the moment Ivan returned, looking tired and swarthy from the sun and the dust, sitting down to their evening meal at the small, low garden table.

There was no Ivan any more, no Vassya, no fields, no nightingales, no hearth, no home, nothing. Nothing was left her, nothing but the slowly cooling ashes, the dark cellar and in it a gravely wounded, dying youngster, an enemy whose mother would not live to welcome home.

When Maria got back she saw the four cows lying down not far from the cellar, and there was Chum welcoming her as he would his true mistress, running about her, wagging his tail and yelping affectionately. She set the heavy stove down on the ground, and then, stepping carefully, descended into the cellar. There was little light to see by. Listening to the breathing of the German, she guessed that he was asleep. Maria sighed and lay down beside him, tucking in the hay so she would not touch him. "Let him sleep," she thought. "And tomorrow I must bury that dead German who's lying in the street."

Utterly exhausted, she fell asleep at once. She dreamed of her father and mother. Each held her by the hand, they were both young and good-looking, they were taking her somewhere and it was such fun because they were in the midst of a noisy, glittering fair: there were jolly merry-go-rounds, a band was playing, shiny beads of every colour were on display at the booths, and under glass lay sweet honey cakes and long candies wrapped in red paper with bushy frills at the ends. Maria asked her father to buy her a candy and he, jungling the copper coins in his pocket, chose the largest one there was. "Here you are, eat it, daughter," he said. Maria took the candy and shuddered with horror: it wasn't a candy, it was someone's hot hand, sticky with blood...

She moaned and whimpered in her sleep and did not feel the dying German boy pressing his face to her hand, she did not hear him whisper choking with tears: "Mama... Mama."

At daybreak, when the German saw that Maria had awakened he gave her a weak smile, sighed, tapped his chest with a forefinger and said in a husky whisper:

"Werner Bracht", repeating the name again and again.

He made the sign of the cross with his fingers and traced in the air the name "Werner Bracht" on an imaginary tombstone.

"Werner Bracht," he said again. "Werner Bracht."

"Your name's Werner, is it?" Maria asked.

"Werner Bracht," he said softly.

Maria looked at his pallid face and his bloodless lips.

"So your name's Werner," she said pensively. "Ah you, Werner, Werner! You didn't want to start this war, did you? And you never thought, you poor thing, that you'd die in this village of ours, which hasn't got even a proper name, it was simply called Team Three of the Lenin Collective Farm. And even that it isn't called any more."

"Lenin?" the German asked.

"Yes, Lenin."

"Lenin karasho, Hitler nicht karasho," he said.

"That's how you talk now," Maria said with a harsh rebuke. "Now that you're at death's door Lenin has become good and Hitler bad? Right? And what were you about before? I'll bet you also hanged and robbed people and set their homes on fire."

He understood from the tone of her voice and the look in her eyes that she was blaming him for something very wicked, and he tried to tell her that neither he nor his parents had wanted to fight, that his father had been arrested twice by the Gestapo and tortured brutally, that his elder brother had been killed at Vyazma, leaving three young children.

Maria listened hard into the foreign speech, trying to understand what this wounded boy was talking about so heatedly, why he was looking at her with tear-reddened eyes, but she could not understand a thing.

"Alright, you can't be held to answer now. You lie down and wait,

I'll go and milk the cows. Maybe I'll nurse you back to life, you poor thing, and then you'll see right from wrong for yourself."

Maria took the mess-tin and climbed out of the cellar. Day was breaking. The cows lay side by side calmly, chewing the cud. Chum appeared from behind the apple tree. Behind him, timidly wagging her tail, came a scrawny white bitch. Maria knew the dog, her name was Lady and she belonged to Fenya whom the Germans had executed.

"Come here, Lady, come to me, good doggie," Maria said. "So you've survived, have you? Oh well, stay with us then, there's room for you."

She milked the cows and went down into the cellar. Holding up the German's head, she told him in a soft voice:

"Here, drink some milk."

Reluctantly he took two gulps, and said again:

"Werner Bracht".

"I know, I'll remember your name," Maria told him. "You stay here alone for a bit, I must go and bury your mate, and do something about the dead horse. They're still lying there in the street."

Werner Bracht understood that she had to go away and do something and that she would come back.

"I'll be back, don't worry," Maria said.

The sun had risen. Only here and there whiffs of rosy smoke still curled up from the black ruins. The dead German had already become covered with purple spots, his unshaven cheeks were bloated, and flies swarmed round his half-open mouth. Bending over him, Maria searched his pockets and found several letters, folded in four and frayed along the edges, a cigarette holder with lots of tooth marks on it, an opened pack of cigarettes and a nearly empty matchbox. She looked at his boots. They were almost new boots with wide, hard legs.

"You've no use for boots now, and they'll do me well, seeing that I've been left bare-footed thanks to you," she was thinking. She tried to pull them off, but the boots wouldn't budge. The corpse had stiffened a long time ago, and the feet would not bend. Maria went back home, as she now thought of the cellar, took the sharp bayonet she had found the day before, and gave Werner Bracht the letters she had taken from his dead mate's pocket.

"Read them meanwhile," she told him. "After all, he was a comrade of yours, and you understand the language. Read them, it'll help to pass the time..."

Although no sound disturbed the silence and there was not a living soul about, save the two dogs trotting behind Maria, she walked quickly, glancing about her all the time for fear that someone would attack her from behind and strangle her with his hands, or someone else would shoot her from a distance. She could not fight off fear, a sticky, nauseating fear, and she almost forgot that only two or three days ago she had prayed for death and wanted to put an end to her life herself. But even in those terrible days when her husband and her son were murdered before her very eyes and when Sanya died in the maize field, even then her unborn child had reminded her, faintly at first and then more and more powerfully of its existence, demanding its right to live. Now that Maria had found a place to live in, securely hidden from the eyes of men, and started making ready for the winter, procuring everything that might come in useful, the indistinct yet imperious appeal of her unborn child filled the whole of her being, and the thought of dying frightened her.

Squatting beside the dead German, she ripped the seams on his boots with the point of the bayonet and pulled them off easily. She cast a cursory glance at the brown socks with holes on the heels, wound the length of wire she had round the corpse and dragged it to the shell-hole not far away, stopping often and breathing laboriously. She stood for a minute on the edge of the shell-hole, then took the wire off the corpse and pushed it down. The body rolled easily down the steep side and lay face down on the bottom.

"It's not proper for you to lie like that," Maria said. "Your children will grieve and weep over you, I suppose..."

She went down the street, took the spade Fenya had dropped in her kitchen garden, tore off a large burdock leaf, gingerly slid down into the shell-hole, turned over the body, covered the face with the burdock leaf, and started shoveling earth on top. The soil on the slopes of the shell-hole was soft and flaccid, but Maria soon tired, sweat trickled down her neck and her tattered dress stuck to her back. Still, she toiled on diligently, trying to give the man a proper burial.

"Well, that's that now," she spoke aloud, wiping the sweat off her brow. "Sleep in peace. No hungry dogs or beasts will get at you now."

The dogs—Chum and Lady—were lying on the rim of the shell-hole, watching Maria. "Of course the dogs are hungry, they can't live on milk. I guess I'll have to let them eat the dead horse," Maria was thinking. She remembered that in the backyard of the collective farm there had always been a mountain of salt, caked to the hardness of stone, from which the shepherds hacked off huge lumps and took them away to the pastures for the sheep to lick. Maria herself had often taken some for the cows and the calves.

She went to the farm. The mountain of salt was intact and only covered with a thick layer of ashes and red brick dust. The rest of the day Maria was busy with the dead German horse. It was a hard job getting it unharnessed. And skinning the animal was no easier for someone who'd never done it before. She hacked up the horseflesh into pieces with the bayonet, surprised that it was still quite fresh, then cleaned out the cart into which the horse had been harnessed, and put the horseflesh in it, sprinkling each layer thickly with salt. She hauled the cart into the shade of the only surviving wall of the team's office, went to the maize field, cut a lot of leaves, neatly covered the horseflesh with them and put some soot-black bricks on top, to keep them in place.

The skeleton of the horse was left lying in the middle of the street. Chum and Lady were picking it clean, grunting and licking their muzzles.

During the day Maria made several trips back to the cellar to see how Werner Bracht was. She found him sleeping, his arms thrown out. His breathing was uneven, laboured and wheezy, and he kept shuddering in his sleep. Looking at his waxen feet, the strange yellowness of the nails looking all the deader for the dirt around them, Maria said to herself: "No, fellow, you're not long for this world."

She went and sat on the stone slab near the cellar. It was a mellow hour preceding dusk. The cows returned from the river along the path they knew well. The dogs, replete with horseflesh, were dozing at Maria's feet. Pigeons were circling in the clear blue sky above. They had appeared from beyond the horizon, and were flying low over the black waste, now almost touching ground, now soaring in fright from this unrecognisable place where there were no slate roofs on the cottages any longer, no cottages, and no dove-cotes where it had been so nice to rest after a flight into the steppe.

Maria recognised the pigeons. They belonged to Styopka, the son of the lame Uncle Kornei. Styopka was the same age as Sanya, but unlike her he was a poor scholar, and his father only allowed him to get the pigeons he had long been hankering after when he started doing much better in school. That was three years ago. At the district centre Styopka bought some beautiful red-winged tumblers and all the villagers admired them. At dawn they woke up the village with their loud cooing, they strutted about dragging their wings along the ground, and when Styopka flushed them they performed such breathtaking somersaults in the clear sky that even the old men stopped and stared, craning their necks and smacking their lips appreciatively. Two pairs of his pigeons he gave Vassya for a present.

The pigeons kept circling over the village, flying low where their

home had been only a few days ago, flying off again and coming back
to look for their lost haven.

All of a sudden an old red pigeon with a white star above his short
beak swooped down abruptly, frightening Maria with his flapping
wings, alighted on her knees, fidgeted for a bit and then, blowing out
his beautiful, pearly neck, started calling his flock. And there were all
the pigeons at Maria's feet, they surrounded her trustingly, shaking
their wings and cooing imploringly.

Maria could not help crying.

"Poor little orphans," she whispered tenderly. "You've no roof
over your heads, no one to tell your troubles to. You can't stand a
cold winter, you're afraid of deep snow and hunger, you can't do
without people. Don't fret, I'll fetch a lot of corn cobs, grind the
grains between two stones, and you'll have food enough to last you
the winter."

After that the flock, placing their trust in the only human being
there, spent every night in the old apple tree, in the morning they
surrounded Maria, waiting while she ground some maize for them,
then they flew off into the steppe to feed on the wheat left unreaped
in the fields, and in the evening returned home to Maria. They would
sit on her shoulders and her head, and let her take them into her
hands, bringing them close to her face to peer into their amber eyes
and kiss them on their short, strong beaks.

The day after she had buried the German, Maria decided to clean
out the well, cluttered with dead cats and dogs. The water in the river
smelt of slime and could not be drunk. It was a problem getting the
large dogs out of the well, and as she pondered she suddenly
remembered that Zorka, one of the four miraculously spared cows,
had been trained by her mistress just before the war to wear a harness
and pull a cart loaded with straw, brushwood or the grass she used to
mow in the ditches lining the roads.

The harness she had taken off the dead horse would come in useful, Maria thought. But it turned out to be much too big for the short
cow. With the help of wire Maria shortened the breech-band and the
traces, fitted the handle of her spade under the traces in place of the
swingle-tree, harnessed the cow, and got down to the back-breaking,
filthy job. Carefully, she lowered herself into the well. She tied wire
round each dead body and shouted to the docile cow:

"Hey, Zorka, come on, giddy up! "

Spreading her legs wide and bracing her feet against the projecting
timbers, Maria pushed up the next body, dumped it on the ground,
unwound the wire round it, and went back into the well. When she

had done with all the dead things, she scooped all the water out of the rather shallow well, and cleaned the sandy bottom, cluttered with all sorts of junk: rusty pails, tin mugs dropped by children, cans and bottles. When she climbed out she was wet through, covered with filth and shivering with cold. She ran to the river, pulled off her dirty rags and quickly washed herself clean. While she was there she thought she'd go along the abandoned Soviet trenches on the other side of the river. Naked, her long, wet hair hanging loose, she stepped carefully with her bare feet over the rifles, lying in the trenches, over the cartridge cases and balls of barbed wire, thinking with fear and pity of the men who had died only the other day in these hastily dug dark, damp ditches. Under her feet she saw scraps of white paper, trampled letters—the last messages which the soldiers had received from their families; dark, greasy rags and the gleam of unspent cartridges in the niches.

Where the long trench made a turn she nearly fell down, tripping over a rolled-up greatcoat, stiff with blood. It must have done as a pillow for someone wounded in the head; he had lain there, bleeding copiously, and then he was carried away and the greatcoat was left behind. Maria tried to unroll it, but the blood had congealed, and she had to use all her strength to unstick the stiff folds.

She needed that coat. There was hardly anything left of her dress. She ran to the river, looking behind her all the time as though there was anyone there to pursue her, put the coat in the water, rubbed it clean of blood with sand, wrung it out with great difficulty, and carried it home. She found some smouldering coals in the neighbouring yard, put some dry brushwood and weeds over them, fanned the fire to a good flame, and squatted near to warm herself, holding the heavy, wet greatcoat in her outstretched arms.

Afterwards, she milked the cows, fed the dogs, and took the messtin down to Werner Bracht. He looked worse. He looked at Maria with feverish eyes, ran his tongue over his dry lips, and took no more than a sip of milk. His hands were damp and hot.

"What am I to do with you? How can I help you?" Maria asked, shaking her head sadly. "Where can I find a doctor when there's only death and devastation all round?"

Werner Bracht did not speak, and only smiled weakly. Maria was afraid that he would die that night in complete darkness, and so she melted a little horse fat over the fire, twisted a bit of rag to make a wick, lit it, and placed this oil lamp of sorts in a corner of the cellar.

The tremulous tiny flame barely illumined the German's haggard, boyish face. He gazed at the flame for a long time with unblinking eyes, then held his hands out to Maria and said, as in that first minute: "Mama... Mama..."

And Maria realised that she was the last person this doomed German was to see in his life, that in these bitter and solemn hours of his parting with life she stood for everything that still tied him to the living—his mother, his father, the sky, the earth, his native German soil, the trees, the vast and beautiful world which was slowly withdrawing from the dying boy's consciousness. The skinny, dirty hands stretched out to her, the dimming glance, beseeching and despairing, told her that she was his only hope, that he had not lost hope that it was in her power to save his dwindling life and fight off death.

And then all the grief and horror she had suffered during those terrible days overwhelmed her, and she burst into sobs. She dropped her head on Werner Bracht's hands, her damp, uncombed hair covered his face, and she began to keen:

"Oh, my darling son Vassya! My poor mite, don't leave me, stay with me if only a little longer, don't leave me all alone..."

In her feverish thoughts everything had become fused together—her little boy, hanged by the Germans, the dying young German soldier, Ivan, Fenya, the murdered Sanya, and all the deaths she had seen in those short days that were so full of horror and blood, and clinging to Werner Bracht's hot hands and tear-stained face she sobbed her heart out, while he stroked her rough hands with weakening fingers and whispered: "Mama, Mama..."

Just before daylight he fell into a coma. A gurgling breath burst in fits and starts from his bared and bandaged chest, his lips twitched and his wide-open, staring eyes expressed nothing, neither pain nor suffering, only that strange and uncanny estrangement from everything which comes to a man at that last, invisible line which divides life from death.

Clasping her knees, Maria sat motionlessly beside Werner Bracht holding his cooling hands. When she saw through the chink in the trap opening that the sun had risen, she got up, snuffed out the burning wick, and opened the trap door. Cool, fresh air burst into the cellar and ruffled the fair hair on the helplessly lolling head of the dying man.

Maria climbed the ladder and stopped on the top rung. The world was radiant in its autumnal beauty. The sun was shining, feathery clouds sailed across the blue sky, thinning out and lazily dissolving. The smell of smoke and burning had almost gone, and through that vanishing smell there wafted from the fields the scent of dew-sprinkled straw, of withered grasses, and the first early morning frosts. A flock of geese flew unhurriedly southward, calling to one another with their exciting, guttural cries. And right below a man, little more than a boy, by name of Werner Bracht was dying, sent to his senseless, stupid death by the wicked and avaricious rulers of his country, by people whom he, a poor peasant's son, had never seen or wished to see, and at whose pleasure he now lay dying before he had really lived, before he had known love or hate...

Werner Bracht died at about noon. Maria closed his eyes for him, smoothed his tousled hair, and placed her hand on his cooling forehead. Looking intently into that boyish face, she thought: "So you've done your span on earth. From what I could see you were still an honest, clean lad with no murders or blood on your soul. Like all children you missed your father and mother. That's why you clung to me and called me mama... When you, children, are in trouble or pain you always remember your mothers... But I wonder what you'd have grown into if you hadn't been killed, if you hadn't died? God alone knows. Your friends and elders would have quickly taught you to do what they're doing themselves... And you, too, would go killing people and raping girls like Sanya, you'd execute people and burn their homes down on their own land, not yours... Maybe it's better, after all, that you died while you were still clean..."

She sat beside him a little longer. Then she wiped her tears thinking that life had to go on, no matter what, that she had to carry the body out of this dark, gloomy hole where she was fated to live, and afterwards fix up this wretched dwelling of hers for the coming winter...

Carrying out the body was not easy. First, she dragged it to the ladder, with difficulty stood it upright, and started pushing it up, her heart pumping strenuously as she hefted the dead weight. When the body was half out of the trap door, she squeezed past it into the open and now tried to free the legs which had got stuck in the rungs. She struggled with them for a long time, afraid all the time that she was hurting the dead boy. At last she laid out Werner Bracht's body on the piece of tarpaulin she had found in the German dug-out, bound it with wire and dragged it to the shell-hole where the day before she had buried his mate. Now, she laid Werner Bracht beside him and heaped earth over his grave.

And again Maria was left alone among the dead. Bleak, autumn days dragged slowly one after the other. There were no rains as yet, but the cold of October was already in the air. In the morning the dry grasses were sprinkled with silvery rime. Cranes, geese and ducks were flying south with loud, parting cries. Sometimes they alighted on the river shallows to take a rest and feed, and when the sun came up they took off with a loud flapping of wings and continued on their journey. In the middle of the day the sun melted the rime, but towards evening it grew chilly again.

Maria did not have an idle moment. What worried her was how she was to procure fire in the winter. She had no lighter and no matches, and so she dug out a small niche in the cellar and set her oil lamp there where the tiny flame could not be put out by a puff of wind. She had made the lamp out of an old tin, which she kept filled with the fat she had melted out of the dead calves, and a twist of rag for a wick. She remembered how her grandfather used to strike fire with a piece of flint, and, in case her light failed, kept at hand the dried heart of a sunflower stalk, a piece of flint she had found on the river bank and a broken mowing-machine blade made of strong steel.

Every morning she went and dug potatoes to bring home to her cellar. She laid in a store of beets, cabbages and carrots, she hacked off armfuls of maize ears, made something like a mill out of two hard stones and every day managed to grind enough flour to keep herself in bread.

She had all the water she wanted. The well which she had cleaned out became filled again from the pure underground springs, and she always kept the large German thermos full. She had a hard time setting up the iron stove she had brought from the dug-out. It took her hours to cut a hole in the roof for the pipe with the bayonet, and more hours to fetch bricks from the blasted cow-shed, mix clay, and build a base and side walls for the stove so as not to get burnt alive in her den.

With the bayonet she felled maize stalks, tied the bundles with wire and carried them home to cover up the entrance, and before long she had quite a heap. She lighted her stove in the daytime only, first making sure that there was no one about who might notice the smoke curling from the pipe.

Winter was coming. For almost a whole week in October Maria went every day to the cow-shed, blasted by the Germans, to clear a passage through the pile of bricks to the far corner of the shed where the four cows could stay out of the rain and snow. The passage she managed to make was narrow and jagged, but she was glad all the same that the animals would have a roof over their heads on blizzardy, cold winter nights, and thick brick walls to protect them from the vicious winds blowing from the steppe.

She had to think of herself now, of finding something to wear. What she needed most was a needle, so she could stitch together something like a dress from the torn sacks and pieces of tarpaulin she had found in the trenches. It was growing colder with every day, and she went about in the soldier's greatcoat worn on her naked body. The wind stole under the skirts of the coat and, shivering, she had to seek warmth in the cellar much too often.

She succeeded in making a needle of sorts from wire: one end she bent in to make the ear, and the other she sharpened to a point on stone. She next washed Werner Bracht's socks, ripped them and wound the thred into a ball. She could do some sewing now.

Two more trips to the trenches behind the river rewarded her with such useful finds as a soldier's tunic, some blood-stained underwear, several knapsacks and footcloths. She washed all these things in the river, dried them and carried them away into her cellar. She stitched the bits and pieces together and made herself a kind of dress. From two of knapsacks she made a rather large square to cover her head and shoulders. The boots she had taken off the German who was killed together with his horse only needed the seams she had ripped open to be done up again, and now she could wear them, using a tunic torn in two for winding round her feet. She shortened the too-long greatcoat, and from the cloth made a pair of mittens and also slippers to wear at home.

"Well, I'm all prepared for winter now," she told herself.

She dreaded meeting anyone, but at the same time she longed to share her loneliness with someone, to pour out her troubles and hear human speech. She was afraid she'd forget how to talk, and so addressed long speeches to the cows, the dogs, and the pigeons. Some three weeks later she noticed that she had begun to talk to herself. She heard herself saying out loud:

"I'll go and fetch water now... We can't do without water, and it's so clean and cool in the well just now..."

Or else:

"I must get some beets for the cows, and some ears of maize too. The nights are getting longer, the animals need more fodder, otherwise there'll be no milk..."

Once, when she was washing her things in the river, she suddenly saw two horsemen approaching the site of the burnt-down village. "It's them, Germans," Maria thought in a panic, and crawled into the rushes. "If they notice my cellar I'll be done for, I'll freeze like a dog in the snow. And if they start looking for me, they'll find me and kill me..." Luckily, both dogs were with her and, her panic communicating itself to them, they clung silently to her legs. The cows were feeding in the maize field and were too far to be seen from the road.

The men rode slowly down the village street, stopped for a

moment without dismounting, then turned back, and galloped off into the steppe. Maria noticed that both were armed with rifles and sat their horses with soldierly smartness. "It's them, of course, none but the damned Germans," Maria thought. "Sniffing around to finish off anyone who got away with his life..."

Maria was sadly mistaken, but she was not to know it until much, much later. If she had not been mistaken she would not have had to suffer the hardships of those long winter months. Those two riders were partisan scouts whose job was to find out how many Germans there were in the villages, who had been appointed village elder or *polizei*, which of the villagers had been executed and who had been driven off into slavery. The partisan detachment was located in the dense forest a long way from the village, on the bank of a big river into which the nameless village stream discharged its waters. On returning, the scouts made a full report to their commander, and said this about Maria's village:

"Team Three of the Lenin Collective Farm has been wiped out by the Germans. The village has been razed to the ground, not a cottage, not a living soul has survived, it's a dead black waste."

The commissar of this partisan detachment was the former chairman of the Lenin Collective Farm, who knew Ivan and Maria, and all the villagers well. Together with the commander he heard out the scouts' report, sighed sorrowfully, dropped his head and said:

"It was a good team. I'm sorry for the people, and the village too. You say not a cottage, not a living soul has survived? The fiends burnt everything, destroyed everything? They won't get away with this. We'll pay them back for everything when the time comes. For everything in full..."

Thus, Team Three of the Lenin Collective Farm was crossed off the lists, and all the people who had inhabited the village were recorded as dead. And it was decided that there was no sense in going there any more: what use was that black waste to anyone?

The Germans did not come back either. None knew better how thoroughly and precisely their punitive squads carried out their orders. If their orders were to burn down the village, herd off all the inhabitants to Germany, and destroy all the animals, no one need doubt that they would do just that. And so when the commander of the punitive squad made his report, the tiny dot, denoting the village on the German maps, was crossed out with a fat brown cross.

In the meantime, the village continued to live a peculiar life of its own, unknown to anyone. It was evidenced by the barely perceptible whiff of smoke, when Maria had the stove going in her cellar, which filtered through the maize stalks and melted away.

Team Three, which had been struck off the lists, was alive in the person of its only surviving member, a woman named Maria.

This was how the team began to live anew. It was a cold day in October. It had rained at sunrise, a dreary, persistent drizzle, then the rain stopped, the raw, chilling wind subsided, but the bleakness did not pass and everything wore a dark, droopy look. Maria put on her boots and greatcoat, climbed out of the cellar, and stood contemplating the river, the thinning forest beyond, and the maize field which in that one night had lost its yellowness and turned grey.

Folding her arms, Maria looked long and sadly at the unharvested field, remembering that right next to it lay tons of potatoes, beetroots and carrots that no one had dug up, that the late water-melons had been left to the mercy of the crows, and that farther away, behind the hill, a whole field of abandoned sunflowers, their heads heavy with seeds and drooping low, were wilting wastefully.

"So much effort gone to waste," she thought, sighing. "The work our team put into those abandoned fields... There's no counting the nights when the tractor operators, the truck drivers, the shepherds, the milkmaids, and the cart drivers went short of sleep... I knew all those people. Every single one of them. We all toiled together on our common land, we all danced at the weddings together, we all went to the funerals when our parents were buried..."

As she talked thus to herself that October morning, remembering her fellow villagers, her heart ached with a nagging sense of guilt, of debt she owed her vanished team.

"But what can you do?" she asked herself. "You are the only survivor, so you must work for all of them, you mustn't fail them."

Tormented by her helplessness, she looked about her and said:

"How can you do it alone? Look at all this wealth that needs to be gathered in! D'you think you can manage? That maize field alone measures all of sixty hectares, and you've only two hands, that's all you have..."

"The sunflowers are shedding their seeds. Pity. It was my Ivan who delivered the sowing seeds there in the spring, and Sanya's father who ploughed that field and sowed it... And now the birds are pecking at the sunflowers, they're dry and shedding. What am I to do, sit twiddling my thumbs and just look on while everything goes to waste?"

"Silly fool, what can you do? One might think you owned a harvester or a fleet of trucks. There's no less than thirty hectares of those sunflowers."

"No, I don't own a harvester, that's true. But I do have a German bayonet, a very sharp one. Good for chopping off the heads of the sunflowers. I'll harness Zorka and we'll cart the sunflowers away..."

"Cart them where? Or do you perhaps have store-houses, or maybe you've already built a granary?"

"No, I have no store-houses, but they needn't be carted away, they can be stacked right there, in the field..."

"And when it rains, and snows?"

"No matter. The sunflower heads can be covered with maize leaves, if they're covered properly, with care, they won't rot."

"Oh, what a fool you are, Maria! A fool woman, that's what you are. Alright, let's suppose you will manage five or six hectares of sunflowers. But what about the twenty-five hectares of potatoes? The ten hectares of beets? The six hectares of carrots? And those sixty hectares of maize? Can you manage the whole lot?"

"No, not the lot. But at least I'll gather a little of everything, so it doesn't all rot and go to waste. Our people will come back, our people from the collective farm named in honour of Lenin ... they'll come back and thank me..."

"They will come back, you say? And what if they don't, if they never come back? What if the Germans have already seized the whole of Russia, the whole of the Soviet Union? What if there'll never be any collective farms any more, and only estates owned by Germans?"

"Then I'll kill myself together with my unborn child."

"You silly fool, it's for the sake of your unborn child that you've got to take good care of yourself and not sweat your guts out on the collective-farm fields. What more do you want? You weren't killed, you weren't driven off into slavery. You've found this nice burrow to live in, you have a stove, plenty of everything for the winter: all the potatoes and beets you want, a whole cartload of horseflesh, and four milch cows. All you must do now is to hold out, give birth to your child and wait. D'you understand, you fool woman? Wait for better days..."

"No, I can't live like that. Supposing I do sit it out here like a she-wolf in her den, give birth to my child, and fatten on the free collective-farm food, and supposing I'll live to the day when our people come back. They'll come here and ask me: how did you live here all this time, a front-rank member of the collective farm, wife of a Communist hanged by the enemy, and mother of a Young Pioneer murdered together with his father? Did you think only about yourself, forgetting all others? Forgetting those people who, together with you, with your father and mother, together with your husband had put so much honest toil into these fields here, watering them with their sweat?

So it was only your own welfare you thought about, Maria, was it?"

On that bleak morning, Maria stood beside her cellar holding this inner debate and, crushed by her sorrow, she really did not know what to do, all alone on these vast, abandoned fields. What use would it be if she, a pregnant woman who was growing weaker with every day, tried to gather in the crop, and who would need the pitiful fruit of her back-breaking toil in this sad world of blood and death with not a living soul in it?

Since time out of mind the local people had been laid to rest in the cemetery on the outskirts of the village, beyond the blasted cow-shed, at the foot of the hill slope. Maria made her way there. The dogs followed at her heels. She stopped at the first grave she came to. The wooden cross on it was awry. The old folk said that the grave belonged to Ivan's great-grandfather, the first peasant to settle on this site and the first person to be buried here. A serf, he had fled from his owners to this remote spot, and though he lived to be ninety-six, he never found his fortune and eked out a wretched existence till the end, barely keeping the wolf from the door.

"Ivan is dead ... and my Vassya too," she said, weeping. "There's not a living soul in the village... Just I alone... People say that you were the first to settle here, and you gave the village its start... You were the first, and I am the last..."

Slowly walking round the graves, Maria came to the corner where her mother was buried under some poplars, planted by Ivan. The white-trunked trees had already shed nearly all their leaves, and they made a soft, damp carpet underfoot. Only a few rusty leaves still clung tenaciously to the thin branches, murmuring indistinctly in protest against the cold gust of wind. The mound of clayey earth seemed to have sagged, and the cross made of four white-washed bricks was all but buried in the fallen leaves.

Maria went down on her knees.

"Mother," she whispered. "Can you hear me, Mother? It's me, your daughter. Speak to me, Mother, tell me how to live in this world..."

Sobbing, she fell forward and pressed her cheek to the cold, damp earth.

"Why don't you speak to me, Mother?" she whispered. "Say something! Tell me what for you brought me into the world? You wanted your daughter to be happy... You cherished and loved me. You taught me sense, you told me to be honest, to love people and our land, to be a good wife and mother... I was all that, truly, I had everything and now I have nothing, not my dearly beloved husband, not my darling son, not happiness, not luck, and no place even to lay down my poor head..."

The poor village cemetery was wrapped in silence. Dark, leaden clouds hung low over the desolate land. The rusty leaves on the poplars murmured sorrowfully. The withered grasses drooped heavily, clinging to the ground. Only here and there on the graves the low, woody stems of the periwinkle, though already touched with auburn, pathetically tried to remain green as a last reminder of the people who were no more.

Maria rose from her knees and looked about her. She remembered how every year the villagers, observing the customs of their forefathers, came here on Remembrance Day, how after work they washed, put on their Sunday best, put the pies, baked the day before, the hard-boiled eggs, salt, bottles of wine and vodka in their baskets, and went in a body to visit the graves of their parents and relatives, to commemorate them with words of gratitude and a drink, to sit and talk about various mundane matters as in their living presense.

The cemetery was always tidied up for Remembrance Day; people planted periwinkle around the graves, sprinkled the paths between with white river sand, mended the crosses, whitewashed the tombstones, and those of them who had railings round their family plot painted them afresh. On that day the cemetery was always crowded. The men, freshly shaved and preserving a solemn air, spread home-woven cloths on the ground, and then the women, wearing bright shawls and dresses, set out the food, the bottles and the thick glasses, and the commemoration began. None of the dead were forgotten, young and old alike, people who had died a long time ago and those who had been buried only recently. The nearest relatives were commemorated first, after that the more distant ones, then the relatives by marriage, the kinsmen, and just friends and fellow villagers. The drink gradually made them maudlin, they wiped their tears with clean handkerchiefs, and someone started a song. They were sad, plaintive songs, the ones their fathers and grandfathers used to sing, all about the bitterness of parting, the peasants' sad lot, the hard toil in the fields. As they sang, it seemed to all of them that the forgotten voices of the dead were imperceptibly and softly joining in these songs, familiar to all of them since childhood, and it sounded to them, intoxicated with wine and memories, as though the dead were singing with the living. And that's how it should be, because Remembrance Day united the generations, as it were, and made people kinder and better...

But on this gloomy autumn day there were only the dead there.

Followed by the dogs, Maria went round all the graves, wishing each one of the dead, whether she had known them or not, to rest in peace. It was only the very old people, who died before she was born or when she was a little child, whom she had not known. She knew everyone who had died in the last twenty years, and she stood for a while beside each grave measuring her life and her conscience against theirs and wondering what they would have done in her place.

"Old Arseny is buried in this grave," Maria remembered. "He died from the sword wounds he got from Wrangel's men in 1920, when I was seven years old... And here lies Luka Vassilyevich, chairman of the Village Poor Committee. He urded the villagers to fight for the commune, for Lenin. The kulaks tied him to an old elm tree and stabbed him with pitchforks. I was eight at the time... Now on this cross here is written the name of my aunt, Varvara Pavlovna. She was the first person in our village to join the Communist Party, she died of typhus when I was nine... And this whole row I know well, buried in these graves are people I'd seen, known and spoken to—tractor drivers, shepherds, bee-keepers, milkmaids and stablemen. They built up our collective farm, hard workers all, undaunted by hunger or cold, they were buried with honours, a red banner covered their coffins and speeches were made, thanking them for everything they had done for the community..."

A sharp pain pierced Maria's heart. Here, where many of the villagers had found eternal peace, there were no graves of her husband and her son, the two people dearest to her. For a long time Maria stood there, whispering incoherently:

"I'd plant some flowers on your graves, beautiful flowers... I'd sprinkle clean white sand all around, on every little path... I'd come here to you, my darlings, and I'd prepare a place for myself so we'd all be together ever after... Who'll tell me where you're buried? No one will tell me, and I'll never see your graves..."

As she was leaving the cemetery, Maria stopped once again at the grave of Ivan's great-grandfather, bowed low to the cross, and spoke as if she were addressing a living man:

"You were the first, and they did not bring dishonour on your memory, neither those who lie here with you, nor those who were executed or driven off by the enemy. And I, the last one, shall not dishonour it either..."

Wrapping her greatcoat around her, she hurried home, to her den.

A dreary, cold rain poured all night. Maria's sleep was fitful, she often woke up, looked at the weak light in the niche, and thought that come morning she must get down to the work that stretched interminably before her mind's eye.

In the morning, she dressed as warmly as she could, climbed out of the cellar and stood there, thinking. Her glance fell on the sign she had leaned against the apple tree and the small pile of charred nails she had managed to collect. Picking up a stone she started nailing the sign to the thick trunk. The nails bent, the strong old tree would not yield easily. She bruised her left hand badly, but still she did nail the sign where she wanted it. She walked back a few steps and read out loud:

Team Three. Lenin Collective Farm.

With a mirthless laugh, she said:

"What are you waiting for, my good team, it's time to start work!"

From the cellar she fetched her bayonet and a piece of tarpaulin and went to the sunflower field. There seemed no end to it. With a sigh, Maria spread out the tarpaulin on the ground and started hacking off the heads. They were so dry and brittle that they scratched her bruised left hand, but the German bayonet was sharp and cut them down easily. Maria carried them on the tarpaulin to the heart of the field and dumped the heads ready for threshing where no alien eye could see them. She started along the length of the field working on four rows of sunflowers at once, and when, by midday, she neared the end, where the sunflowers had begun to thin out, she saw the beehives, which had been set up there when the sunflowers were only just flowering.

The collective farm's bee-keeper was Maria's cousin, quiet, hunch-backed Kiryusha. He took a course in bee-keeping before the war, being disabled he was not mobilised, he never thought of marrying and lived with his mother in a small, clean cottage, built for them by the collective farm. Kiryusha doted on his bees and migrated with his hives to the steppe, wherever it was best for them. Sometimes Maria came to visit him and, eating the fragrant honey from the comb, let Kiryusha talk for hours about the life of bees, about their swarming, their chyle, and their drones. Kiryusha and his mother had been rounded up with all the other villagers by the Germans and taken off somewhere, and the orphaned bees were left to die a slow death from the winter frosts.

Maria counted the hives—there were sixty families. When the cold set in the bees stopped flying, there was no humming to be heard, and on the entrance boards lay the dead bodies of those who, flying home to their hives, had lacked the strength to crawl in and froze to death.

"I'll have to cover the hives with something, if only with sunflower stalks, otherwise the whole apiary will perish in the winter," Maria was thinking. "At this time of year Kiryusha already had them back in the village and put them in the winter shelter. Only now there's no Kiryusha, and no shelter."

She put one of the frozen bees in her palm and said softly:

"You poor little things, you're left without your master, and there's no one to care for you..."

Remembering how Kiryusha used to prepare the bee-garden for the winter, she made the entrances smaller in all the hives, and knocking on the wooden walls with a finger listened to the humming inside.

"You'll have enough honey to last you the winter," she said. "None was taken this autumn, and I'll do something about your homes to protect them from the snow and frost."

She went back to cutting the sunflower heads and continued until she felt hungry. A big, nice heap lay in the middle of the field where no one could see it.

Maria locked the fingers of her tired, numb hands behind her neck, and said:

"You've done your day's quota, my good woman, rather more than your quota. But you've got to work for the whole team, not just yourself, you know. When, God willing, our people come back, you'll report to them and say: comrade collective farmers, I did my honest best, I did everything I could for you, and if there's something I left undone or overlooked, it's because my strength failed me, so don't hold it against me..."

It was already late afternoon. When she came home she quickly milked the cows, fed the dogs and the pigeons, drank some milk and fell asleep at once. At daybreak she went back to the field and again cut sunflowers until dark. She did that for about ten days until her hands and legs grew numb and stiff from weariness. For a change, she dug two long deep holes, one in the potato and the other in the beetroot field, and devoted the next week to digging up the crop. With her home-made needle she stitched a large sack for lugging the potatoes and beets into their respective holes.

Days passed. No people ever appeared. And who'd ever want to come to the burnt-down village which even before had never attracted outsiders, miles away as it was from anywhere? One would think that a living person could not have endured this utter loneliness, all alone among the dead. Only someone very strong in spirit can get used to any privations and put up a brave struggle. Maria was neither brave nor very strong in spirit. Yet this small woman, who had lost everything and everyone and loved people with a motherly love, little by little became used to the strange life she was living. She almost stopped fearing the sudden appearance of Germans, and in the daytime she went about quite openly, although she was prepared to instantly hide in the maize at the slightest hint of danger or crawl away and lie low somewhere.

It grew colder with every day. There were more and more rains. Sometimes in the morning there was a blustering wind and the first snowflakes whirled in the air. Maria worked without rest every day: cutting sunflowers, digging up and storing potatoes, beets or carrots, or else fixing the hives up for the winter.

She became used to silence. There was no one to talk to. The two dogs always came with her to the fields and she talked to them, and in the evenings she'd have the same kind of one-way conversation with the cows and the pigeons. Songs were a great help. More often than not Maria sang as she worked in the fields, she sang in an undertone the songs she remembered hearing from her mother when she was a child. She was only a little girl then and did not know why the village women called her father, whom she hardly ever saw, a "red" and the rich man Elisei a "white", nor why her mother, as she sat spinning in the evening, would drop her head and sing under her breath. Now, she remembered the heart-gripping words of her mother's plaintive songs, and wielding her bayonet without a pause she sang:

> At my window I
> Sit and gaze and see
> How a swallow flits
> Back and forth alone.
> In the eaves above
> There's a nice, warm nest,
> Where her mate awaits
> His beloved one,
> With the swift grey wings,
> And the snow-white breast...

The German bayonet flashed in Maria's hands, the sunflowers fell on the tarpaulin, low, rain-laden clouds sailed overhead, and she, barely controlling the sobs bursting from her throat, sang:

> As I watch her fly
> To her nice, warm nest,
> Bitter tears I wipe,
> From remembering.
> Like that swallow's mate
> Once I used to wait
> For my darling love

> *To come home to me,*
> *Wicked fate had built*
> *Her another nest,*
> *In the cold, dark sod,*
> *There for evermore...*

Maria went on working till dark, her tired hands and legs fair killing her. But, as usual, she milked the cows, fed the dogs, and then in the faint light of her oil lamp tidied up her underground dwelling. She made a habit of doing this every night, and gradually she made her dark cellar look like a tiny lived-in room. From the cartridge cases she had found in the trenches she knocked together a small table. She dried the hide of the dead German horse in the wind and laid it on the earthen floor. From the boards she had dismantled in the German dug-outs she built herself a plank bed. She put bunches of wormwood in the corners of her room to rid the dogs of fleas. At night she kept both of them with her so their barking would not betray her to the Germans if any came there. The dogs seemed to understand: at the merest suspicious sound outside they only growled softly and looked at Maria as if asking her whether they must sit still or were allowed to bark.

On this particular night there was hardly any sleep for Maria. Just as she lay down on her plank bed she heard the unmistakable howl of wolves. Until about three years prior to the war wolves did come prowling round the village sometimes, but then the hunters found the den in one of the distant gullies, and killed the she-wolf together with her six cubs. The he-wolf, it is true, got away with the rest of his pack. Since then there had been no sight or sound of any wolves. And suddenly here they were howling much too close to home.

The dogs sprang up and bared their fangs. The fur on their backs stood up on end. The howl sounded again. Chum began to growl.

"Quiet, doggies, quiet," Maria hushed them, sitting up. "The wolves can't get in here, and I've propped the cow-shed door with a log. So just sit quietly."

Suddenly, Maria heard the frightened bleating of sheep. What sheep? They had never had any in the village. The collective farm flocks were kept far away in the steppe, no less than sixty kilometres away, where the shepherds had a mud-hut to live in, a well, and a store of emergency fodder. Maria then remembered that the flocks belonging to the neighbouring sheep-breeding state farm sometimes approached the village as they roamed the steppe. "That must be them," she thought, leaping to her feet. "But what can I do? How rescue the sheep? The wolves will get them."

She grabbed her burning oil lamp, pushed open the trap door and, calling the dogs, jumped out, waving the lamp. The two dogs shot out after her. Maria saw a cluster of sheep under the apple tree, and the wolves a little further away. Lady had already planted herself beside the sheep, she was growling and baring her fangs, while Chum, in a frenzy of rage barked huskily into the darkness. The wolves' green eyes flickered a short distance away.

Raising her lamp high, Maria screamed at them: "Clear off, damn you, go away, and may you croak, blast you! "

Evidently, a human shape holding a burning lamp and the ferocious dogs frightened the pack. The wolves had been prowling the desolate steppe for many days in search of food, and had felt quite safe. They circled for a bit round the now unattainable sheep, and scurried off, vanishing in the darkness.

Maria was afraid to leave the sheep unguarded, and so she put on her greatcoat, and boots, armed herself with her spade, called the dogs, and sat down on the stone slab under the apple tree to wait for morning. The dogs lay down at her feet, pricking up their ears. It was a cold, starry night. The wind whistled in the denuded branches above. A despondent, drawn-out howl sounded just once more from somewhere beyond the hill, and then all was quiet again.

Myriads of stars twinkled in the dark sky, some brightly and others faintly. Gazing at the starlit sky, Maria thought of her miserable lot. She had not believed in God even as a little girl, but she well remembered how her old granny took her to church every Easter. The church was very far, but usually they walked the thirty versts. Maria liked walking with her granny, gazing about her at the spreading green fields of wheat, the grass growing along the country road, the poor little chapels at the crossroads, and to listen to the noisy, jolly cawing of the rooks who at that time usually built their nests on the edge of the forest which, though still almost transparent, was already bursting into green leaf.

Maria also liked it in the church, where everything was so thrilling and solemn—the trembling candlelight, the smell of hot wax and incense, the hazy reflection of human faces in the glass on the icons, and the people themselves, dressed in their finery, so dignified and serene. The old priest intoned in his quavering, senile voice, and from somewhere above the choir responded, and Maria listened rapturously to the droning of the basses like distant thunder, punctuated by the trilling of the sopranos and the tenors, their voices rising higher and higher to the very dome.

And when in the stuffy, dusky church all the candles were lit at once, when the choir joyously announced in powerful, ringing voices that Christ had risen from the dead, when the big and small bells in the tall belfry started ringing, and when the people came out in a gay, talkative crowd and went about the church yard kissing one another, Maria's heart overflowed with bliss in which everything was merged into one: the spring, the good people, the hundreds of flickering candles, and the awareness that the unknown meek Christ, crucified by wicked villains, had arisen from the dead, was hovering over people and looking down on them lovingly from the gold samite of the gonfalons.

Later, when Maria joined the Young Pioneers, the patrol leader, a dark-haired boy who was already a member of the Komsomol, took her aside one day, having heard that she went to church, and asked her in a calm, formal tone:

"Is it true that you go to church?"

Maria dropped her eyes.

"Aren't you ashamed of yourself?" he asked, raising an eyebrow.

"What's there to be ashamed of?" Maria asked. "My granny goes and takes me with her."

"Your granny is an ignorant, illiterate person, it's pardonable in her case, but you are a Young Pioneer, a future member of the Komsomol, daughter of a Red partisan! Don't you know that there is no god, that it's all an invention of the priests, and that all that church splendour—the icons, the candles, the incense and the rest of the stuff—is a stage show put on by the priests to befuddle people's minds?"

"I didn't know that," Maria replied in a small voice. "We weren't taught about priests' shows in school."

The patrol leader burst out laughing at this.

"You will, all in good time. Just now I ask only one thing of you: don't go to church, don't disgrace our Young Pioneer troop and dishonour the memory of your Communist father. Learn well in school, read books, and you'll arrive at everything yourself."

Maria remembered that conversation. When she came home for the holidays she told her mother about it and plied her with questions about her father—how he had lived and what he had believed in. Stroking the girl's fair head, the mother said:

"Do what this patrol leader of yours says, he's a clever boy, he finished school. Your father did not believe in God. It wasn't God he worried about, it was the poor people..."

Maria stopped going to church after this talk with her mother. Besides, she had no one to go with—her granny had died. As Maria grew up she began to understand that people themselves had invented

God instead of creating a paradise on earth where no one would starve, quarrel or kill one another. The hikes she went on with the Young Pioneers, the campfire songs in the forest glades, the lessons in school which she could not finish because she was needed at home to help her mother, and also what she learnt from the Komsomol, confirmed her conviction that the most important thing in life was to do good to people.

Sitting under the apple tree that night and guarding the sheep from the wolves, Maria gazed into the starry sky and thought that her whole life, all her losses, everything she had so far experienced, had been only a prelusion to the immeasurably difficult task which she had to accomplish now, at a time of her frightening loneliness, not just for her unborn child but also for the men and women who had toiled on these fields not just for themselves and their children but for many people whom they had never seen or known, and whom they would never see or know. The immense size of the collective farm fields terrified her. They had been a full-time job for the entire team of sixty-three people and all the tractors, reapers, trucks, and horses there were, and now it was up to her alone to reap everything the team had grown. "I'll just have to do it, there's no choice," Maria thought. "I'll work day and night, I'll dig up the potatoes and beets in the day-time, and the sunflowers and maize can be cut just as well in the dark."

When light came, she counted the sheep. There were nine. She put them in the shed together with the cows, where there was plenty of room for all of them.

November came. It was growing ever colder. On most days it rained, and more and more frequently there was an outburst of snow. Undaunted, Maria went to work every morning, cutting off sunflower heads, breaking off maize ears, and digging up potatoes and beets. She had long forgotten the taste of bread, and lived on milk and potatoes. However, she realised that she had to eat more nourishing food if she did not want to fall ill from malnutrition, and so several times she beat butter in the German thermos with the lid screwed on tight.

"If I fall ill, God forbid, it'll be the end of me and my baby," she said to frighten herself into eating more.

And now she lost count of the days, she did not know what month it was and did not care. Her fingers and palms were covered with blisters. She felt that before long she'd have no strength left at all, and decided to take a day off. In the evening she heated some water, washed herself as best she could, and slept soundly all night.

When she came out in the morning the sun was shining, but gave little warmth. The night frost had bound the rain puddles with ice and decorated the dry grasses and bare apple branches with sparkling rime. Maria went down to the river. The water had frozen, and the ice was gilded by the sun. Carefully she walked across, went along the line of trenches and only now noticed that there were more of them in the distance. "I'll go and take a look," she decided.

She walked slowly, looking about her all the time for fear that someone might see her in that open country. The trenches were like the ones Maria had been in before. They stretched in a long wavy line, and behind them, here and there, were smaller holes—machine-gun nests.

Maria lowered herself into a trench and walked along it, looking under her feet. Here, too, there were rifle cartridges, cartridge pouches, bandages trampled into the ground, empty cigarette boxes, and lots of cigarette ends. Several rifles had been leaned against the wall, and hand grenades glittered dully in the niches. The silence in this place abandoned by people after battle was so creepy and strange, that Maria shivered with fear. She stood still, looking about her, and suddenly saw a dead soldier where the trench made a turn. He lay on the breastwork, gripping the handle of his machine-gun. His face and hands were grey, his helmet had been pierced by a bullet. A small red star stood out brightly on his sleeve. Decomposition had already done its dirty work on the corpse, but the frost had arrested the destruction, wrought by death...

Maria stood for a long time beside the dead man. This young political instructor had apparently remained at his machine-gun, covering the retreat of his comrades, firing back at the attacking Germans and pinning them to the ground. Dozens of German helmets had been left lying some distance away from the trench where the machine-gun was aimed. The Germans must have carried their dead away, while the dead political instructor remained on the breastwork with his machine-gun as the last immortal sentinel...

Maria climbed out of the trench, tried to pull the dead man away from his machine-gun, but his stiffened fingers could not be unbent, fused forever to his weapon. Maria took off his helmet. The brown, soft hair stirred in the wind. Blood had congealed to a large black clot a little above his left temple.

Dropping to her knees, Maria looked at the dead man, and said:

"Wait here a little, dearie, I'll go and fetch my spade. You can't be left here like this. Ravens will peck at your body, wolves will tear it to pieces and carry them all over the steppe... You've got to be buried, and I'm the only grave-digger here... If I die there'll be no one to bury me..."

She brought her spade and some wire, and stood for a long time over the dead soldier wondering where to bury him.

"My poor boy, it would be easiest for me to bury you right here in the trench you defended with your life, just lay you down on the floor and heap earth over you. But that wouldn't be right, would it? When the war ends, people will come back, they'll fill in the trenches and no one will ever know where you are buried, no one will find your grave."

Not far from the line of trenches the river bank rose a little, and there, on that rise, a wooden tower had been built for some purpose or other by a group of topographers who came from town. When the war broke out, the collective farm was ordered by the district military command to pull down the tower, as it might serve the enemy as a reference point for artillery fire. The tower was duly pulled down and the boards chopped up for firewood, but there was still the square of levelled ground on which it had stood. And that's where Maria decided to bury the young political instructor, so his grave would be seen from afar.

The top layer of earth had frozen during the night, and when at last she had broken it up she started digging the grave, resting every so often and glancing back at the dead man. She realised that she'd never be able to get his stiff hands unclenched and would have to bury him together with his machine-gun. Therefore, it had to be a much bigger grave.

When she had done with digging the grave, she went back to the breastwork, wound the wire round the body and the machine-gun again and again, and started dragging it to the grave. The load was terribly heavy: she thought her every breath was the last. She stopped, rested for a bit, then tied the end of the wire into a loop, strapped it over her chest, stuffing the coat lapels under it so it would not cut into her flesh, and hauled. She stopped to rest after every five or six steps. When she reached the grave, she slipped the wire strap over her head, and stood thinking: "I must turn him face up so he'll lie in the grave in the Russian custom on his back, facing east."

Squatting down, she tried with one hand to turn over the body and with the other to push along the heavy machine-gun. At last she had the dead man lying on his back, but the machine-gun proved too much for her and remained with the wheels up. Maria saw before her the face of a mere youth with a thin, dark moustache above his grinning, lipless mouth. "He must have grown this moustache to look older," she thought pityingly. "Pleased with it like the child he was..."

Evidently the advancing Germans could not be bothered with the dead machine-gunner who had kept them at bay for such a long time. His officer's map case and opened holster were still attached to his belt. Maria undid the belt, took the pistol, slightly touched with rust, from the holster and, after a moment's thought, shoved it in the pocket of her greatcoat. In the map case she found some newspapers, a stale rusk, a tobacco pouch embroidered with bright silks, and a lighter. From his tunic pockets she took out several letters, a pencil, and a photograph of a beautiful and very young girl with her hair in two pigtails. Written in a large schoolgirlish handwriting on the back of the photo was: "To darling Slava from his loving Lena. Hoping we'll meet soon."

"No, Slava, you won't see your Lena, and your Lena will never see you again," Maria whispered tearfully.

She started pushing the body slowly to the grave, and suddenly shrieked with horror. Two field mice scampered out of the dead man's sleeve and quickly disappeared in the thick, rime-covered grass.

"Oh my God, my God! " Maria whispered in despair. "Even beasts are frightened by the deeds of men, yet it's people from whom they seek salvation from fire and death..."

Maria laid the body down on the bottom of the grave, feeling sorry that she could not properly fold the hands which still gripped the machine-gun, filled it in with earth, built a small mound and placed the bullet-pierced helmet on top.

Back in her cellar, she read everything she had found on the dead soldier. The first thing that came to hand was a letter from the boy's mother.

"Dearest Slava, my darling son," she wrote. "It's over a year now since you left us and went off to the front as a volunteer. There has not been a day when you were not uppermost in my thoughts and I did not cry. I've been left all alone, you know that. Your father is fighting somewhere near Leningrad, he writes me that he was wounded, stayed for six weeks in hospital and has now returned to his unit. You left home after your father, and I was hoping that Klava, my darling daughter and your young sister, would stay with me and together we'd wait for you, our warriors, to come back to us. I had no idea that Klava was training for a nurse on the quiet from me, and a month ago she went off to the front and I never heard from her since. Can she be dead? I beg you, Slava, my boy, do this one and only thing for your mother: guard your young life, after all you're still only a child! Don't rush first into the face of death, be careful. I want you to know that if you are killed I won't survive it. Write to me as often as you can, my darling boy. I kiss you a thousand times. Your Mother..."

Maria read this letter through a film of tears. The words became blurred and she was thinking: "Poor, poor mother. You're living alone somewhere, and you no longer have a son, just as I don't have my Vassya, and no one in the world can revive our sons and bring them back to us."

The son's answer was unfinished. Evidently he had started writing it just before the fray, which was to be his last, and had no time to finish it.

"Dear Mother," he wrote. "Thanks for your letter, I was very glad to receive it. Don't be sorry that Klava went off to the front. She did the right thing, she did what her conscience told her to do. And you really shouldn't tell me to take care of myself. How do you picture it? That I, a Communist, the political instructor of my company, should hang behind in a moment of danger? Of course, I don't stick out my neck unnecessarily, like anybody else I have no wish to die, but when I have to I'm in duty bound to be in front.

"You cannot imagine, my dear mother, the enormity of the terrible evil we are fighting against. Consider yourself fortunate that you did not have to see what we saw in the villages we liberated. Burnt-down houses, mountains of dead bodies, gallows, tortures, executions and all manner of humiliation—that's what Hitler's Nazis have brought to our land. We've got to, Mother, we absolutely must defeat this black evil, this brutal, ferocious band of murderers and rapists, otherwise they'll enslave the whole world.

"We, Soviet soldiers, are fighting for the future of mankind, for truth and the clean conscience of the world. When you have this conviction, this idea, you are not afraid of death, and if I die, please don't cry and don't feel sorry for me. Just remember that your son, like thousands of other men who did not spare themselves, laid down his life for a rightful cause.

"We are retreating at present, but only temporarily, mother dear. We shall be victorious. We are definitely going to win. My company has a difficult job to do today: we are to cover the retreat of our comrades, and I'm sure..."

On this the letter was broken off. Maria lay down on her plank bed, covered herself with her greatcoat, stretched out her tired legs in utter exhaustion, yet she could not sleep. The two dogs snored peacefully on the floor, the oil-lamp flickered faintly in the niche... Maria was haunted by the thought of the two men she had buried: the German boy Werner Bracht, and Slava, the young political instructor. She felt a motherly regret for both of them. Their young lives had been cruelly and stupidly cut short by the war, whereas both could have lived for years and years.

"Look how everything's set up in the world," she lay thinking. "Two women gave birth to two boys. Those boys were like all the other children: clean of heart, no bad in them whatever. Just children. Then one of them began to be taught all kinds of nasty things by wicked people, who drummed it into his head that he was born to be a master, that everything was permitted him—to kill and rob, and even though he may have tried to protest he was forced to put on a uniform and do whatever his cursed commanders and comrades, brutes all of them, made him do. And it was only when he was mortally wounded that he must have understood that he was dying for the most vile and wicked cause there is. And then, just before the end, his conscience came awake and he wept bitter tears, called me, a strange Russian woman, mama, and kissed my hands. And in that last hour, I suppose, he saw all the women living in the world as one mother, who loved all her children, fondled them, nursed all the equally good boys, sobbed and suffered, when one of her boys, her darling children was killed... And one of these boys was Werner Bracht...

"The other boy was called Slava. Since infancy he was taught to do good; he was told that all people on earth should be happy, they all wanted to live, to eat the food they had grown, that no man had the right to strangle another, that people did not want war, they wanted peace and in peace they themselves would see which way their road to happiness lay, and they would not kill, abuse or humiliate one another... And the boy Slava, born in the free Russian land, understood this and knew, just like my father and my husband Ivan, just like Fenya, like Sanya and many, many other honest people, that he must defend his land and the freedom of the road which alone led to true happiness for all. That's why the boy Slava volunteered for the army and sacrificed his young life for the good, holy cause. When the war ends, people will put up monuments to heroes like Slava, they'll tell their children and grandchildren about them, so they'd always remember those who saved them from slavery and death."

It was almost dawn when she fell asleep. Through her sleep she fancied she heard a cock crowing. And then a second, and a third one.

"How silly, how could there be any here?" she mumbled and went back to sleep. And then a cock crowed so near and in such a loud, rousing voice that Maria sat up, rubbing her eyes.

"Am I asleep or awake?"

When she came outside and peered into the pre-dawn twilight, she flung up her arms in amazement: dozens of chickens were strutting about her yard.

"Where have you been wandering for two whole months, poor things?" she cried.

She cut a lot of sticks in the wood and made perches in the cowshed, and also nests for the hens and pigeons from the cartridge cases she had. But at first neither the chickens nor the pigeons would go inside, shying from the dark, narrow entrance Maria had cleared in the mountain of blasted bricks. She only managed to lure in the frightened birds, who had gone wild in their homelessness, by tempting them with ground maize.

And once again the days dragged monotonously and bleakly. Winter had come. It was frosty. The weather was changeable. There would be days of snowfall, blessedly concealing the ugly black waste under a pure white carpet, the placid scene marred only by the black chimneys and the remains of walls. After that, the weather would turn warm, the snow would sag heavily and melt. Water would glisten in the ruts of the deserted road. Sometimes, after a brief thaw, the frost would strike again, and there would be slippery ice on the ground. The branches of the apple tree would droop low in their armour of ice, and in the utter, desolate silence Maria could clearly hear them ringing softly as they flinched from an onslaught of wind and dropped long, crystal icicles on the ground.

First thing in the morning, Maria tended to her livestock, which was increasing in number. One late afternoon three brown horses came plodding to the village, their heads drooping, and their shoes, hanging by a nail, slapping on the ground. They were appallingly scrawny, more like skeletons than live horses. The sharp bones on their cruppers stuck out, the ribs protruded, and their eyes were rheumy. All three were saddled and bridled. Under the saddles they had dark blue horsecloths with red stars on the corners. The saddle on one of the horses had slipped under her belly, and she shuffled behind the others, stumbling all the time.

Maria's heart cringed with pity for the wretched animals.

"How did you manage to stay alive?" she exclaimed. "Where are your riders, and who were they? They're lying dead in the steppe somewhere, I shouldn't wonder."

Indeed, how did these cavalry horses come through the fray alive? How did they survive, wandering about the wastes and plains for more than two months?

The iron bit made it difficult for them to chew the dry grass and bruised their mouths. The hard saddles and girths rubbed their backs and sides raw, and the raw-hide bridles, dragging along the ground behind them, kept tripping them up.

Sighting Maria from afar, the horses stopped, pricked up their ears and whinnied piteously. All three came to her and stood round her with their heads low. Their forelocks, manes and tails bristled with burs, blood tricked from the bruised corners of their mouths, and their backs, which Maria saw when she had taken off their saddles and bridles, were covered with festering wounds, the hairless skin hanging in tatters.

"Oh, you poor, poor things! " Maria sobbed.

Very carefully, with the lightest touch of her fingertips she smeared their backs with butter, gave them some maize to eat, and using her bayonet relieved them of their slapping shoes. Gratefully and meekly the horses went into the cow-shed, and for the first time in those long days and nights of wandering about went to sleep in a warm place with no pangs of hunger to keep them awake.

Every morning Maria let out the horses, cows, chicken and sheep. She cleaned out the shed, then took the animals to water in the river. There was one place in the river which she checked every day, breaking the thin ice with her spade and not letting it freeze hard. It was there she watered her animals. She always walked in front, with the animals she had saved following her docilely. They seemed to be basking in their attachment to this loving woman, the only living person anywhere, who had such gentle hands and such a warm, calm voice. This lonely little woman fed them, watered them, combed out their matted fur, rubbed them down with a piece of sacking, carefully picked the sharp, prickly awns out of their mouths, and every touch of her warm hands seemed to bring back to them those days when their masters reared them, tended them and cared for them, and when they gratefully paid back the people with everything they had to give. Now that they had this good woman to look after them it seemed to them that there had been no frightening explosions in their life, no devouring fires from which they fled helter-skelter, no hunger, no thirst, no endless wanderings in search of a human being to save them. It seemed to them now that those horrors had been no more than a bad dream, and that in the whole world there existed only this woman, their friend and kind mistress who had rescued them from death, fed them, sheltered them from the snows and fierce cold, so that they could live and bless the sunlight, bear their young according to the laws of earthly existence, and eventually, when came the time set by wise nature, to calmly depart from this world, ceding their place under the sun to others.

1943. 1st Byelorussian Front. The Commander-in-Chief,
Konstantin Rokossovsky, in the town of Gomel at a meeting
to mark the liberation of the town

1944. 1st Baltic Front. Through liberated Polotsk

1944. A women's air regiment arrives
in Byelorussia to take part in battle
operations

1944. 3rd Ukrainian Front. On the offensive

Across the shallows to Odessa

1944. Battle for the liberation of Sevastopol

1944. The Black Sea Fleet. The battles in the Crimea
are over

The frontier has been restored!

The Crimean Conference of heads
of government of the USSR,
the USA and Britain.
Right to left: Stalin, Roosevelt
and Churchill

Nazi POWs in Moscow. 1944

A tank column being unloaded for the front. The slogans read: "To storm Berlin!"

All of them recognised her footsteps from afar, and every morning, on hearing her low, rather husky voice, they welcomed her with neighing, lowing, bleating, clacking and cooing. She let them out and they surrounded her, all of them wanting to touch their saviour. The horses kissed her chilled face with their velvety lips; the pigeons, cooing, alighted on her head and shoulders; the chickens bustled at her feet; the cows rubbed their necks against her sides with subdued moos; the sheep, flocking together, gazed at her with devotion, blinking their whitish eyelashes. The dogs, who never left Maria's side, sat down a little distance away and tactfully wagged their tails. After watering her animals Maria drove them off to the maize field and resumed her endless work—breaking off the maize ears, cutting the sunflower heads and piling them up. She worked in any weather, anxious to rescue something of what her team had planted in the spring. On frosty days her hands and feet ached from the cold, her lips got chapped and bled. Time and again she wept from pain and pity for herself, calling herself a crazy fool, and wanted to drop everything, keep a good fire going in her stove and stay in her warm den, letting everything go hang. But it was a momentary weakness. Instead, she rubbed her face and hands with snow, ran up and down to warm her toes, and doggedly continued doing her job.

Sometimes the weather turned warm in the middle of the winter, the snow melted and copious rains fell, but this did not make it any easier on Maria: heavy clumps of mud stuck to her German boots, and plodding across the ploughed-up fields was a nightmare.

The only thing that gladdened her heart was that one of the shell-holes was already brimming with maize ears, and that a good half of the sunflower heads had been chopped off, stacked and securely covered.

When the strain became quite unendurable and she wanted to collapse in the middle of the field and never get up again, she took a day or two off. But even then she did not sit twiddling her thumbs: she cleaned out the cow-shed, heaped the manure a few metres away from it, or else went to the abandoned trenches collecting everything that might be of use to people later: catridge cases, balls of telephone wire, discarded greatcoats, hats, gas-masks, shovels, axes, crow-bars, mess-tins, mugs, spoons, and other such things.

"Everything will come in handy," she reasoned. "Why let things go to rot and rust? Maybe not all our team has been murdered by the Nazi bastards. Maybe someone is still alive. When people come back they'll have to start from scratch..."

On those days of enforced idleness Maria would take Slava's map case and, calling her dogs, make the rounds of the various sections of the collective farm, jotting things down in the note-book she had found in his tunic pocket. She recorded all her finds: in Rooks' Gully she discovered two rusty tractors, two cultivators, and nine metal drums of machine oil. It must have been Sanya's father who hid the tractors in the bramble thickets in the nick of time before the Germans descended on them. In a remote field she found a good cart, six harrows and a seeder, abandoned there by someone, and elsewhere, a heavy roller, drifted over with snow.

Maria left the pages covered with Slava's writing in the note-book. He had written down the names of all the soldiers in his company who fell in battle, as well as the names of the wounded and the raw youngsters sent as reinforcement. Against the names of the latter he had written a few words characterising them, evidently meaning to have a talk with them later and give them what help they needed.

On a cold day in December Maria decided to go to one of the farthest sections which adjoined the land belonging to the neighbouring collective farm. This section was rarely ploughed, and was mostly left as grazing ground for the calves. The neighbours, whose village was about forty kilometres away, did not plant anything on their land either, as the steppe here was cut up with shallow gullies and abounded in washed-out hollows and salt-marshes. The land was difficult to plough, and so for years it lay fallow.

It was a frosty day. The low sun, outlined by spectral, rainbow-coloured rings, threw a yellowish light on the snow-clad steppe. The snow creaked under Maria's boots and dazzled her. She walked slowly, waddling like a goose. She could feel her belly straining against the greatcoat. "It's five months already," she thought. "My darling child, you'll have to come into the world not in a nursing home, not in a hospital, but in a dark cellar in the middle of a black waste."

She had been living all alone for nearly four months. She hardly felt afraid now. This place was the back of beyond, a long way from the highroad, it was no use to anybody, the Germans had carried the war far to the east, and an encounter with the enemy no longer threatened her, she realised. All that weighed down on her spirit now was her terrible grief, her heartache which no tears could alleviate, and her miserable loneliness.

Here was the boundary of the collective farm. The desolation was utter. The flatness of the snow-clad field was relieved only by the small boundary posts with the numbers written on them in black tar, and a forgotten hayrick which had turned dark from the autumn rains and was merely sprinkled with snow.

Pushing her frozen hands into the sleeves of her greatcoat, Maria stood looking about her. Nothing disturbed the white silence. Somewhere far away battles unprecedented in fury were raging, guns roared, people died in their thousands, the very ground moaned, while here, in the empty, snow-clad field, lit by the yellow sun, the silence was so complete that Maria could hear the breathing of her dogs, and it was as if there was no war, no deaths. nothing but this eternal, deap blue sky, the unattainable remote sun, and this land which was now resting under the cold snow, to awaken from sleep with the first rays of the springtime sun, and begin anew its endless, blessed work essential for the life of people, animals and grasses.

Suddenly she fancied that she heard muffled, indistinct human voices. Loosening the knot of the square of tarpaulin she wore over her head and shoulders, Maria listened. From where that hayrick stood came the crying of a child, the sound of two other voices, also children's voices, and then Maria clearly caught the words:

"Stop crying, you hear? Keep quiet, or else the Germans will come and hang all of us."

The dogs, on the alert, kept glancing from the hayrick to Maria, trying to tell her that there was someone inside that hayrick. Their new mistress had trained them not to rush headlong to challenge an unknown danger with furious barks, but to wait for her signal.

Maria raised her hand in warning, and started for the hayrick, all but tiptoeing lest the snow would creak under her heavy boots. She stopped beside the hayrick and whispered to the dogs: "Quiet! "

The child's feeble crying came from within.

"Don't cry, Dashenka," she heard. "D'you hear? Don't cry. You're not the only one who's hungry. Tania wants to eat, and Natasha, and Lara, and Andryusha, all of them are hungry but they're not crying, see..."

Maria went round the hayrick and saw a path, trodden in the snow. A barely visible whiff of vapour filtered through the melting snow at the top of the tall rick. Maria's heart cringed: "There're children inside! Little children! Stranded... Hungry..."

Bending down, she pushed apart the hay and saw the swarthy face of a skinny girl, brown eyes wide with fear.

"Don't be afraid, children," Maria said softly. "Come out, there are no Germans here... There's just me alone. My name's Aunt Maria... Come out, please come..."

The girl, who must have been about thirteen, crawled out. She was so emaciated that Maria trembled with pity.

"Where are you from, children, and how many are you?" she asked, putting her arms round the girl.

The girl burst into sobs, fell on the snow and, hugging Maria's legs, muttered incoherently:

"We're not very many... Seven... We're from Leningrad, from a children's home... We're evacuees... We rode in a train for a long time, and then the Germans bombed our train, our teachers were all killed and many of the kids burnt to death... And those of us who weren't killed ran away... We ran for a long time and lost our way... There were eighteen of us, and now only seven are left... Eleven died from hunger, three girls and eight boys... Oh, Auntie dear, kind Auntie, be good to us ... we're all so cold and hungry..."

Squatting and holding close the thin little body, barely covered with tatters, Maria mumbled through her shuddering sobs:

"Poor, poor chicks... My own darling children... Come out, all of you... Come out... I'll feed and wash you, you're going to live with me... I'm all alone, all by myself... I haven't heard the sound of a human voice for such a long time..."

The children started crawling out of the hayrick. Skinny, almost naked children, crushed by fear and hunger, their eyes brimming with tears, they flocked round the sobbing Maria, clung to her, clutching their arms round her neck and her shoulders, crying their hearts out.

Trying to hug and warm them all, Maria kissed their dirty knees, their poor sunken tummies, their long uncut hair, full of prickly, dry awns.

They walked single file across the snow-clad steppe, a pathetic, straggling procession that neither the transparent sky, nor the cold sun, nor even the indifferent frost-bound earth had a care about. Maria walked in front carrying two three-year olds—Dasha, whose crying had revealed the orphans' wretched haven to her, and a boy—Andryusha. Galya, the girl who first came out of the rick and was the oldest among them, carried on her back a girl named Olya, who was in a doze and too feeble to walk. Natasha, Tania and Lara stumbled along behind, barely able to drag their feet.

All that evening Maria heated water on the stove, washed the children one after the other, scrubbed their heads, gave them some warm milk to drink and settled them for the night, while she herself got down to laundering their tatters.

All the children fell asleep at once except for the two oldest girls—Galya and Natasha. Watching Maria through half-closed eyes, they sighed, tossed and turned quietly, and then started telling Maria about their long and terrible ordeal, speaking in whispers so as not to waken the others.

"From Leningrad, our children's home was evacuated in lorries, at night," Galya began. "It was very cold, and we rode for a long time over ice. German planes circled above us and threw bombs, and then searchlights lit up the sky, it was really black, and our aircraft gunners fired at the Germans... We were brought to some station, put into a train, and no one told us where we were going...."

"And in Leningrad everyone was starving, and no one had running water because the Germans had surrounded the town," said Natasha. "We were still given bread and jam at the children's home, a small piece of bread the size of a matchbox and a teaspoonful of jam... Only a few of the children died, just nine boys and four girls..." Galya gave a quavering sigh. "People were dying in the streets. A person would be walking along, then he'd fall down and die ... he'd be lying there on the pavement for a long time, until someone buried him... A doctor lived in the house next door to us, and d'you know what his daughter did? She cooked her sandals, cut them up and ate them... She vomited every day, and died beside her gate...

"It was so frightening when the Germans started bombing our train... They started in the morning when we were still asleep. We jumped up from the explosions, and the coaches were already burning and tumbling down the embankment... In our coach we had a teacher, Yevgenia Vassilyevna, a very old, kind lady... She always wore a black dress, and she wore glasses because she couldn't see well... When we jumped out of the coach we saw her lying at the foot of the embankment with her head torn off and blood pouring... And her glasses still on..."

Galya turned away to the wall and cried.

"Don't cry, child, don't cry and don't be afraid," Maria told her. "Everything will be well now... I had a son, Vassya, a little younger than you ... the Germans hanged him..."

Maria burst into tears, and now it was Galya who comforted her:

"Auntie, don't cry, don't. You told us yourself that everything would be well now."

After a silence, Galya resumed her woeful tale:

"When the Germans blasted our train, all the children ran away from it. There were a hundred and sixty of us in the train. Some were killed, some were burnt alive, and what happened to the others we don't know... We walked for days across the steppe and through forests. At night we crawled into shrubs or haystacks so the Germans wouldn't catch us. Sometimes we went into villages and the women cried and gave us bread, bacon and eggs. In two of the villages the women wanted to keep us, divide us up among the households, but we saw live Germans come, all of them were drunk and wearing dirty greatcoats. They were firing at people, dogs and cats with their tommy-guns... We got scared, and when it grew dark we ran into the steppe again... We walked for days and were terribly thirsty. Once we found some empty food tins and some wire. We tied the wire to the tins and when we came to a pond or a river, we filled them with water, like little pails, and took them along..."

"But what did you eat, you poor things?" Maria asked.

"Anything there was. We dug up potatoes and ate them raw because we had no matches and could not make a fire. We ate sunflower seeds too. And once we came upon a deserted orchard and picked a lot of apples."

"And those three girls and eight boys, what happened to them? Did they die from hunger?"

"Yes, from hunger," Galya replied matter-of-factly. "At first they had diarrhoea, water flowed and flowed from them, then they grew quite weak and died in two days. We buried them, made crosses from twigs to put on their graves, we all cried a bit, and then went on."

Maria stroked Galya's dark hair, pressed her cheek to hers, and said softly:

"Sleep now, child. That's all over. When our people come back everything will be fine."

And so the seven little tramps, orphans from one of Leningrad's children's homes, came to live with Maria in her cellar. All the tunics, underwear, greatcoats, footcloths and things Maria had brought home from the abandoned trenches, washed and stored away for a rainy day, came in useful now. For several days in a row she sat stitching things for the half-naked children, using up almost all the thread she had from unripping the Germans' socks.

The arrival of the children seemed to revive Maria. She told them all about her village, the coming of the Germans, the murder of Ivan, Vassya and Fenya, she told them how she buried poor Sanya in the maize field, and then that German boy Werner Bracht and Slava, a political instructor. She told them how the cows, dogs, sheep, horses, chickens and pigeons came to her for she was the only human being there.

As before, she went out to work every day, warning the children not to climb out of the cellar, except if their need was urgent, and to keep their voices low so as not to attract notice.

For the first few days she fed the children on cabbage soup with horseflesh and maize gruel with milk, and then she slaughtered a sheep and five chickens. Before her very eyes the emaciated children began to look better, and a bit of colour appeared on their chapped, gaunt faces.

Little Andryusha was the first of the children to call her mama. One evening, when Maria returned to the cellar, after work, he flung himself on her neck and shouted joyously: "Mama's come! Mama's come! "

And Dasha, clapping her hands, repeated:

"Mama's come! Our Mama's come! "

"Yes, of course, I'm your mama, who else's?" Maria said, holding back her tears.

Later, Galya, Natasha, Tania, Lara and Olya, standing round Maria asked her shyly:

"Can we also call you mama?"

"But I am your mama," Maria said hollowly. "I had just one son, and look how many children I have now, such good children too..."

The winter days were short, and the nights long. Blizzards howled in the open fields, the whistling wind swept up clouds of snow. But in the cellar, hidden from the eyes of men, it was always warm, the firewood, stored up by Maria in good time, crackled in the stove and the oil-lamp threw a faint light on the children's faces. Every night Maria told them a bed-time story and very softly sang her own mother's favourite song:

> Snowflakes, white and fluffy,
> Covered all the fields,
> All a'sparkle was the world,
> But my grief was not relieved...

Huddling together, the children listened to the sad words:

> There's a shrub stands in the field,
> All alone it stands,
> Neither withers it nor droops,
> But no leaves it bears...

Tears streamed from Maria's eyes, she wiped them furtively lest the children should see them.

> Day and night I pine and sorrow,
> Day and night I cry,
> Snow will melt where fall my teardrops,
> And new green grass will grow...

Maria told them about their collective-farm team, taken off somewhere by the Germans, and about each of the villagers individually. She told them with justified pride how hard they had worked on the land, how neatly the wheat and maize fields were kept, how well-fed and groomed were the cows, what high milk yields they always had, and how sweet were the water melons and musk melons they grew.

"When the Germans came, they set fire to our village and marched all the people off no one knows where," she said bitterly. "Our team's no more, and the collective farm itself is no more. Even the sign they tore off, threw it on the ground and squashed it with their feet."

"But we saw this sign, it's nailed to the tree," Natasha said.

"It's I who nailed it up," Maria told them. "I felt sorry for our people who worked so hard. I took that squashed sign and nailed it to the apple tree. When I look at it I seem to see all our people, our green fields and orchards... One day, looking at that sign, I remembered everything that made our life before the war, and decided to work for the whole team, so it wouldn't vanish without a trace... I've been working all the time, cutting sunflower heads, breaking off maize ears."

"Is there a lot left to do?" Natasha asked.

"No end, children," Maria smiled sadly. "We were sixty-three on the team, and now it's just me alone."

Coming home one evening Maria caught the older girls looking at her in a peculiar way as if they wanted to tell her something. At long last, Galya worked up the courage to speak and, tugging at her dark plait, said:

"Mama, we want to help you. It's too much for you alone. We're big girls—Natasha, Tania, Lara and I. Olya will stay at home with the little ones, and we four will go out to work with you."

Maria cut up another of the greatcoats she had found in the trenches and made boots for the four girls, soling them with horsehide. She also made four pairs of mittens, and when she had them clothed warmly enough she took them to work with her.

"Well, now, that's a real team we have," she told them. "Things will get moving now. But I'm afraid that I'll have to be the team leader, girls, because we've only one bayonet, which means that I'll cut the sunflower heads, Galya will carry them to the pile, while Natasha, Tania and Lara will break off the maize ears."

Work went much faster now. The heaps of sunflower heads and maize ears grew by leaps and bounds. Maria's large new family lived in peace and quiet: every morning the four older girls went out with her to work, the well-fed younger children did not get up to any mischief and stayed in the cellar, all the animals were fed and watered on time...

It seemed to Maria that nothing could now disrupt the measured course of the life which had kindled on the dead black waste, that the quiet about them had come to stay, and that no one would ever appear in this remote, snow-drifted valley or on the abandoned and forgotten fields on the rise.

And then suddenly one night, when all her children and the two dogs were sleeping soundly in the warm cellar, Maria was wakened by a hollow roar some distance away. She sat up and listened. The sound did not subside. Now it came nearer and then Maria fancied that the earthen walls of the cellar trembled and the oil-lamp in the niche winked alarmingly. Now the sound rolled away, growing fainter and fainter.

She got up, put on her boots and greatcoat, and covered her head with the square of tarpaulin. Cautiously, so as not to waken the children, she climbed out of the cellar and closed the trap door. The cold made her shivery. There was no moon. Stars twinkled in the dark sky. The snow was a pale blue. Pale red flashes flickered in the eastern sky far beyond the river. It was from there the deep, growling sound came, and Maria understood that the fighting front was approaching this snow-drifted, desolate steppe once again, that thousands of guns were roaring, and more villages and towns were going up in flames again.

She could not know that on this winter night a decisive battle was being fought around the large town on the Volga now reduced to ruins by the incessant bombardment, that amid the roar of guns, shell explosions and whistling bullets was achieved the turning-point in the war, which would bring liberation to many millions of suffering people.

Maria did not know this, but she did guess that the distant roar of guns she had heard after months of silence meant that the Germans were retreating and the Soviet Army was advancing. And that frosty night she had her first glimmering of hope that Soviet people would soon come to the village.

In the morning she told the children:

"Can you hear that noise? It's our people coming."

They heard the distant cannonade every day and every night now. But weeks passed and it seemed that the battle was being fought in one and the same spot and there was no breaking out of that vicious circle. The cannonade was heard more and more faintly, and then not at all. Now the sound came from somewhere to the north, behind the hills, approaching and then receding, until at last Maria did not know what to think at all.

The days grew longer and the nights shorter, the sun shone more warmly, and in the mornings a smell of thawed out earth was already wafted from fields far away where the snow still lay in sagging, dirty patches. The warm wind dried the puddles and there was the feeling of approaching spring in the air. There were days when the wind blew from the north, when dark, low clouds blocked out the blue of the sky, when snowflakes whirled in the air and afterwards there was pouring rain, and then the sky cleared up once again, the sun came out and the warmed earth steamed.

Following Maria's example, the children wandered about the village in the hope of finding something that might be of use, and they never came back empty-handed: they brought back a hoe, a pitchfork, a shovel, an axe, or a pailful of charred nails, nuts and bolts.

Once when Maria was hanging up the children's laundered clothes to dry on the apple tree, always glancing about her warily, Galya came running to her in fright and said, gulping the words nervously:

"We had such a scare, Mama! We were stacking the bricks over there ... beside that wall," she pointed to the remains of the team office. "We stacked more than two hundred bricks ... and then under the wall we found ... three skulls and some bones ... some people must have burnt to death there..."

Maria turned pale and clutched at her heart. She would have fallen if Galya had not held her up and screamed:

"What's wrong, Mama?"

"Three skulls, you say?" Maria asked, unclenching her bloodless lips with an effort. "Two big ones and a small one? Is that right?"

"Yes, Mama, two big ones and one small one, they were lying together and we left them like that."

"Let's go there, child, it's them... My Ivan, my son Vassya, and Fenya."

They were, indeed, the remains of Ivan, Vassya and Fenya. Before leaving the village the German punitive squad took down the bodies from the poplar and threw them into the burning team office.

Kneeling before the heap of charred bones, Maria kissed the sooty skulls, clawed the ground in a frenzy of grief, screaming words of love and a mother's despair, and her lament rose to a heart-rending inhuman howl.

The frightened children thronged round Maria, hugged her and screamed:

"Mama, Mama, don't! Mama darling, don't! "

The word "Mama" smote at her heart, and she started up, rose to her feet, stood biting on her soot-covered hand to still her screams and, finally recovering control, told the children curtly:

"Bring me the case which stands in the corner."

It was an ordinary cartridge case with two iron handles. When the girls brought it and set it at Maria's feet, she told them:

"Go and bring me some burdock leaves. Never mind that they're withered."

She lined the case with the brittle leaves, and paused for a moment. Crushed by the children's hands, they had a bitter smell.

"Put all the bones in, don't leave any out," Maria said.

Surrounded by the younger children, Maria watched the big girls with unseeing eyes as they rummaged through the ashes, laid the white fragile bones in the case, and placed the skulls on top—the small one in the middle, and the big ones on either side. When they had shut and latched the case, Maria said:

"Let us go."

She walked ahead, the girls carrying the case behind her. The youngest children, looking grave and forlorn, followed, holding hands.

Maria dug the grave herself. The spot she chose was next to the graves of her father and mother. Silently, she shovelled the damp soil with her heavy spade. The steaming earth smelt of spring. Rooks were bustling about in the bare branches of the poplars. At the foot of the grave mounds the first tender blades of new, green grasses had sprouted through the brown, drooping remains of the old.

They lowered the case into the grave, and when clots of earth began to drum hollowly on the lid, Maria wiped the sweat off her brow and looked at the children.

"I've had to bury so many people here, and I was sorry for all of them," she told them. "And here I've buried my own, but my heart has already turned to stone because I've wept out all my tears, and spent all the strength I had..."

At home, she lay down and, staring at the ceiling with dry, inflamed eyes, Maria felt her unborn child kicking peremptorily. She had felt it moving before, but the kicks were feeble, she barely noticed them, and here it was masterfully demanding its rightful place under the sun. Knowing neither the fear of death, neither illness nor the bitterness of loss, neither love nor hate, the child was already prepared to embark on its fated road, fraught with suffering and happiness, and, obeying the powerful call of life was pushing about in its mother's dark, warm womb with its tiny elbows, knees and head...

A month passed. The sun shed more and more warmth. The April rains washed clean the earth, playful brooks ran through the dry ditches, the small village river clouded and swelled, and down it floated tufts of cotton wool, dirty bandages, chips of wood and whatever had collected on its flat banks the autumn before. New green grass appeared on the water meadows. Couch-grass, goose-foot and the ever-present dandelions sprouted on the breastwork of the empty trenches, on the clayey rim of the communication trenches, around the concrete pill-boxes and the low roofs of the dug-outs. Even the dead black waste of the village changed in appearance: the warm western winds and gentle rains removed the soot from the chimneys, it flowed down, seeped into the ground and everywhere pale-green, new grasses shot up to gladden the eye.

Together with the children Maria took off the covering she had put on the bee-hives for the winter, examined all the hives, swept out the dead bees and wax-dust, opened wide the entrances and stood there for a long time, deep in thought, listening to the merry buzzing of the bees making their first flight. She was finding it ever harder to walk. Her time was near, and rather shy of the children she tried to hide her heavy, sagging belly with her greatcoat.

Her first pains started at dawn. Hunching from the pain in the small of her back and her hips, barely able to make a step on her dragging feet, she lit the stove, put some water on to heat, scrubbed clean the German aluminium thermos and whetted the German bayonet on a piece of hard stone.

When the sun came up she roused the children and told them in a weak voice:

"Go outside, children, look at the pigeons and the chickens. Go, please, and don't come back ... until I call you."

The children climbed out of the cellar, leaving the trap door open. A rosily yellow sunbeam peeped in and lit up the earthen wall. Lying on the floor and writhing with pain, Maria heard the merry whistling of the recently arrived starlings and the distant cackle of geese...

She bit through the hot bag of waters, thinking: "People born in the bag are supposed to be lucky." She tied the cord with a strong thread, and cut it with the bayonet.

The baby cried in a thin, feeble voice.

"Welcome, my darling son... Welcome, my Vassya boy, my own, precious boy..." Maria whispered faintly.

She bathed the newlyborn child in the German thermos filled with warm water, wrapped him in a soldier's footcloth, held him close, and lay still.

With the baby lying beside her, she listened to his soft, even breathing, and felt that her entire life, all her thoughts and hopes, everything she had in this world was contained in the soft breathing of the child she had born. His little head, with soft whitish fluff on the pulsating forehead, lay in her armpit, and she, swivelling her eyes, could not look her fill at his wet, half-open mouth, his pink, toothless gums, and the all but imperceptible bubbles of saliva which came and went at the corners, repeating his calm, rhythmical breathing.

Her son was sleeping. Clear blue skies showed through the open trap door. She could hear the children talking in muted voices and, though she could not make out the words, she knew that, huddled together under the apple tree, they were talking about that mysterious and awe-inspiring happening that had just taken place in the dark cellar, and she wanted to get up, call all the seven of them, hug them all, press them to her heart and protect them with her body so that nothing in the world should ever dare to take them away from her or threaten their lives. In that moment it seemed to Maria, drained of strength by the delivery, that she had indeed born all these defence-less children whom the war had stranded in the desolate, bleak steppe, and that it was up to her, their mother, to avert death from them.

Sleep was overcoming her. With a weak hand she stroked her son's fluffy head and whimpered. She felt as if she had born not just this baby and the seven children gathered round the apple-tree, but that in the maelstrom of cruelty, murder and bloodshed, with the bullets whistling and the guns roaring, she had born all the children in her war-ravaged land who demanded protection and love of her, their mother.

"You're going to live," she whispered. "All of you will live..."

Nothing could stop life—not death, not fire, not the wounds inflicted on the land.

At the end of April, the scorched apple-tree unexpectedly showed signs of returning life. There were no leaves as yet, only leaf-buds burgeoning timidly here and there, the half-dead, black branches were still bare but white blossoms with reddish hearts were already opening shyly to adorn them.

"You poor things! " Maria cried, touched by the sight. "Look at the pretties, struggling back to life! "

She stood under the tree, waiting for the children. Before day-break they had taken the animals to water, and they had been away for such a long time that Maria began to worry. Suddenly she saw three horsemen emerging from the forest. They were holding the smallest children in their arms, and the older girls were skipping beside them, shouting gleefully. Maria saw the glitter of Soviet battle orders on the men's chests. They turned out to be the scouts of a Guards' cavalry regiment which had broken through into the rear of the retreating German forces.

Maria would have fallen in a dead faint if one of the horsemen had not dismounted quickly and held her up.

When she came to, she told the scouts about her ordeal in the burnt-down village. They looked at the bullet-ridden sign nailed to the apple-tree, rode at a walk, accompanied by the children, round the fields Maria had harvested, and then, with their caps doffed, stood beside the fresh grave at the cemetery.

Later that same day they reported everything to their regimental commander.

* * *

The year was 1943.

The first thunderstorm that spring had just passed. The trees in the thin oak coppice, the grass in the green flood meadow, and the greyish-blue shrubs of new wormwood along the sides of the country road sparkled with raindrops, and everything smelled fresh and young and had a radiant look, as usual after a violent, early rainstorm.

Our Guards' cavalry regiment was splashing through the puddles on this country road with the aim of surrounding the district centre before nightfall and making a surprise attack on the German chausseurs ensconced there.

Our regimental commander, an elderly major, rode at the head of the first squadron with the three scouts who had been to the burnt-down village and told us about Maria.

We saw her just as we started across the shallow little river, over-grown by rushes. She was standing on the low slope, bare-foot, her hair flowing, and held a baby in her arms. Around her clustered children, cows, horses, sheep and chicken. A flock of white-winged pigeons wheeled above the group.

When we approached, the commander halted the squadron and dismounted. Limping slightly, he went up to Maria, looked into her eyes, took off his cap, kneeled before her, his smart cape sweeping the mud, and silently pressed his cheek to her small, rough and limply hanging hand.

* * *

The sun rose higher in the sky. After the night's warm rain everything smelled young and fresh in the old park—the thick-crowned trees, the green lawns, and the flowers in their beds. Grey and black thrushes were fussing and preening themselves in the bushes. A boy and a girl, primly holding hands, passed by along the walk, sprinkled with yellow sand. A handsome woman in a white dress walked unhurriedly, pushing a pram before her. Down below, at the foot of the hill, the roofs of the old town gleamed in the sun.

The Madonna in the stone niche gazed at the children, the birds, the domes of the churches and monasteries with impossibly blue eyes. I looked hard into the face of the Mother of God, remembering the story of another Maria, mother of man, a simple Russian woman, and thinking:

"Yes, the time will come when wars will disappear from the face of the earth, there will be no murders, no robberies, no lying, no perfidy, no slander. White, black and yellow people will become brothers. They will know neither oppression, nor hunger, nor humiliating poverty. They will know joy, happiness and peace.

"It shall be. And it may be that grateful people will erect the most beautiful, the most majestic monument to the Mother. White, black and yellow brothers will gather together all the gold in the world, all the precious stones, all the treasures of the oceans and the bowels of the earth, and the image of the Mother of Man, the symbol of our incorrupt faith, hope, and everlasting love, created by the genius of new and unknown makers, will shine over the world..."

Translated by Olga Shartse

Konstantin Rokossovsky

(1896-1968)

Marshal Rokossovsky was born in Warsaw into the family of an engine-driver. In 1918, he joined the Red Army and proved himself a brave and capable officer. His talent as a general revealed itself during the Great Patriotic War when he distinguished himself during the fighting for Smolensk and was an Army Commander in the Battle of Moscow. As Commander of the Don Front at Stalingrad, Marshal Rokossovsky accepted the capitulation of Field Marshal von Paulus. Later, he commanded the armies of the 1st and 2nd Byelorussian Fronts, and was one of the authors of the plan to rout the Nazi Army Group Centre in Byelorussia.

After the war, he was Deputy Minister of Defence and held other important military posts. The following is a chapter from Rokossovsky's book (in an abridged form) describing a major event of 1944—the operation to liberate Byelorussia, code-named *Bagration*.

A Soldier's Duty*

TWO MAIN ATTACKS

The main action in the summer campaign of 1944 was to take place in Byelorussia according to the General Headquarters of the Supreme Commander-in-Chief plan. The operation would involve troops of four fronts (army groups): 1st Baltic commanded by Ivan Bagramyan; 3rd Byelorussian commanded by Ivan Chernyakhovsky; the 2nd Byelorussian Front on our right commanded by Ivan Petrov; and finally the 1st Byelorussian Front. GHQ deemed it possible to inform the front commanders about the entire planned strategic operation. It was a correct decision. Knowing about the overall plan the front commanders had an opportunity to clarify the mission of their troops and show greater initiative.

Trying to hold out in Byelorussia the German command deployed large forces there: Army Group Centre commanded by General Field Marshal Busch (one Panzer and three field armies); part of the divisions on the right flank of the 16th German Army from the North group and Panzer divisions from Army Group North Ukraine were also operating in the zone of the coming offensive. On the whole there were 63 German divisions and 3 brigades numbering 1,200,000 officers and men along the front from Sirotino to Kovel on June 23. The enemy had 9,635 artillery pieces and mortars, 932 tanks and 1,342 aircraft.

The troops on the right wing of our front faced the German 9th Army which blocked the way to Bobruisk. The German 2nd Army assumed the defensive on a 400 kilometre sector in Polesye facing the centre and right wing of the 1st Byelorussian Front.

We prepared carefully for the coming battle. Extensive work was done on the terrain, particularly the area of our frontlines, before the plan was drawn up. We virtually had to crawl on our hands and knees. Investigation of the terrain and the state of the enemy defence convinced us that it was expedient to deal two attacks from different sectors of the front's right flank: one would be inflicted by the 3rd and 48th armies from the Rogachov area towards Bobruisk and Osipovichi, the other by the 65th and 28th armies from the area of the Berezina River's lower reaches and Ozarichi in a general direction towards Slutsk. Both attacks were planned as main attacks. This con-

*English translation © Raduga Publishers 1985

tradicted the established views according to which only one main attack was to be made in the offensive for which purpose the command concentrated its principal forces on one sector. Having adopted a rather unconventional decision we were scattering our forces to some extent but there was no other way out in the marshes of Polesye, or rather no other way to achieve success in the operation.

As a matter of fact the terrain in the Rogachov and Bobruisk sector enabled us to deploy there only the 3rd and part of the 48th Army at the beginning of the offensive. If this force would not be supported by offensive actions on another sector the enemy could prevent a breakthrough here and transfer forces from the sector that had not been attacked. Two main attacks would solve all the problems: the principal force of the front's right wing would be committed to battle simultaneously which could not be done on one sector due to its relatively small length; the enemy would lose any real opportunity for manoeuvre; successful operations even on one of the sectors would put German troops in a difficult position, while energetic progress of the offensive would be secured for our front.

The final plan for the offensive was elaborated at GHQ on May 22 and 23. Our ideas concerning the offensive by the troops of the front's left wing on the Lublin sector were approved, but the decision to deal two blows on the right flank was subject to criticism. The Supreme Commander-in-Chief and his deputies insisted that one main attack be made from the bridgehead on the Dnieper River (in the Rogachov area) held by the 3rd Army. Twice it was suggested that I go out into the next room to consider the GHQ proposal. After each exit I was compelled to defend my decision with fresh force. Seeing that I firmly defended our viewpoint Stalin approved the operational plan as we had proposed it.

"The persistence of the front commander shows that the organisation of the offensive has been carefully considered. This is a reliable guarantee of success," he said.

The entire operation was code-named Bagration. The troops of the four fronts had to carry out important strategic and political missions: to liquidate the enemy bulge in the Vitebsk, Bobruisk and Minsk area, to smash and destroy a large grouping of enemy armies Centre, and liberate the Byelorussian Soviet Socialist Republic. Subsequently, they would begin liberation of fraternal Poland and switch military operations to the territory of Nazi Germany. Major importance was attached to organising interaction, particularly between the 3rd and 1st Byelorussian fronts: their troops were to advance rapidly to the west and link up their flanks west of Minsk.

Our officers and men were faced by a most gruelling mission: to cross the almost impassable marshes and woodlands fighting all the way and at a rapid pace. The men were preparing themselves for the feat. Not far from the frontlines infantrymen were learning to swim, to cross swamps and streams by means of anything that came in handy and find their bearings in a forest. Many means were made for going over wet land: swamp skis, sleds for machine-guns, mortars and light artillery pieces, boats and rafts. Tank crews were also training. I remember how General Batov showed me once tank practice grounds on a swamp in the army rear area. For about one and a half hours we watched tank after tank negotiating the bog. Together with the military engineers the tank crews furnished every tank with fascines, logs and special triangular structures for crossing wide trenches. I must commend our fine military engineers for their hard work and ingenuity. In 20 days of June they defused 34,000 enemy mines, made 193 passages for tanks and infantry on the sector of the main attack, and lay dozens of crossings over the Drut and the Dnieper. Not to mention the numerous corduroy and graded earth roads for wheeled vehicles!

In this stupendous work by enormous masses of troops the tone was set by the Communists and Young Communist League members. They were the uniting force in all units. They served as a model for everyone.

In early 1944 we experienced certain difficulties inevitable in war. The troops suffered losses in fierce fighting during the offensive carried from the Kursk bulge to the Dnieper, and there were also heavy losses in Party ranks. Here is but to mention one figure: Party organisations ceased to exist in 1,224 compaines due to Party members dying heroically in battles for the liberation of the Soviet land. The links of the Party with the people, the soldiers were indistructible, and the people's finest sons were immensely attracted to it. This process, so beneficial for the front's troops, was organised and headed by the political administration under Lieutenant General Galajev, a man of great intelligence and excellence. By the beginning of the Byelorussian operation most of the units had full-fledged and well functioning Party and YCL organisations: the companies had five to ten Communists, ten and up to 20 YCL members. It should be emphasised that in accepting new members priority went to the soldiers who had distinguished themselves in action. As a result the influence of the Party increased enormously in all military matters.

After receiving the GHQ directives, as commander I had to work a great deal with the personnel of my HQ and commanders of the front's armies. Everything having to do with the coming offensive was elaborated on the spot: troop control at the initial stage and in the course of the operation, camouflage of troop movements, delivery of materiel and ammunition, selection and preparation of routes and roads, as well as certain ruses which would mislead the enemy as to our intentions.

Particular attention was paid to reconnaissance both in the air and in the field by all the arms and radio intelligence. Pilots of the 16th Air Force Army took aerial photographs of all enemy fortifications in the Bobruisk sector and the maps with the data obtained were immediately distributed among the troops. The armies of the right wing alone made four hundred missions, and our courageous scouts captured more than 80 identification prisoners and important documents.

We demanded from the HQs of all levels constant control from ground and air to ensure that everything that took place in the front's troops was carefully camouflaged. The Germans could see only what we wanted them to see. Units were concentrated and regrouped at night, while in the daytime trains travelled from the front into the rear with dummy tanks and artillery pieces. In many places engineers laid and built decoy crossings and roads. Numerous guns were concentrated on secondary sectors which after making several artillery attacks were removed to the rear and replaced by decoy batteries. Front Chief of Staff General Malinin was inexhaustible in inventing such ruses.

Extensive work was carried out in all the units—armies, corps, divisions and regiments—to prepare for the offensive. The average strength of the divisions reached 6,500 officers and men. The Byelorussian Partisan HQ acted jointly with us, and close contacts were maintained between the partisan groups and the regular units. The partisans were assigned specific missions, where and when to hit Nazi German troop communications and bases. They blew up trains along the Bobruisk-Osipovichi-Minsk, Baranovichi-Luninets and other railways. All their attacks were made in close conjunction with us and in accordance with the coming operation.

By June 20 and the following days the front's troops took up their assault positions. On both breakthrough sectors there was a superiority over the enemy of 3 to 4 times in manpower and 4 to 6 times in artillery and tanks. We had strong mobile groups capable of surrounding enemy forces. More than 2,000 aircraft covered and supported the offensive from the air.

The troops were equipped with motor transport, prime movers for artillery, self-propelled artillery and other technical means which greatly increased the ability of our units to manoeuvre.

Soviet working people had concerted all their efforts to provide their armed forces with everything they needed to achieve victory over the enemy.

With the aim of studying the situation on the Kovel sector (the front's left wing), branch commanders and I set out for Sarny. We were forced to travel on an armoured train, because Bendera bands and other Nazi hirelings still roamed the forests. Subsequently we flew to the troop control points on our irreplaceable U-2s.

The four armies taking up the first lines here were improving their defences and had begun to prepare their headquarters for future battles. These forces will be dealt with later when their combat operations will begin. Now I would like to describe an outstanding encounter I had. The 1st Polish Army was approaching the Kovel-Lublin sector. It had been formed at the request of the Polish Patriots' Union and consisted of volunteers of Polish nationality.

It was with a feeling of delight that we went out to meet our comrades-in-arms. The army was commanded by General Zygmund Berling, an imposing, serious and well groomed commander. It was clear from his appearance that he was a veteran soldier with vast combat experience. Berling was an officer of the Polish regular army. Having taken part in the fighting when the Nazi aggressors had invaded Poland, he had now decided to continue fighting the enemy in Polish units shoulder to shoulder with soldiers of the Red Army.

The general reported on the state of his army and immediately said that his colleagues and he hoped not to remain in the second echelon for long. This produced a good impression on me, as did the troops. I felt they were ready for military action and eager to engage the enemy who had enslaved their country. In talks with the officers and men I promised them that they would all be given an opportunity to display their abilities in battle.

We met other leaders who were organising and taking care of this first major force of the future Polish Army. Member of the Army's Military Council General Alexander Zawadski was an old Polish revolutionary, a miner in the past, member of the Polish Workers' Party who was tremendously popular among Poland's working people and well loved among the troops. He had a keen mind, was engagingly pleasant and full of uniting energy. General Karol Swierczewki was the second member of the Military Council. He had served from private to general in the Red Guards and the Red Army and commanded an international brigade in Republican Spain. Subsequently, General Swierczewki took command of the 2nd Polish Army.

I regard it as my duty of a friend to mention among the first organisers of new Poland's armed forces the army's chief of staff V. Korczica and chief of the operations section V. Strazewski. The army's staff was a close-knit body by that time. Particularly fruitful work was done in the 1st Army by officers Jaroszewicz, Poltorzycki, Biewzuk, Rodkiewicz, Kiniewicz, Pszczolkowski, Yuzwiak, Guszcza and Waryszak.

We spent a few days with our Polish friends, and then returned to the front's right wing.

On the night before July 24 generals Telegin, Kazakov and Orel and I set out for the 28th Army. The observation post of Army commander Luchinsky was installed in a forest. A tall tower was built rising to the level of the pine tops. We decided to watch from here how the battle would develop.

GHQ representative Georgi Zhukov who had favoured the idea of a single main attack from the Dnieper River bridgehead by the 3rd Army set out for the latter place. As he left Zhukov joked that Gorbatov and he would extend us a helping hand across the Berezina and pull us out of the marshes towards Bobruisk. Actually things turned out the other way round, I might say.

The offensive of the 1st Byelorussian Front began on June 24. It was heralded by strong bomber attacks from both sectors of the breakthrough. For two hours the artillery pounded at the enemy defences on the frontlines and suppressed his fire system. At 6 a.m., units of the 3rd and 48th armies launched the offensive, and an hour later both armies of the southern assault group pitched in. Fierce fighting began.

On the Ozerane-Kostyashevo sector the 3rd Army achieved inconsiderable results on the first day. The divisions of its two rifle corps captured only the first and second lines of enemy trenches on the Ozerane-Verichem sector repelling fierce infantry and tank counterattacks and were forced to dig in. The offensive developed no less easier in the zone of the 48th Army. The wide marshy floodlands along the Drut River largely slowed down the crossing of infantry, and tanks in particular. Our units dislodged the Nazis from the first line of trenches here only following two hours of pitched fighting and occupied the second line at twelve noon.

The offensive was most successful in the zone of the 65th Army. Supported by aviation the 18th Rifle Corps broke through all the five lines of enemy trenches in the first half of the day and advanced

5-6 kilometres deep by mid-afternoon capturing the enemy's strong-points of Rakovichi and Petrovichi. This enabled General Batov to commit General Panov's 1st Guards Tank Corps to the breakthrough and the corps advanced rapidly into the rear of the German troops. Exploiting the success of the tank corps, the infantry of the 65th Army reached the Grachi-Gomza Sekirichi line by the end of the day.

Crushing enemy resistance, units of the 28th Army reached Brodtsy, Ospino and Rog.

Thus, as a result of the offensive's first day the southern assault group breached enemy defences on a 30-kilometre front to a depth from 5 to 10 kilometres. The tank corps extended the breakthrough to 20 kilometres. A favourable situation arose which we took advantage of to commit General Pliyev's cavalry-mechanised group to battle at the junction between the 65th and the 28th armies. The group advanced to the Ptich River west of Glusk and crossed it in several places. The enemy began to retreat north and north-west.

Now all efforts were to be aimed at moving rapidly to Bobruisk.

On June 24 in the evening Zhukov called me and congratulated me right away on our success saying that we would have to extend our hand to Gorbatov from the southern bank of the Berezina.

At the end of the third day General Batov was already on the Berezina south of Bobruisk, and General Luchinsky's troop had crossed the Ptich River and taken Glusk. The southern group of the front's right wing had been swung for action.

Fighting continued unabated in the zone of the northern strike force throughout the night before June 25. The enemy repeatedly counterattacked attempting to dislodge our units that had wedged into his defences and hurl them back into the river. The attempts failed.

The 3rd Army resumed its offensive after short artillery preparation fire in the morning of June 25. In the middle of the day, to step up the breakthrough, General Gorbatov committed two tank brigades to battle, and on June 26 Bakharov's entire 9th Tank Corps joined in from the Dobritsy line with the aim of driving deep into the enemy rear, occupying the Staritsy area and straddle the Mogilev-Bobruisk highway.

The 16th Air Force Army was ordered to assist the advance of the northern group. Thousands of bombs rained down on the enemy retreating to the Berezina.

Breaking into the enemy's rear the 9th Tank Corps reached the eastern bank of the Berezina in the Titovka area, and in the morning

of June 27 straddled all the roads and crossings north-east of Bobruisk. Now the rifle units of both armies in the northern group moved
forward more rapidly, surrounding the enemy Bobruisk force from
the north-east.

By this time the 65th Army's 1st Guards Tank Corps was already
north-west of Bobruisk cutting the western retreat routes of five
German divisions.

The front's main forces were to move on forward to Osipovichi,
Pukhovichi and Slutsk. It was our task to wipe out the surrounded
enemy forces as quickly as possible. In Bobruisk the mission was
assigned to the 65th Army and south-east of the city to the 48th
Army.

THE ROUT

Up to 40,000 officers and men of the German army were locked
in a circle with a diameter of some 25 kilometres. We had sealed the
German routes to the south and west firmly, but on the first day of
the encirclement the enemy in the north and north-west was held
only by units of our tank corps. Apparently the commander of the
9th German Army sought to take advantage of this. On June 27 he
ordered commander of the 35th Army Corps von Lützow to break
out either to Bobruisk or to the north to Pogoreloye to join the 4th
Army. Von Lützow decided to destroy all his equipment and advance
north. The German corps failed to break out. The 108th Rifle Division sent by the army commander to support Bakharov's tanks straddled the highway going to Mogilev. On the right flank our troops
reached the Berezina in the Svisloch area.

On June 27, at the end of the day, massive explosions and fires
began on enemy positions: the Nazis were destroying artillery pieces,
tractors, tanks and motor vehicles they were slaughtering the cattle
and razed to the ground all the villages. The covering forces consisting
of picked officers and men resisted stubbornly and even counterattacked. However, General Gorbatov's and Romanenko's troops
tightened the ring with increasing strength closely interacting with
the 65th Army.

In the Titovka area the enemy launched up to 15 counterattacks
attempting to break out to the north. Here is an eyewitness account
of the commander of the 108th Division, General Teremov: "...The
fiercest attack developed in the forward area of the 444th and 407th
regiments. The forces deployed in the area were mainly those of

our artillery regiment. Not less than 2,000 enemy officers and men
supported by rather strong artillery fire advanced towards our positions. The guns opened fire against the attackers when they were
700 metres away, machine-guns at a distance of 400 metres. The Nazis
continued their advance. Shells burst in their very midst. Machine-
guns mowed down their ranks. The Nazis stepped over the bodies
of their dead men. They pressed forward disregarding all considerations... It was an insane attack. We saw a terrible sight from our observation post. There was not a shade of military valour in it. The
Nazis were in a dazed state. The movement of this mass of soldiers
was like an obstinate herd of animals rather than troops seeking to
impose their will on the enemy at any cost. Nevertheless, it was
impressive."

Our aviation discovered large concentrations of German infantry,
tanks, artillery and other equipment in the Dubovka area. The aviation was ordered to attack: 526 aircraft took off and bombed the
enemy for a whole hour. The Nazis ran out of the forests, rushed
about in the clearings, many attempted to swim across the Berezina
but even this did not save them. Soon the bombed area became an
enormous cemetery scattered with bodies and equipment destroyed
by the bombs.

In two days our troops killed more than 10,000 enemy officers
and men and took some 6,000 prisoners; they captured 432 guns,
250 mortars and over a thousand machine-guns. The German force
south-east of Bobruisk was wiped out.

Simultaneously, our troops launched attacks to capture Bobruisk.
There were more than 10,000 German soldiers in the city, and surviving groups of them from the units defeated east of the city filtered
through all the time. Bobruisk commandant General Hamann managed to set up a strong all-round defence. Houses were used as weapon
emplacements, barricades built across streets and tanks dig into the
ground at streetcorners. The approaches to the city were thoroughly
mined.

In the second half of the day on June 27 the 1st Guards Tank and
105th Rifle corps attacked the enemy that still held the city but
with no success. Fighting involving great bloodshed continued all
night and all day. In the night before June 29 the enemy pulled back
a considerable part of his forces to the centre and concentrated major
infantry and artillery forces in the northern and north-western areas
of the city. The commandant of the German garrison decided to leave
the city at night and break through in a northwestern direction.

After a strong artillery and mortar barrage the positions of the

356th Rifle Division were attacked by panzers, followed by assault officer battalions and then the rest of the infantry. Officers and soldiers, all drunk, pressed forward despite the crushing fire of our artillery and machine-guns. Hand-to-hand fighting began in the darkness. The men of the 356th Division fought heroically resisting the enemy onslaught for an hour. At the cost of enormous losses the Nazis managed to drive wedges into the division's defence in some places.

At the break of dawn the advance forces of the 48th Army crossed the Berezina under artillery cover and engaged the enemy on the eastern outskirts of Bobruisk.

At eight in the morning regiments of the 354th Rifle Division captured the city's railway station. Pressed on all sides by our troops the Germans attempted to break out to the north-west once again and attacked the valorous 356th Division. They succeeded in breaching its defence line. Some 5,000 officers and men headed by the commander of the 41st Panzer Corps, General Holmeister, attempted to escape through the gap but failed.

The troops operating north-west of the city wiped out these fleeing enemy units as well.

The 65th Army in close cooperation with the 48th Army took Bobruisk on June 29.

As a result of this operation our troops cracked the enemy's formidable defences on the southern face of the Byelorussian bulge, and advanced some 110 kilometres. This made possible a rapid drive against Minsk and Baranovichi.

On June 28 GHQ assigned the following mission to the 1st Byelorussian Front: part of its forces were to advance on Minsk, while the main forces were to move towards Slutsk and Baranovichi and cut off the enemy from southwestern escape routes, and in conjunction with the 3rd Byelorussian Front to encircle as quickly as possible the Minsk group of German troops.

After fierce fighting Minsk, Byelorussia's capital, was cleared of the enemy by the end of July 3.

A distressing picture unfolded before the eyes of its liberators. The city lay in ruins. The few surviving buildings were mined and ready to be blown up. Fortunately, they were saved by the units that burst into the city. Mines were removed from the buildings of the 11-storey Government House and the Central Committee of Byelorussia's Communist Party.

The citizens of Minsk who had suffered terribly welcomed the heroes enthusiastically. The whole country celebrated the liberation of the Byelorussian capital.

The German troops in the Minsk pocket were to be wiped out by the 2nd Byelorussian Front strengthened by the 3rd Army transferred from our front.

Troops of the 1st Byelorussian Front's right flank continued their rapid advance to the west.

The battle which took place on the 1st Byelorussian Front's left wing in July and the offensive launched by the troops of our left neighbour—the 1st Ukrainian Front—a week earlier developed into a harmonious cooperation of the adjacent flanks of the two fronts. Our success was largely due to the fact that by launching the offensive the 1st Ukrainian Front deprived the enemy of all possibility to reinforce his troops on the Lublin sector in the same way our actions prevented the enemy from directing his troops against the 1st Ukrainian Front. This operation, a continuation of the Byelorussian operation, had been planned by GHQ well in advance.

The spectacular offensive waged by the Soviet troops in July, in which five fronts took part, resulted in the defeat of the German army groups North (16th Army), Centre (4th, 9th, 2nd and 3rd Panzer armies) and North Ukraine (4th and 1st Panzer armies, 1st Hungarian Army). Enemy defences were smashed along an extensive front.

Finally, the time had come when the enemy who had unleashed the war had to go through everything that had happened to the Red Army at the beginning of the war. But we realised that our setbacks were largely due to the element of surprise in the treacherous enemy attack and were temporary, and we did not lose faith in the victorious outcome of the war. The enemy was suffering defeats after the victories he had scored and had no hopes for a more or less favourable end to the war whose flames he had fanned.

The Nazi catastrophy was imminent. Replacing one general by another did not help the German command either. Our reconnaissance learned that the unfortunate Field Marshal Busch who had commanded Army Group Centre had been replaced by Model, who commanded the North Ukraine Army Group and now combined the two posts.

When the troops of the front's right wing reached the Svisloch-Pruzhany line and the approaches to Brest conditions were just right to surround the enemy Brest grouping. This task was to be carried out by the 70th Army interacting with the 28th Army.

The 47th Army was to advance towards Siedlce in the southwestern direction after crossing the Bug River, defeat the enemy units facing it and prevent German troops, east of the Siedlce-Lukow line, from retreating to Warsaw. Kryukov's 2nd Guards Cavalry Corps was fighting in the same sector.

At the same time the offensive waged by these armies secured success for the troops commanded by Chuikov, Bogdanov, Berling and Kolpakchi which drove west after crossing the Bug River. Overcoming enemy resistance they captured the cities of Chelm, Wlodawa on July 22 and liberated many other towns and villages.

On July 23 the 2nd Tank Army liberated Lublin. On July 25 the tankmen reached the Vistula River in the Deblin area. Here, General Radziyevsky who had replaced the wounded Bogdanov yielded his sector to the 1st Polish Army which had been advancing behind the tank army. The Soviet tanks were assigned to advance along the right bank of the Vistula to the north, capture Warsaw's suburb Praga on the march and hold on to it until the 47th Army arrived. The 1st Polish Army was to cross the Vistula on the Deblin sector and capture a bridgehead on its western bank.

On July 28 the front's main forces on the Brest-Siedlce-Otwock line had to deploy their front to the north having encountered the stubborn resistance of enemy troops. Everything pointed to the fact that the German command had mustered large forces in this sector with the aim of counter-attacking in the southern direction east of the Vistula and prevent our armies from crossing the river.

Since the enemy kept his main force east of Warsaw, our troops on the front's left wing had an opportunity to advance to the Vistula rapidly. General Kolpakchi's 69th Army reached the river on July 27. The troops crossed the river near Pulawy and established a bridgehead on its western bank by July 29. The 1st Polish Army attempted to drive across the Vistula on July 31 but failed. However, by that time we could use the whole 8th Guards Army for operations on the western bank. In the morning on August 1 it began to cross the mouth of the Pilica River near Magnoszew.

During the day General Chuikov's troops established a bridgehead on the western bank of the Vistula 15 kilometres wide and some 10 kilometres deep. By August 4 the army managed to span the river with several bridges with a 16-ton carrying capacity and one with a 60-ton capacity. Vasily Chuikov was able to send his tanks and artillery over to the bridgehead. The front's engineers set down to building a wooden bridge on piles.

The front's command post moved together with the troops. As a rule it was transferred to the next site only when communications had been established with all the front's troops there.

This time we had moved with our command post to Wlodawa, a small town on the western bank of the Western Bug; simultaneously, Malinin and Maximenko were preparing the next command post in the village of Konkolewitsa not far from Siedlce where fighting was still going on.

On the very eve of our departure enemy aviation had bombed us at night in Radoszin; it was our good fortune that there were no casualties. I mention the fact to emphasise that enemy aviation had a special mission to discover our command posts and bomb them. In our turn we never failed to pay the enemy back in kind: commander of the 16th Air Force Army General Rudenko did everything to attack enemy command posts. At that moment, however, the 16th Air Force Army was mostly engaged in covering the crossings on the Vistula.

The troops of our neighbour on the right—the 2nd Byelorussian Front—were advancing very slowly on the Belostok sector. It was faced by a very strong enemy grouping still capable of repelling the offensive. But it was unable to attack the right wing of our front. Credit for this went to the units of the 2nd Byelorussian Front, and we fully realised this.

When the enemy saw where he was most threatened it was too late: the Magnoszew bridgehead was firmly held by the 8th Guards Army, while the bridgehead south of Pulawy was also reliably secured by the 69th Army. The German command began to transfer troops from areas east and north-east of Warsaw and attacked our bridgeheads. The Guards were hit with particular strength.

Our secret agents, air and radio intelligence confirmed that enemy troops were being transferred in a hurry to the Magnoszew bridgehead. Chuikov's Guards had to be assisted, and we asked our Polish comrades-in-arms to help us. Turning the line along the Vistula over to a cavalry corps, Zygmund Berling led his troops in a forced march to the bridgehead. They took up defence on the 8th Guards Army's right flank. We also succeeded in bringing a tank corps of the 2nd Tank Army there.

These all proved to be timely moves. The enemy attacked the bridgehead with tremendous force, but it was too late! Our defences turned out to be unshakable here. The frenzied attacks that lasted for many days yielded nothing for the Nazis except enormous losses.

The enemy committed his entire aviation to battle attempting to bomb the bridgehead and crossings. But the hundreds of enemy bombers were attacked by Rudenko's air force army. The crossings were also successfully covered by the front's powerful AA-guns.

The comradeship between the Soviet and the Polish units grew stronger in the hard fighting. The men of the 1st Polish Army fought bravely against the Nazi invaders and won universal respect.

Turning to the past we see with profound satisfaction that the group of fronts commanded by GHQ carried out the Byelorussian operation brilliantly. As a result Army Group Centre was routed and a major defeat dealt to Army Group North Ukraine; Byelorussia, a large portion of Lithuania, and a considerable part of the Polish lands east of the Vistula were liberated. The Soviet troops crossed the Niemen and Narew rivers and approached the frontiers of East Prussia. The Nazi troops had suffered a major defeat.

The 1st Byelorussian Front made its contribution to this immense achievement.

Translated by Sergei Sosinsky

The 1941-1945 Great Patriotic War

1945

In 1944-45, the Red Army, advancing westwards, began its struggle to liberate the peoples of Europe from Nazi occupation. Years of bitter struggle, long and arduous battles, crippled land and burnt down and devastated towns and villages had been left behind. The Red Army entered the final stage of the war as a formidable and powerful force.

Soviet soldiers helped save the world from the danger of Nazi enslavement. They fought shoulder to shoulder with the armies of the anti-Hitler coalition, the Polish Army, the people's liberation army of Yugoslavia, the Czechoslovak corps and resistant movement fighters in many European countries.

This section describes the events of the very last days of the Second World War. Its authors include Marshal Konev; writer Vsevolod Vishnevsky, who attended the negotiations on the surrender of Berlin; poet and prose writer Vassily Subbotin who was among the troops which stormed the Reichstag; and Yelena Rzhevskaya, who happened to visit the underground "Führerbunker" in the first hours after the fall of Berlin.

All materials in this edition are based on documents and personal evidence of people who were in the thick of events in the final minutes of the Second World War.

Sholokhov's famous story, The Fate of a Man, *concludes Volume Two and the entire edition.*

Ivan Konev
(1897-1973)

"The Soldier Marshal" was the nickname given to Commander Konev, because his tall, erect figure was so often to be seen in the front-line trenches.

The son of a poor peasant and a soldier during the First World War who already then showed innate bravery in action, Konev became an ardent supporter of Soviet government from the very first days following the 1917 Socialist Revolution. During the Civil War he was commissar of the famous Armoured Train 102 operating on the Eastern Front.

In the war against Hitler, Soviet troops fighting under his command inflicted crushing defeats on the Nazi invaders at the town of Kalinin, in the Ukraine and in Poland. Then came the tremendous operation carried out with the troops of the First Byelorussian Front under Zhukov which culminated in the encirclement and capture of Berlin and finally, the liberation of Prague. After the war Marshal Konev held a number of important military posts.

Nineteen Forty Five is his book about the final battles of the war. The central chapter of this book, "The Berlin Operation", is published in this edition in an abridged form.

The Berlin Operation

On April 1, 1945, G. K. Zhukov, Marshal of the Soviet Union and Commander of the First Byelorussian Front, and I were summoned to the General Headquarters of the Supreme Commander-in-Chief in Moscow. Stalin received us, as usual, in the Kremlin, in his large study with its long conference table and the portraits of Suvorov and Kutuzov on the wall. Also present were members of the State Defence Committee, Chief of the General Staff A. I. Antonov and Head of the Chief Operations Command S. M. Shtemenko.

No sooner had we exchanged greetings than Stalin asked:

"Are you aware how the situation is shaping up?"

Zhukov and I answered that, according to the information we had, we were. Stalin turned to Shtemenko and said:

"Read the telegram to them."

Shtemenko read the telegram aloud; its essence was briefly as follows: the U.S.-British Command was staging an operation to capture Berlin with the aim of taking the city before the Soviet Army could do it. The main forces were being organised under the command of Field Marshal Montgomery. The direction of the main attack was being planned north of the Ruhr, via the shortest road between Berlin and the main British forces. The telegram listed a series of preliminary measures taken by the Allied command, including the organisation of an assault group and concentration of troops. The telegram ended with a statement that, according to all the available information, the plan to capture Berlin before the Soviet Army could do it was regarded in the Allied headquarters as quite feasible and the preparations to carry it out were proceeding apace.

As soon as Shtemenko finished reading the telegram Stalin asked Zhukov and me:

"Well, then who is going to take Berlin, we or the Allies?"

It happened that I had to answer the question first, and I said:

"It is we who will be taking Berlin, and we shall take it before the Allies."

"So that's the sort you are," Stalin said with a faint smile and, at once coming to the point, asked me straight out: "And how will you be able to organise forces for it? Your main forces are at your southern flank, and you'll apparently have to do a good deal of regrouping."

"You needn't worry, Comrade Stalin," I said, "the front will carry out all the necessary measures, and we shall organize the forces for the offensive in the direction of Berlin in due time."

Zhukov reported that the troops were ready to take Berlin. The First Byelorussian Front, abounding with troops and equipment, was at that time aimed directly at Berlin via the shortest route. Stalin heard us out and said:

"All right! The two of you must work out your plans right here in Moscow, at the General Staff, and as soon as they are ready, say, in a day or two, report them to General Headquarters, in order that you may go back to your fronts with approved plans."

On the morning of April 3, we reported our plans at General Headquarters. The first to be considered was the plan of the First Byelorussian Front. Stalin made no remarks of any particular significance. Then I reported the operational plan of the First Ukrainian Front, no special remarks were made on my plan either.

After our plans were approved the draft directives of General Headquarters to both fronts were read out; the directives had been drawn up with our participation.

The directives to the front assigned the capture of Berlin to the First Byelorussian Front, and charged the First Ukrainian Front with routing the enemy in the region of Kottbus and south of Berlin. It was assumed that by advancing in the western and north-western directions we would, not later than on tenth or twelfth day of the operation, seize the Beelitz-Wittenberg line, i.e., a number of points south and south-west of Berlin, and would reach the Elbe.

The First Ukrainian Front was to strike the main blow with the forces of five infantry and two tank armies.

According to the plan, there should be at least 250 guns per kilometre in the penetration area on the right flank of the front, in the main direction, for this purpose the front was reinforced with seven additional artillery breakthrough divisions.

In the centre we were to strike a blow at Dresden with the forces of two armies and also reach the Elbe.

On the left flank the front was to remain on the defensive. Kurochkin's left-flank 60th Army was assigned to the Fourth Ukrainian Front, which operated, if we may say so, in the Czechoslovak direction.

Besides these main, fundamental decisions—the direction of the blow, composition of the groups and concentration of artillery—nothing else was discussed at GHQ. All that was connected with the logistic support of the operation was decided in the usual manner, without special discussion. Moreover, the front had all it needed.

On the whole, the task of the First Ukrainian Front amounted to the following: by advancing south of Berlin and helping in its capture, to split the front of German fascist troops in two and make contact with the Americans.

As things worked out, in the course of the Berlin operation the armies of the First Ukrainian Front not only helped to take Berlin, but together with the troops of the First Byelorussian Front directly participated in storming the city.

The question is: did anybody foresee such a possibility at the time the plan for the Berlin operation was being endorsed at GHQ, and, if anybody did, who did and to what extent?

At that time I reasoned approximately as follows.

According to the initial plan, Berlin was to be captured by the First Byelorussian Front. However, the right flank of the First Ukrainian Front, on which the main assault group was concentrated, was just south of Berlin. Who could at that time say how the operation would develop, what surprises were in store for us in the different directions and what new decisions or corrections we might have to make in the course of events?

At any rate, I did then have an idea that, owing to a successful advance of the troops of the right flank of our front, we might find ourselves in an advantageous position for a manoeuvre and attack against Berlin from the south.

I felt it was premature to give voice to these considerations, although I had the impression that Stalin also, without saying it beforehand, thought such a variant possible.

My impression grew stronger when Stalin, while approving the composition of the groups and the direction of the attacks, began to pencil on the map a boundary between the First Byelorussian and the First Ukrainian fronts. In the draft directives this line ran through Lübben and then somewhat south of Berlin. While pencilling this line, Stalin suddenly halted it at the town of Lübben, which was about 80 kilometres south-east of Berlin, and stopped short. He did not say anything, but I think Marshal Zhukov also saw a certain implication in this. The line of demarcation was cut short at about the point we were supposed to reach on the third day of the operation. Subsequently (apparently depending on the situation), it was tacitly assumed, the commanders of the fronts could display their own initiative.

To me, in any case, the end of the boundary at Lübben meant that the rapidity of the penetration, as well as the speed and manoeuvrability of the operations on the right flank of our front, might subsequently create a situation which would make our attack against Berlin from the south advantageous.

Could this halting of the boundary at Lübben have suggested competition between the two fronts? I admit that that could have been the case. At any rate, I do not exclude this possibility. This becomes all the more plausible if we think back to that time and recall what Berlin meant to us and how ardently we all, from soldier to general, wished to see that city with our own eyes and capture it by the force of our arms.

As a matter of fact, the drawing of the line of demarcation brought the planning of the operation to a conclusion. The GHQ directives were approved.

The Second Byelorussian Front took part in routing the Berlin group in the northern, maritime direction and thereby actively contributed to the capture of Berlin. However, the part of the plan pertaining to the operations of the Second Byelorussian Front was endorsed several days later after Zhukov and I had already left.

The aim of the Berlin operation was to rout two army groups—Vistula and Centre—then capture Berlin and, upon reaching the Elbe, make contact with the Allies.

The accomplishment of these tasks would, in our opinion, make further organised German resistance impossible. The end result of the operation was to be a victorious consummation of the war in Europe.

In preparing for this major strategic operation it was necessary to consider a number of its special features, particularly the probable strength of the enemy's resistance. The Hitler command had concentrated large forces for the defence of the imperial capital and the approaches to it, had extensively deployed their defences in depth and built a system of fortifications and all sorts of obstacles on the Oder Line, the Spree Line and all the approaches to Berlin from the east, south-east, south and north.

Moreover, the terrain around Berlin offered quite a few additional obstacles—woods, marshes, numerous rivers, lakes and canals.

Nor could we disregard the fact that the Hitler command and the Nazi government stubbornly pursued a policy aimed at breaking up the anti-Hitlerite coalition and had latterly resorted to direct attempts at reaching separate agreements with our Allies, hoping, as a result of such agreements, to transfer their troops from the Western to the Eastern Front, against us.

That the attempts of Hitler and his associates to reach separate agreements with our Allies failed is now a matter of history. But even then, during the war, we would not believe that our Allies could come to any agreement with the Nazi command. But in the atmosphere of that time, replete not only with facts, but also with rumours, we had no right to rule out this possibility altogether.

This circumstance lent the Berlin operation what I would call a special poignancy. And, at last but not at least, we had to consider the fact that, when finally faced with the necessity of draining the bitter cup of military defeat, the Nazi leaders would prefer to surrender Berlin to the Americans and the British, would open all roads to them and fight us savagely to the last man.

The Soviet Command knew that the Berlin operation would tax us to the extreme.

The Hitlerites were intent on protracting the operations. We, on the contrary, were striving for the greatest possible speed. The operation was planned for a duration of only 12 to 15 days, so as to give the enemy no respite and to prevent them from prolonging the operation or withdrawing from our attacks.

We had only 12 days to carry out an extensive and complex redeployment of troops.

I have had occasion to read some of the erroneous statements which appeared in the Western press to the effect that on the first day of the Berlin operation the attack was launched at both fronts—the First Byelorussian and the First Ukrainian—according to a single plan. This is not true. The fighting at both fronts was co-ordinated by GHQ, but the fronts, as usual, exchanged information and operations and intelligence summaries. It is only natural that on the first day of the operation each of the fronts chose its own method of attack based on its own estimate of the situation.

At the First Byelorussian Front it was decided to carry out a powerful artillery preparation at night and to launch the attack by the glare of searchlights.

The First Ukrainian Front chose an entirely different method. We planned a longer artillery preparation than our neighbour in order to secure and support the forcing of the Neisse and the penetration of the enemy's main line of defence on the opposite, western bank. We wanted to conceal the crossing as much as possible and it was therefore not at all to our advantage to light the penetration zone. On the contrary, it was much better to prolong the night. The artillery preparation was to last 2 hours and 35 minutes, of which one hour and 40 minutes were allotted to the support of the crossing and 45 minutes to organising the attack on the western bank of the Neisse.

During that period we expected to disrupt the whole German system of command and subdue their artillery and mortar positions, while our air forces, operating at a still greater depth, had to complete the rout of the enemy by concentrating their attacks on his reserves.

The night before the beginning of the offensive I arrived from near Breslau at the observation post of General Pukhov's 13th Army. The observation post consisting of a small dug-out and a slit trench was situated on the edge of an old pine forest; below it, directly before us, was a precipice and, beyond it, the Neisse and the opposite bank, also observable over a rather long distance. Through a stereoscopic telescope we had an excellent view of all that was going on in front of us.

In war, such conveniences have to be paid for. Observation from this point was particularly effective because it was so close to the enemy, but this, in its turn, afforded no insurance against rifle and machine-gun fire from the other side of the river. Everything turned out all right, however, except for one bullet that grazed the support of the stereoscopic telescope. The smoke screen was used towards the end of the first phase of the artillery preparation. In the observable zone it proved to be very effective—dense and precisely as high as necessary. It was skilfully laid by our attack planes flying at a low level and a very high speed exactly along the Neisse line. It should be observed that the smoke screen was laid along a frontage of 390 km. Being of such length, it did in some measure mislead the enemy as regards our crossing points on the Neisse.

The powerful artillery preparation and the smoke screens disrupted enemy troop control, disorganised their fire system and weakened their defence. As early as midday prisoners testified that individual soldiers, as well as small German units, had used our smoke screen in their own way—they had merely abandoned their positions and withdrawn to the rear.

Our artillery preparation was not hampered by our smoke screens. Our fire was fully adjusted to the topography of the area, all the primary targets having been spotted beforehand.

Subsequently, during the crossing, more smoke screens were laid. The weather was fine, the velocity of the wind was only 50 km/s, and the smoke slowly crept into the depth of the enemy's defences, filling the whole valley of the Neisse, which was just what we needed.

The forward battalions started crossing the Neisse at 6:55 a.m. under smoke screen after a 40-minute artillery attack.

It took the first echelon of the main forces one hour to cross the river. As soon as bridgeheads were seized on the western bank of the Neisse we began to launch bridges along the entire penetration sector. The advance battalions crossed in boats, towing assault bridges. The moment an assault bridge was made fast to the opposite bank, our infantrymen crossed it at the double.

Light boat bridges were launched in 50 minutes, the bridges for 30-ton loads—in 2 hours, and for 60-ton loads—in 4-5 hours. The latter could carry tanks of all types. Part of the field artillery was hauled across the river by rope simultaneously with the crossing of the forward battalions.

About 10-15 minutes after the first soldiers had reached the western bank of the Neisse the first 85-mm anti-tank guns were also hauled across. That immediately gave us a sense of stability on the first small bridgeheads.

In addition to the bridges we also used ferries for the crossing; the ferries transported to the opposite bank of the river the first groups of tanks for direct support of the infantry.

We owed our success in forcing the Neisse to the hard and dedicated work of our engineering troops. They organised 133 crossings in the main attack area alone. The 3rd Guards and 13th armies had, in the zone of their advance, 20 bridges, nine ferries, 12 assault troop crossings and 17 assault bridges.

The penetration of the front was successful both in the main and the Dresden directions of the attack. After heavy fighting, units of the 3rd and 5th Guads and the 13th armies, having forced the Neisse, penetrated the enemy's defences on a frontage of 29 km and advanced 13 km.

The first day of the offensive was also successful for our assault group—the 2nd Polish Army and our 52nd Army—in the Dresden direction. After forcing the Neisse and repelling several furious enemy counterattacks they advanced 6-10 km west.

The troops of the main group approached the second line of the enemy's defences on the very first day and engaged the enemy. But the breakthrough in this difficult wooded area was hard to exploit. The Nazi troops launched persistent and in some cases fierce counterattacks almost at once. On the very first day the Nazi command sent against us not only their tactical, but also their operational reserves.

As regards the unique features of the Berlin operation I should like to emphasize that the forcing of the Neisse, the capture of bridgeheads on its western bank, the penetration of the first line of the enemy's defences, the attack against the second line and its penetration, the further advance towards the Spree, its forcing and the penetration of the third line of German defences were all carried out as a single and continuous process.

As far as I am concerned, it was the first time in the Great Patriotic War that I had had to force a river, then, without any interruptions, immediately break through the enemy's defences, which had a well developed fire system obstacles, fortifications and minefields, and then break through the second and third lines of defence, involving the forcing of another river. I think that this single, continuous process of developing an operation deserves some attention from the point of view of operational skill.

The troops were in very high fighting spirits. The soldiers and officers had to surmount incredible difficulties, but their stamina was literally doubled because they realised that, as a result of this last enormous physical and moral effort, we could finally achieve complete victory over the enemy. They were firmly convinced that this time we would at last bring the war to an end.

Now it is time I said something about the enemy. At the time of the breakthrough the defences were held by the enemy's 4th Panzer Army. As a result of our attacks in the main and secondary directions, this army was severed into three isolated parts. One of them was cut off on our right flank, in the vicinity of Kottbus (we later called it the Kottbus Group). The central part continued to fight us in the forest near Muskau, while the third part was also cut off on our left flank in the area of Görlitz. Subsequently we called this part the Görlitz Group.

Thus the whole orderly system of the enemy's defences, which envisaged an appropriate sequence of committing the reserves to action, was disorganised. And this was very important, because precisely such a disruption of the integrity of hostile forces and of the system of their control is a *sine qua non* for successfully developing an operation to a great depth.

In the course of three days' fighting we routed four Nazi divisions which held defences in the first line along the Neisse—the 342nd and 545th infantry divisions, the 615th special action division and the Brandenburg motorised division. As a matter of fact, very little was left of these divisions.

Trying to check our advance, the Hitler command committed to action against us in the second and third lines of defence six panzer and five infantry divisions from their reserves, actually, however, there were only ten divisions because one of them was incomplete and could be disregarded.

The fighting was furious, the Nazis hurling 60-70 panzers into each counterattack and sending against us anything they could lay their hands on. Small wonder. We were delivering a blow at their weakest spot, and if they did not foresee a complete catastrophe they had a presentiment of a good deal of trouble.

Later, when I analysed the events of the first days of our offensive, I often wondered why the Germans had so hastily, as early as the second line of the Neisse defences, committed to action their operational reserves, to the point of using some units from the GHQ reserves. It seems to me they were psychologically affected by the fact that Berlin was already very close and the territory where they could still try to stop us was rapidly diminishing.

Moreover, the generals were aware of how our successful breakthrough south-east of Berlin might end. They must have feared the appearance of so large a group of troops, including tank armies, in an area with plenty of operational room and a chance for manoeuvring towards Berlin.

Despite our extensive use of smoke camouflage at the beginning of the operation, the enemy's air reconnaissance was bound to discover our tank concentrations.

This danger and Hitler's order to hold the Neisse line at all costs prompted the Germans to use the main operational reserves as early as the second line of defence. The enemy actually made it easier for us to accomplish our subsequent tasks.

By that time the Nazi generals were badly shaken, although, it seems to me, it hardly occurred to them that a crisis was on hand and that the situation was essentially hopeless. Moreover, their distressing situation was aggravated by the fact that Hitler continued to attribute all the failures at the front to treachery; this charge was levelled at the generals who were defeated by the troops of the First Ukrainian Front on the Neisse line. When Hitler was informed that the Soviet troops had broken through in the vicinity of Kottbus he was shocked, but insisted that it was a result of treachery. I want to emphasize that on the Neisse line his generals served him faithfully to the very end and even when it dawned on them that catastrophe was imminent they tried to postpone, if not prevent it.

On the morning of April 17, I gave instructions to prepare as soon as the situation would allow it, an advanced observation post near the Spree in the area of the crossing intended for Rybalko's 3rd Guards Tank Army, and set out in the same direction.

By midday I reached the Spree without any particular difficulties. What I saw on my way was nothing out of the ordinary for a man accustomed to war. Of course, at war one may see things one would like to forget, but can't.

I recalled the terrible picture I had seen one winter morning in 1944, after the completion of the Korsun-Shevchenkovsk operation. During the war I never saw so many dead on such a comparatively small territory. The Germans had made a hopeless attempt to break out of the pocket at night, the attempt was made at a terrible cost. Bloodshed was not included in our plans: I had ordered the capture of the encircled group, but since General Stemmerman, who commanded the group, ordered a breakthrough at all costs we had to oppose force by force. The Germans moved at night, trying to break through in close column combat formation. We stopped them with fire and tanks, which crushed in the horrible winter field a jostling and, I should say, poorly controlled crowd. And the tankmen were not to blame, for tanks, as is well known, cannot see at night. It all happened in pitch darkness and a snowstorm. Towards morning the snowstorm ceased and I drove across the field of battle in a sledge, for it was impossible to cross the field in anything else. Despite our victory the sight was so distressing that I prefer not to recall it in all its details.

On the way to the Spree, however, the human casualties did not at once strike the eye: in the forest one cannot see so well. What caught the eye much more often was the machines and equipment—burned down, smashed and stuck in rivers and marshes.

The battle raged on and I could hear its incessant din ahead of me, as well as on the right and left, on both sides of the corridor we had forced for ourselves. The sappers who moved with the advance units had already made passages in the mine fields and had demined the numerous abatis.

War experience is a great thing. The soldiers who had begun to fight in '41 and '42 near Moscow, in the steppes of the Ukraine or near Stalingrad were now close to Berlin. They were worthy of the glory of Suvorov's heroic soldiers whose valour they even exceeded. Of course, they had not served the term that soldiers had in Suvorov's time, but, if we consider that they were soldiers of the Soviet Army, take into account all their fighting experience during those three or four years, remember all they had seen and had gone through, and add up all their trials and tribulations, we may rightfully say that with such soldiers we could not only capture Berlin; we could have stormed the sky itself.

When I recall the war and compare its different stages, I feel that at times we underestimate the path we traversed in mastering the art of war during those years. In the fourth year of the war we thought it natural that we could perform such combat missions which, if mentally transferred to the first stage of the war, would be considered incredibly difficult and bordering on the impossible. As for the beginning of the war and the correlation of forces at that time, we are now inclined to forget so important a factor for the Germans at that time as their being absorbed in the war, their offensive zeal resulting from their continuous victories on the battlefields of Europe over a period of two years.

Now, in April 1945, we had driven the world's strongest army back almost to Berlin. What we now had to do no longer presented insurmountable difficulties for our army which had matured and was imbued with an offensive spirit and a determination to put an end to fascism once and for all.

I was hurrying ahead to the Spree because I wanted to see the 3rd Guards Tank Army crossing the river with my own eyes. Our further ability to manoeuvre and the Germans' further ability to resist depended on how fast our tank armies, followed by our infantry, made the crossing. The more we accomplished the less they would be able to do, and vice versa.

When I reached the river, I gathered from the reports of our scouts and from my own observations that, in general, things were turning out rather well. But since we had to fight all the way there, we had been unable to forestall the enemy. The Hitlerites had managed to deploy some units on the bank of the Spree and were able to open fire. But I could feel that the fire was uncoordinated and poorly organised; in other words, we did not face a system of concentrated and heavy fire. That is, we did not face one as yet. To give the Germans time to organise it, would have been an unpardonable mistake on our part.

I summoned Rybalko and, together, we followed an advance detachment to the very river. It occurred to me that somewhat lower down there might be a ford. Rybalko was of the same opinion.

The desire to win time at all costs dictated the following decision to us: without waiting for bridges to be launched, we should try to ford the river in tanks, especially since they were proof against the machine-gun and submachine-gun fire which the Germans were delivering from the western bank. In the advance detachment we picked the best, bravest and well-trained crew and ordered it to ford the river.

At this point the river was about 40-60 metres wide. Before our eyes the tank rushed ahead and crossed the river, which turned out to be only about one metre deep.

A good beginning is half the battle. One after another the tanks crossed the river, the enemy's fire was subjugated, the Nazis were driven out of their positions and within 2-3 hours (before the first bridges were launched) a few forward tank brigades were already on the opposite bank of the Spree.

By that time one of Rybalko's corps had found another ford somewhat to the right and also crossed the river on the march. Lelyushenko's 3th Guards Tank Army, which had reached the Spree south of us and had encountered strong German resistance, turned our way and, finding yet another ford, began to cross the river.

I was informed that the advance command post had already been equipped in a baronial castle a little further back from the place where Rybalko, Lelyushenko and I were standing, watching the crossing. The mansion was clearly visible. From somewhere beyond, it was being shelled ineffectively by enemy artillery. The Germans had apparently discovered the radio station which had already started working there or they may simply have been delivering fire on a structure conspicuously standing in the forest.

I was in no hurry to get to the advance command post. I was drawn to the river bank by the joyous sight of the rapid and successful crossing (a ferry was already in operation and the launching of a bridge was nearing its end), and also I had to talk to the commanders of the tank armies which after the crossing would have to execute a deep manoeuvre in the enemy rear.

In my mind's eye I saw the end of this manoeuvre at the southern and south-western outskirts of Berlin. This was suggested by the situation. Of course, it was premature to order a subsequent turn of the tank armies to Berlin in the depth of the enemy defences since the conditions were not yet ripe for it and, besides, I had to get permission from GHQ. But I wanted both commanders of the tank armies to feel my mood and sense my confidence that they would subsequently face precisely such a prospect.

We were standing on the bank of the Spree discussing the situation. The army commanders were worried about the burning woods ahead of us. Fires are very troublesome to tanks. They limit visibility which, under combat conditions, is poor anyway; moreover, movement through a zone of fires is continuously fraught with the danger of explosion. The tanks entering a deep gap carry a good deal of their armour, including crossing equipment; the more farsighted crews even carry a fuel reserve, in cans or special barrels.

But, of course, the fires were not their main worry. The principal problem, which both the army commanders and I understood, was that we had to advance while fierce fighting was still proceeding on our flanks nearby. The tankmen were entering the deep gap at the front of the 13th Army, while Gordov's 3rd Guards Army was repelling the continuous violent German counterattacks on the right flank and Zhadov's 5th Guards Army was beating them back on the left flank.

That was, in the main, what we were talking about. Regardless of whether or not the tanks would turn north-west, towards Berlin, I blessed their daring break-away from the infantry to a great operational depth.

Of course, the following question may have occurred to the tankmen: you are sending us into this narrow gap and are ordering us to break away and advance without turning back, while fierce fighting is raging on both our flanks. Won't the enemy cut into our rear and disrupt our communications?

In all fairness to both commanders I must say that neither of them asked me this question. But I, as the commander of the front, deemed it my duty to reassure them and I had moved my advance observation post right into the middle of the gap in order that I might, so to speak, bear the burden of both threatened flanks. I even tapped myself on each shoulder, thereby literally demonstrating how I would, by my presence in the centre of the breakthrough, push both flanks apart, and showing the two commanders that they had nothing to fear.

I want to stress in particular what I have mentioned before, namely, our confidence in each other. Both Rybalko and Lelyushenko with whom I had carried out a number of major operations trusted me, as the front commander, and I trusted them. They knew I meant it when I said that the logistics of their armies would be protected, that I personally was and would continue to be there and that I would do everything to keep my word.

I stayed at the crossing till about six o'clock in the evening. The last conversation with Rybalko and Lelyushenko before their departure ended in the following decision: bravely ahead, don't look back, don't fight the Hitlerites at their strong points, don't under any circumstances, attack them frontally, outflank them, manoeuvre, take care of your equipment and always remember that you must have reserve strength for the final mission. What this mission was we did not say outright, but they very well understood that they would probably have to fight for Berlin.

I left them both in good spirits. Nor was I in a bad mood.

When I reached the castle I telephoned to all those I still had to talk to. I talked to the headquarters of the front, heard the reports of several army commanders, talked once more to the tankmen (they reported they were successfully advancing west of the Spree) and, forming a picture of all that was going on, I telephoned GHQ. I reported the progress of the offensive, the crossing of the Spree and the fact that tanks had begun to break away from the infantry and to advance far in the north-western direction.

A German battery on duty continued firing on the castle from somewhere afar as methodically and wildly as it has been doing all day, and I sat in the castle speaking to Moscow. The audibility was excellent.

I was finishing my report when Stalin suddenly interrupted me and said:

"And with Zhukov things are not going so well yet. He is still battering through the defences."

After saying this, Stalin fell silent. I also kept silent and waited for him to continue. Then Stalin asked unexpectedly:

"Couldn't we, by redeploying Zhukov's mobile troops, send them against Berlin through the gap formed in the sector of your front?"

I heard out Stalin's question and told him my opinion:

"Comrade Stalin, this will take too much time and will add considerable confusion. There is no need to send the armoured troops of the First Byelorussian Front into the gap we have made. The situation at my front is developing favourably, we have enough forces and I can turn both my tank armies toward Berlin."

After saying that I specified the direction in which the tank armies would be turned and, as a reference point, named Zossen, a little town 25 kilometres south of Berlin and, according to our information, the Nazi General Staff Headquarters.

"What map are you using for your report?" Stalin asked.

"The 1:200,000."

After a brief pause, during which he must have been looking for Zossen on the map, Stalin said:

"Very good. Do you know that the Nazi GHQ is in Zossen?"

"Yes, I do," I answered.

"Very good," he repeated. "I agree. Turn the tank armies toward Berlin."

Under the circumstances I regarded our decision as the only correct one.

With the First Byelorussian Front, which was advancing toward Berlin from the west, experiencing difficulty in penetrating the carefully organised enemy defences distributed in depth it would have been strange to reject so promising a manoeuvre as a tank attack against Berlin from the south through the gap we had already made.

As soon as Stalin hung up, I called the commanders of both tank armies on the HL and instructed them with reference to turning the armies toward Berlin. In greater detail these instructions were incorporated in the directives of the front, which about three hours later were sent to GHQ and the troops.

On the night of April 17, the 3rd and the 4th Guards Tank armies of the First Ukrainian Front turned toward Berlin; as a result of joint operations of the First Byelorussian and the First Ukrainian fronts this turn subsequently led to encirclement of the whole Berlin group of Hitlerites and the fall of Berlin. The turn of the tank armies of the First Ukrainian Front from the south in the direction of Berlin was, in my opinion, a quite natural manoeuvre largely unexpected by the enemy and aimed at smashing them in their most disadvantageous position.

I believed that this manoeuvre would prove successful.

To make it quite clear what happened in the days that followed we must resort to the calendar and, in retrospect, compile a day-to-day diary of events.

April 20

Overcoming all the lines of defence prepared by the enemy beforehand and breaking through the formidable obstacles presented by the woods and marshes, of which there are very many on the approaches to Berlin, the troops of our main assault group advanced day and night.

The Sixth Tank Corps of Rybalko's Army captured the town of Barut, an important strong point on the approaches to Berlin. The same day Rybalko's tankmen penetrated deep into the so-called Zossen line of defence.

This line was not only one of the links of the Berlin chain of defences; it was important in itself and, what's more, its importance was symbolic.

The German Army General Staff HQ had for long been located in deep underground shelters in the centre of the Zossen fortified area. Many operations had been conceived, planned and controlled from there. And now, on their way to the final goal—Berlin—our tankmen broke into these Zossen positions which protected the Hitler General Staff HQ.

I, personally, happened to be in Zossen only late in the day on April 23, after the complete capture of this area. The German General Staff could hardly have expected, when launching their Barbarossa Plan, that four years later they would urgently have to abandon their underground headquarters in Zossen. The Hitlerite generals and staff officers abandoned it in such haste that they managed to flood and blow up only part of their underground quarters.

As a result of the operations of our main assault group on April 20, we drove a deep wedge into the enemy defences and by the end of the day severed the Vistula Group of German armies from the Centre Group. That day the German front was actually cut in two. The left flank of the Vistula Army Group was driven north where it collapsed under the blows of our tank armies. The right flank of the Centre Army Group was hurled to the south.

The Nazi command continued to call its army group defending the Berlin direction the Vistula Group, although after all that had happened this designation sounded ridiculous.

To complete the above picture, I shall quote the statement of one of the officers of the German General Staff, published in volume four of the War Diary of the High Command of the German Armed Forces. The officer, whose name was not mentioned in the publication of the diary, wrote the following:

"When, on the night of April 20, I reported to Hitler the breakthrough of Soviet troops in the Kottbus area, which resulted in the collapse of the Eastern front and the encirclement of Berlin, Hitler and I were for the first time alone. A few hours earlier Hitler had decided to transfer his headquarters, the General Staff of the Wehrmacht, as well as the Army General Staff and the Air Force General Staff, to the so-called Alpine Fortress, i.e., the area of Berchtesgarten and south of it. Hitler listened attentively to the very tragic report and again found no other explanation of the success of Soviet troops than the word "treachery". Since there were no witnesses I mustered up some courage and asked Hitler: 'My Führer, you speak so much about treachery on the part of the military command, do you really believe that there is so much of it?' Hitler cast something like a sympathetic glance at me, thereby intimating that only a fool could ask such stupid questions, and said: 'All our failures in the East are due to treachery.' I was under the impression that Hitler was firmly convinced of it."

That was how Hitler's headquarters estimated the situation on the night of April 20. The author of the above statement was alone with Hitler for the simple reason, as he said himself, that everyone else in the Imperial Chancellery was busy packing or loading the things to be shipped to the new headquarters in the Alps.

For Berlin the danger of encirclement was becoming very real indeed. Although Hitler could still get to Berchtesgarten in a round-about way, he could no longer supervise from there the operations of the whole Berlin Nazi group, which was threatened with encircle-ment and utter defeat by our troops.

It was apparently these events, which Hitler did not expect and which shattered his recent hopes of prolonging the war, that in the end made him stay in Berlin.

April 21

Having recovered from the perplexity caused by our breakthrough the Nazi command took urgent measures to check at all costs the Soviet advance on Berlin from the south. On April 21, to meet us and to defend the outer Berlin line, as well as the towns of Zossen, Luc-kenwalde and Jütterbog, they detached from Berlin a number of infantry and panzer units—all they could lay their hands on at the time. The list of units that were sent shows what feverish haste they were in. It included a training panzer battalion, a brigade of assault guns, three labour and two construction regiments, two flying schools and units of the Friedrich Ludwig Jan Infantry Division, which was just being formed.

It took our tank armies all day to break the rather stubborn resistance of these units and the remnants of those which had been smashed before. The difficulty was that even though these units were committed in haste, they were based on such well-prepared centres of resistance as Zossen, Kumerdorf and Luckenwalde. More-over, in this area our tankmen had to overcome numerous road blocks and obstructions, ditches, marshy floodplains and other large and small obstacles.

Nevertheless, by the evening of April 21 our tankmen had defeated all the enemy groups they encountered and were close to the outer Berlin defences, i.e., in the suburbs, only 24 kilometres from the southern boundary of the Nazi capital. That day our tankmen cap-tured Wünzdorf, where the command post of the Vistula Army Group had but recently been located. Towards evening the Berlin circular road was also cut in a number of places.

April 22

By evening, as a result of the offensive of the 8th Guards, 69th and 33rd armies of the First Byelorussian Front and the 3rd Guards, 3rd Guards Tank and part of the forces of the 28th armies of the First Ukrainian Front, the Frankfurt-Guben enemy group was about to be pocketed at any moment. In the north, east, south and, partly, in the west, this group was already encircled by a continuous front of three infantry armies of our front.

Rybalko's Army advancing toward Berlin from the south was, by evening, separated from Chuikov's 8th Guards Army attacking in the direction of the south-eastern outskirts of Berlin by only a narrow strip about 12 kilometres in width.

An important factor was that the right flank units of the main assault group of the First Byelorussian Front and our tank armies were also about to link up west of Berlin, thereby forming a second, larger circle around the Berlin group.

By the end of the day the distance between the advance units of General Perkhorovich's 47th Army (First Byelorussian Front) and our tank army commanded by Lelyushenko did not exceed 40 kilometres. Thus, two rings of encirclement had formed and were about to close before our very eyes—one around the enemy's 9th Army east and south-east of Berlin, and the other west of Berlin, around the units directly defending the German capital.

Towards evening the distance between the Frankfurt-Guben ring—let us call it the smaller ring—and the Berlin ring—let us refer to it as the larger ring—amounted to 80 kilometres in the western direction and to 50 kilometres in the southern direction. Inside, between these two encirclement rings, was Berlin with all its suburbs.

Still farther west from the Berlin ring were the Nazi units that found themselves between us and our Allies; these units included Wenck's Army.

Having surrounded the 9th German Army and the remains of the 4th in the woods south-east of Berlin, the First Byelorussian and the First Ukrainian fronts virtually cut off from Berlin the main enemy forces that had been intended for its defence, and we were able to deal piecemeal with a group that had but recently constituted a single striking force.

In evaluating the actions of the Germans in the course of this operation military historians often raise the question: could the Germans have withdrawn the 9th Army and the remnants of the 4th Army to Berlin without waiting for them to be encircled?

My answer is that they certainly could have done so, but it would not have altered the situation as a whole. The attacks we had planned were irresistible and we could have smashed the entire Berlin group in any situation.

The closer to Berlin, the denser the enemy defences became and enemy infantry were supported by more and more artillery, tanks and faustpatronen.

April 23

On the northern bank of the Teltow Canal the Germans had established rather strong defences—they had dug trenches, built ferro-concrete pillboxes and dug tanks and self-propelled guns into the ground. The canal was lined with massive buildings with walls 1 metre thick and thicker. Most of them were industrial enterprises, their back, blank reinforced concrete walls facing the canal and forming, as it were, a mediaeval fortress wall rising straight out of the water. All that was excellently adapted to protracted stubborn defence. Some of the bridges across the canal had been mined, others had already been blown up. The canal itself was also a serious obstacle— 40-50 metres wide and 2-3 metres deep.

Now imagine this deep moat with high, concrete, steeply sloping banks. On the 12 km section of the canal reached by Rybalko's tankmen, the enemy placed all they could lay their hands on—about 15,000 men. It should be observed that in city-fighting 1,200 men per kilometre constitute a very high troop density. The enemy also had more than 250 guns and mortars, 130 tanks and armoured carriers, more than 500 machine-guns and unlimited quantities of faustpat-ronen.

Moreover, to the minds of the Nazi officers and soldiers defending themselves on the Teltow Canal, this was the last line on which they could stop us. Behind them was Berlin. And besides Berlin, besides the desperate determination to fight to the end, to die, but to keep us out of Berlin (judging by the bitterness of the fighting, most of the last defenders of the German capital did have such determination), behind them they had the blitz SS court-martials to which all those accused of desertion were immediately delivered.

At that time (this is unanimously confirmed by the testimonies of hundreds of prisoners) the SS and Gestapo were particularly merci-less, shooting and hanging anyone who left the positions or was in any way suspected of having done so.

In those days Hitler behaved, as we know, like a man possessed and even went as far as stating that the German people did not deserve a leader like him. In his hatred of his own people he was ready to take vengeance on them for the ignominious collapse of his bloody adventure.

An atmosphere of hysterically swift reprisals and utmost cruelty reigned in Berlin, because of the fear it inspired this atmosphere undoubtedly prolonged the agony of the German capital.

There were all sorts of people on the Teltow Canal, especially in the Volkssturm battalions, which consisted of regular soldiers, old men and adolescents who wept, but fought on and with their faustpatronen set our tanks on fire.

While the infantry divisions were being brought up, Rybalko and his corps commanders were making ready to force the canal. It was decided that the canal should be forced simultaneously by all three corps on a wide front. But we, nevertheless, determined the main direction in which we should concentrate our artillery fire. We created an artillery fist capable of smashing anything we might encounter. This smashing blow was to open up the way directly to Berlin.

Close to 3,000 guns, mortars and self-propelled guns were concentrated on the front of main penetration sector 5.5 km wide. Six hundred and fifty guns per kilometre of front! It was probably the only case of such intensity of fire power in all my war experience.

The beginning of the preparation was set for 6:20 a.m., April 24. We purposely avoided taking a round figure, say 6:00 or 7:00 a.m., because experienced troops are usually on the look-out for a possible artillery attack or preparation at such times.

On April 23, while the main force of Rybalko's Army was preparing for its crossing on the Teltow Canal, something important happened; through a liaison officer we established connections with General Katukov's First Guards Tank Army, which at that time was also nearing Berlin.

Two of Rybalko's brigades, the 70th and 71st, were still performing the mission assigned to them the night before, i.e., they were advancing to meet units of the First Byelorussian Front.

Meanwhile Lelyushenko's tankmen continued successfully to advance in the Potsdam direction, covered by the 5th Motorised Corps in the west.

Towards evening of that day Lelyushenko's Army was already outflanking Berlin from the south-west. The distance that now separated it from the troops of the First Byelorussian Front—Perkhorovich's 47th Army and the 9th Corps of Bogdanov's Tank Army, fighting their way to join it—was only 25 kilometres.

In the morning the advance units of Zhadov's Army reached the Elbe and by the end of the day were joined by Zhadov's main forces to take up a wide front on the eastern bank of the river—from Elster to Riesa.

The same day the Elbe was reached by General Poluboyarov's 4th Guards Tank Corps, General Baklanov's 34th Guards Infantry Gorps and General Rodimtsev's 32nd Guards Infantry Corps. This was the same Rodimtsev who, only two and a half years previously, while commanding the 13th Guards Division, had held defence on one of the last narrow strips on the bank of the Volga at Stalingrad.

As a matter of fact, the arrival of these three corps on the Elbe meant that the 5th Guards Army had already performed the main mission assigned to it before the beginning of the operation.

On April 23, the enemy had begun some redisposition in the west and was apparently preparing to attack us from the west. We did not know the exact direction of the impending attack, but it was quite clear that such an attempt would be made.

It came to light that Hitler has issued an order according to which Wenck's 12th Army was to discontinue operations against our Western allies, turn its front to the east and create a shock group to relieve Berlin by an attack against Soviet troops advancing towards Berlin from the south. A similar order has simultaneously been issued to Busse's 9th Army, which was also to attack the southern suburbs of Berlin in order to join forces in that area with Wenck's Army.

We foresaw this plan in general outline, and small wonder for it was not devoid of expediency. True, it lacked due regard for the then existing correlation of forces, but that was another matter.

As it turned out later, in those days Hitler literally lived by that plan of a link-up between Wenck's and Busse's armies. He attached so much importance to it that he sent Keitel himself to Wenck's Headquarters to check up on the operations of Wenck's troops.

Naturally, I did not know then what Hitler lived by and hoped for and what missions he assigned to Keitel; I had not even the slightest idea where the two of them were. It was perfectly clear to me, however, that, if the enemy undertook any active operations, they would first of all try to cut off both from the west and the east the troops of the First Ukrainian Front that had broken through to Berlin. I was sure my judgement would prove correct, and it was.

April 24

At 5:00 a.m., April 24, I drove out to Rybalko's to watch with my own eyes the forcing of the Teltow Canal and to be in a position to render any assistance that might be needed.

Since I left so early, after insufficient sleep, I, naturally, felt drowsy. But in those days I could not take a nap even in my car.

Odd groups of Germans were roving here and there. Some parts of the road along which we had to move through the rear of the 3rd Tank Army were not yet completely demined. In a number of places we had to make detours. All around were peat bogs, the ground was soft, and the tanks had made such ruts with their tracks that it was well nigh impossible to travel on wheels; the driver had to keep his eyes wide open and I knew he would not let me down. My driver, G. I. Gubatenko, a Don Cossack, was a cool and fearless soldier and a very experienced chauffeur. We had gone through a good deal together, and he had never failed me.

All along the same tank ruts, bypassing the mined sections of roads, wherever we went that day, came an endless stream of people liberated from captivity. They constituted a real International, these Soviet, French, British, American, Italian and Norwegian prisoners-of-war. Among them were women, girls and youths who had been driven away and were now being set free by our advancing troops. They came with their hastily made national flags, lugging their scanty personal effects in their arms, carts, perambulators, on bicycles and, now and then, on horse-drawn vehicles.

They hailed to Soviet soldiers, each shouting something in his own language. Neither they nor we had any time to stop; they were hurrying, if not directly home, at least to get out of the zone of fighting, while we were hastening to Berlin.

Although the end of April is comparatively warm in these parts, it is rather cool in the mornings, and the rags and tatters in which these people were dressed could hardly protect them against the morning chill. All roads to Berlin were literally jammed with people. They rose at daybreak and set off on their way. However early I started out I always saw them coming.

Although none of them knew their whereabouts and, of course, they had no maps, they nevertheless chose their roads correctly, finding the safest directions and avoiding mines and encounters with the remnants of the routed German troops. For the most part, as I noticed, they walked along the ruts made by the tanks, for there could, naturally, be no mines there.

· When I drove up to Rybalko he was watching the movements of his troops and directing the crossing. The advance detachments began to cross the canal before the end of the artillery preparations.

Everything was shaking. The entire locality was wrapped in smoke. Heavy artillery was demolishing the houses on the other side of the canal. Stones, slabs of concrete, fragments of wood and dust were flying into the air.

Rybalko, the commander of the artillery of the front, the commanders of two air corps, Kozhukhov, commander of an artillery corps, and I, made ourselves comfortable on the roof of an eight-storeyed building, probably an office block. There were no occupants in the building because it was not only under artillery, but also under rifle and machine-gun fire.

At first, when we climbed up on the roof, enemy submachinegunners fired several bursts at us, but missed.

The roof was flat and the huge chimneys of the heating system offered excellent protection against submachine-gun fire. Time and again German soldiers fired a few bursts, but to no avail. Finally I got tired of it and ordered the artillery to strike out at them. They were silenced very quickly, but single shots continued to be fired from somewhere.

From the roof of this building we had a good view of Berlin, especially its southern and south-western districts. The left flank could be seen as far as Potsdam. Our field of vision extended to the right flank where, on the outskirts of Berlin, the troops of the First Ukrainian and the First Byelorussian fronts were to link up.

I remember how vast the city appeared to me. I noted the massive old buildings, in which the district that lay before us abounded, and the density of these buildings, I took note of everything that might complicate our task of capturing Berlin. I also noticed the canals, rivers and streams that crossed Berlin in different directions and were plainly visible from above. Such a multiplicity of water obstacles promised additional difficulties.

Before us lay a frontline city, besieged and prepared for defence. Had there been a reasonable government at the head of Germany it would have been logical, under the circumstances, to expect from it an immediate surrender. Only surrender could have preserved what still remained of Berlin; it would also have saved the lives of many of its citizens. But it was apparently futile to expect a reasonable decision and we had to fight it out.

As I gazed upon Berlin I reflected that its end would spell the end of the war and that the sooner we took the city the sooner the war would be over.

It also occurred to me that at the very end of the war it would, of course, have been good to have fewer casualties, but we could not prolong the struggle and for its earliest possible termination we would have to make sacrifices, especially in materiel, and primarily in tanks.

One more thought flashed through my mind: we must bring up heavy artillery, including the heaviest. I immediately got in touch with my staff, making all haste to report to GHQ that we needed special task artillery of particular power. It was at the disposal of GHQ. I did not know where it was at the moment, but I knew that we had such an artillery.

On my request this artillery was sent to us and it took part in the final battles for Berlin.

In the meantime the Teltow Canal was being forced before my very eyes. I can't say that it took place without a hitch, but in general it proceeded successfully.

At 10:30 a.m. information had reached us on the roof that the 71st Motorised Brigade of Rybalko's Army, while fighting for Schöne-feld, one of Berlin's suburbs, and simultaneously continuing its advance east, had swung round to attack Basdorf from the west, a built-up area whose eastern part had already been occupied on April 23 by units of the 8th Guards Army and the 1st Tank Army of the First Byelorussian Front.

Thus the troops of the First Byelorussian Front linked up with those of the First Ukrainian Front in the rear of the 9th German Army. This completely isolated the 9th Army from the Berlin enemy group.

At about 1:00 p.m. when a boat bridge had been built and the first tanks had crossed the Teltow Canal I left Rybalko's observation post.

The crossing continued all day and all night. In the night of April 24 Rybalko's troops broke the enemy's inner defence line, which covered the central part of Berlin in the south, and burst into the city.

At the same time a new situation, which we had foreseen began to develop on Lelyushenko's left flank and on Pukhov's right.

As I have already stated, on April 22 Hitler ordered Wenck's 12th Army, which had been withdrawn from the Western Front, to march on Berlin from the west and the south-west. This army consisted of somewhat battered units, but the size of the group trying to break through to Berlin was quite impressive, for the army included the 41st and 48th panzer corps and the 38th and 20th army corps.

During the afternoon of April 24 Wenck's Army launched the first panzer attacks in the Beelitz-Treuenbritzen sector in an attempt to penetrate the positions of General Yermakov's 5th Guards Mechanised Corps and units of the 13th Army, which had just moved in, linking up with the tankmen on their flank.

I received the first information on Wenck's thrust while I was on my way back to Front HQ. By the time I reached HQ, everything was all right. The 5th Guards Mechanised Corps had organised a system of defence and, supported by artillery and attack aircraft, as well as Pukhov's units, which had arrived on its flank, successfully repelled all the German attacks.

Wenck's Army which, according to Hitler's plans, was supposed to rescue Berlin had suffered heavy losses during its very first onslaught and had made no gains.

Meanwhile in the Imperial Chancellery Hitler was continuously demanding reports on the offensive of Wenck's Army: he literally raved about Wenck, in whom he saw his only hope of salvation.

Considering this interesting and worrying day as a whole, I must say that its main event was the beginning of the actual fighting for Berlin. Conventionally speaking, this day saw the end of the first stage of the Berlin operation, notably, the penetration of the Berlin defences and the double encirclement of the Berlin group. It marked the beginning of the closing stage of the battle of Berlin and the complete and final defeat of Hitler Germany.

As regards the operations of the First Ukrainian Front the day was vital in all respects.

It was a tiring, but a good day. It was a day in honour of which, after finishing all my work, I would not have felt it a sin to take a little drink before retiring for the night. But I did not have any time for anything outside my work even before going to bed. Nor did my health at that time permit anything of the sort.

April 25

Rybalko's Army and a corps of Luchinsky's 28th Army fought hard in the southern part of Berlin all day long. It was an unusual mission for the tanks. They had to storm a fortified city, seizing one house after another, one street after another.

The bitter struggle, in which one attack followed another, required that we set up a special combat organisation of assault groups. During the fighting for Berlin each such group included from a platoon to a company of infantry, 3-4 tanks, 2-3 self-propelled guns, 2-3 rocket

artillery mounts, a group of engineers with powerful demolition equipment (they played a particularly important role in the fighting for
Berlin) and several guns of accompanying artillery for direct fire support—85 and 122 mm guns, as well as 152 and 203 mm howitzers.

While Rybalko was fighting in Berlin, Lelyushenko's Army continued to fight for the crossings over the Havel, south-east of Potsdam.
Lelyushenko's 6th Guards Mechanised Corps forced the Havel and at
noon linked up with units of the 328th Division of General Perkhorovich's 47th Army. By now the troops of the First Ukrainian and
the First Byelorussian fronts had also made direct contact west of
Berlin, firmly closing the ring of encirclement. After they had linked
up, Lelyushenko's 6th Mechanised Corps and Perkhorovich's 41th
Army continued their advance toward Potsdam.

At the extreme right flank of the front Gordov's Army was engaged in hard fighting against the Frankfurt-Guben Group.

The situation of the 9th German Army, now tightly wedged in
between two fronts—the First Byelorussian, attacking it from the east
and north, and the First Ukrainian, blocking its way in the south and
south-west—was becoming catastrophic. However, the army was still
battleworthy. On April 25 it redeployed and continued to probe for
places where it could break through in the hope of joining forces with
Wenck's Army.

In the west Pukhov's Army and Lelyushenko's 5th Mechanised
Corps continued fighting Wenck's Army on their former lines, where
Wenck had deployed several infantry divisions supported by panzers
on a rather wide front.

I do not think that the commander of the 9th German Army, or
the commander of the 12th German Army, or the commander of
the Vistula Army group could have failed to see what the actual
situation was or that it made all their plans unfeasible.

In their post-war writings the former Nazi generals who participated in this operation, including General Tippelskirch, blamed the un-
wise orders of that period mainly on Hitler and partly on Keitel and
Jodl.

There is a large measure of truth in this. As a matter of fact, having
first helped to organise Wenck's offensive, Keitel succeeded in misin-
forming both sides. He did not completely disclose to Wenck the
tragic situation of the already encircled 9th German Army and the
semi-encircled 3rd German Army north of Berlin, thereby raising vain
hopes. On the other hand, in his report to Hitler he intentionally
exaggerated the actual chances of Wenck's Army.

As a result, Hitler continued to consider his plans feasible. He went on believing that the combined efforts of the 9th, 12th and 3rd armies could still save him and Berlin as well. It is possible that his decision to stay in Berlin was based on these hopes. It should be observed that, however fantastic the grounds for this decision may have been, there was some logic behind it. I must repeat that the Germans hoped against hope that they might succeed in bringing us into conflict with our Allies.

On April 25 Wenck's renewed attempts to break through in the Beelitz-Treuenbritzen area also failed. The attacks were fierce, but we repelled them very effectively with a minimum of losses.

That day seems to have been a psychological turning point for Wenck. He continued to carry out the orders he received, but from his actions it was evident that he no longer pursued a real major aim and that his troops were attacking merely as a blind.

By April 25 all the enemy's attempts to relieve Berlin, all their efforts to cut the First Ukrainian Front in half and sever its shock group from the rest of our forces had obviously failed. Nothing could release Hitler or the remnants of his troops hiding under the ruins of Berlin from the trap in which they found themselves.

The retreat routes of the Nazi army were lined with trees and posts from which dangled corpses of soldiers hanged allegedly for cowardice in battle or unwarranted withdrawal from their positions. I am saying "allegedly" because my impression was that, considering the circumstances, the German soldiers fought stubbornly. It was not Hitler, or Keitel or Jodl, who delayed the inevitable outcome for a few more days or hours. It was the German soldiers.

By hanging their soldiers the Nazi ruling clique strove to postpone their own end. By this I mean their physical end because, morally, they had long since ceased to exist.

A rather large group of Nazi troops, numbering at least 200,000, was surrounded in Berlin itself.

April 25 was, as we see, a day of important events. But the most important of them occurred not in Berlin, but on the Elbe, in Zhadov's 5th Guards Army, where General Baklanov's 34th Guards Corps contacted the American troops. It was there, in the centre of Germany, that Hitler's army was finally cut in half.

In Berlin, near Berlin and north of it were units of the 3rd, 9th and 12th armies, and in the south—the whole Centre Army Group under the command of Field Marshal Schörner.

The meeting of the two Allied armies took place in a calm atmosphere, unhindered by the enemy; it was the result of many years of struggle, of a number of operations and battles which had made the meeting on the Elbe possible. And now at last it took place.

The following is a brief excerpt from the report we sent to GHQ:

"At 1:30 p.m. on April 25, 1945, Units of the 58th Guards Division met in the zone of the 5th Guards Army, in the area of Strela on the Elbe, a reconnaissance group of the 69th Infantry Division of the 5th Army corps of the First American Army.

"On the same day the leading battalion of the 173rd Guards Infantry Regiment of the same 58th Guards Division met, in the area of Torgau on the Elbe, another reconnaissance group of the 69th Infantry Division of the 5th Army Corps of the First American Army."

April 26

The fighting in Berlin raged day and night, but now I should like to dwell on the general nature of the defences of Berlin without timing my observations to any particular day.

I have heard it said that the street battles in Berlin could have been fought with lesser fury, bitterness and haste and, hence, with smaller losses.

These opinions have an extrinsic logic, but they ignore the most important thing—the actual situation, the real stress of the fighting and the real spirit of the men. And the men were imbued with a passionate and impatient desire to put an end to the war as soon as possible.

And those who wish to judge whether or not the sacrifices were justified and whether or not Berlin could have been taken a day or two later should remember this. Otherwise it is absolutely impossible to understand anything about the Berlin fighting.

From April 24 the defence of Berlin was under the command of Artillery General Weidling, former commander of the 56th Panzer Corps. The imperial commissar for the defence of Berlin was Goebbels, while the general supervision of the defence was exercised personally by Hitler together with Goebbels, Bormann and Krebs, the last Chief of the German General Staff.

Goebbels headed the civil authorities and was responsible for organising the civilian population of the city for defence, while Weidling, upon assuming the post of commander of the Berlin defences, received from Hitler a categorical order to defend the capital to the last man.

The Hitlerites organised Berlin for stable and stubborn defence based on a system of intense fire, strong points and centres of resistance. Defences multiplied as one approached the centre of the city. The massive stone buildings were adapted to a state of siege. The doors and windows of many buildings were walled up and only firing ports were left.

A few buildings thus fortified formed an anti-tank base. The flanks were secured by strong barricades to 4 metres thick, which were simultaneously strong anti-tank obstacles. They were built of timber, earth, cement and iron. Corner buildings were fortified with particular care because that made it possible to deliver flank and slant fire. From the point of view of organisation all this was very well thought out. Moreover, the Germans had supplied the centres of resistance with large quantities of faustpatronen, which in street fighting turned out to be redoubtable antitank weapons.

Of no small importance to the system of the enemy defences were underground structures, of which the city had more than enough. Bomb shelters, underground railway tunnels, underground communications were used for troop manoeuvres, by this means troops could be moved and ammunition delivered to firing lines.

The fighting in Berlin required great skill on the part of the commanders who organised it directly in their sectors. This applied primarily to regiment and battalion commanders because it was they who commanded our assault groups.

The advance of the Soviet troops was also rendered difficult by a number of other circumstances. In Berlin, especially in the centre, there were many special ferroconcrete shelters. The largest of them were surface ferroconcrete bunkers capable of sheltering garrisons of 300-1,000 soldiers.

Some of the bunkers were six-storeyed and up to 36 metres tall; their roofs were 1.5-3.5 metres thick and the walls 1-2.5 metres thick, which made them practically invulnerable to modern systems of field artillery. On the bunker platforms there were usually several antiaircraft guns which were simultaneously used against aircraft, tanks and infantry.

These bunkers formed part of the defences within the city limits; Berlin had about 400 of them. In the city there were also many reinforced concrete pillboxes with machine-gunners inside and, upon breaking into a square or the territory of a factory, our soldiers very often ran into their fire. Berlin also had a lot of anti-aircraft artillery, during the street fighting it played a particularly important role as anti-tank defence. Apart from the toll taken by fausts, most of our losses in tanks and self-propelled guns in Berlin were caused by the enemy anti-aircraft guns.

During the Berlin operation the Hitlerites succeeded in destroying or putting out of action more than 800 of our tanks and self-propelled guns. We suffered most of these losses during the fighting within the city limits.

To reduce the losses caused by fausts we screened the tanks with sheets of tin plate or iron. These comparatively flimsy screens damped the fausts' reactive power before they met the tank armour, after which they usually ricochetted without doing harm.

Why did we start using those screens so late? Previously we had not encountered such wide use of fausts in street fighting. Under field conditions we had not been particularly worried by them.

The German soldiers surrendered, as always, only when there was no other way out. The same must be said about the officers. But they had already lost their fighting spirit, and there remained but a gloomy and hopeless determination to fight until there was an order to surrender.

But the mood prevailing in the Volkssturm during the decisive fighting for Berlin may be described as one of hysterical self-sacrifice. These defenders of the Third Reich, including mere boys, believed themselves to be the personification of the last hope of a miracle which, in spite of everything, must ultimately occur.

On the other hand, all Hitler's instructions during that period, all his efforts to relieve Berlin, all his orders issued to that effect to Wenck, and Busse, and Henrizi, the Commander of the 3rd Army, and Schörner with his Army Group, and Gross-Admiral Doenitz, who was supposed to break through to Berlin with sailors, were under the circumstances and the correlation of forces quite unjustified.

But Hitler's plans would not have collapsed of themselves. Only armed action by us could make them collapse. It was the successes of the Soviet troops in the hard fighting for Berlin that day by day, hour by hour exposed the illusoriness of Hitler's last hopes, plans and orders.

Had we acted differently, these orders and plans might have turned out not so fantastic. This is something we must never forget.

By April 26 we began to "shut in" more and more encircled units in the vicinity of Berlin and in the area of the Frankfurt-Guben Group. The prisoners now included commanders of regiments, brigades and divisions, as well as staff officers.

On April 26 we continued to release prisoners from various concentration camps around Berlin. Their numbers kept growing. We liberated many war prisoners and foreign workers around Kottbus where there were many factories, including underground ones. Not far from Berlin Lelyushenko's tankmen freed Edouard Herriot, a former French Prime Minister, the man who had been one of the first advocates of Franco-Soviet rapprochement as far back as the 1920s.

April 27

By April 27, as a result of the operations of the armies of the First Byelorussian Front, which had advanced to the very centre of Berlin, and the operations of the armies of our front, the enemy held in Berlin only a narrow strip from east to west 16 kilometres in length and 2-3 kilometres and, in some places, 5 kilometres in width. The whole strip was now under constant artillery bombardment by our guns.

At the same time the fighting for the liquidation of the Frankfurt-Guben Group was going on apace. Five armies of combined arms—the 3rd, 69th and 33rd of the First Byelorussian Front, Gordov's 3rd Guards Army and part of Luchinsky's 28th Army of the First Ukrainian Front—were thrusting at it from all sides. Krasovsky's 2nd Air Army, which formed part of our front, was charged with smashing this group from the air.

Large forces of all the three armies of the First Byelorussain Front delivered vigorous blows at the German group from the north, north-east and east in an attempt to split the group, but the Nazi troops dodged their blows and, contracting like a spring pressed against the armies of our front, which barred their way to the south-west.

The stronger the pressure that was exerted against them and the harder the blows they received from behind, the more vigorously they tried to break through to our rear. Each thrust from behind seemed to pass through them to us, in front. The enemy concentrated their battle formations and attacked us more and more actively. This was only to be expected, for there was no alternative but surrender. True, they could have fought their way through our battle formations and linked up with Wenck.

During the fighting for Berlin the Nazi troops managed to break through our encirclement twice. They broke through first time and were stopped. Then they broke through for the second time and, as a result of successive attacks advanced quite a long way in the area of Beelitz, where by May 1 they were only about 5 kilometres away from Wenck's Army, which was continuing its attacks from the west.

During that double breakthrough, however, the Hitlerites were unable to do anything to our logistics. They broke through, but were encircled and squeezed in again; they broke through again and were squeezed in once more and kept moving within our encirclement. But be that as it may, this case shows once again that even under the most difficult conditions 200,000 fighting men are 200,000 fighting men, especially when they fight purposefully and desperately.

Western historians at times clearly exaggerate the number of the 9th German Army effectives who, by May 2, managed to break through to the west. Some historians even set this number at 20,000-30,000. This is, of course, a gross exaggeration. As the commander of the front, I can testify that only a few scattered groups, totalling hardly more than 3,000-4,000 men, filtered rather than broken through the woods on various sectors of the front.

The fighting for Berlin was nearing its end.

On the Elbe our troops had three days since linked up with the Americans. South of it, in the Dresden direction, the German units that had counterattacked us were completely checked. And only in the south did there remain the still undefeated large German group—the Centre Army Group under the command of Field Marshal Schörner and the Austria Group which still occupied part of Saxony and the greater part of Czechoslovakia and Austria.

Though the fighting for Berlin had been tense and there were still many tasks facing the First Ukrainian Front, as time went on we had to think more and more of the Schörner Army Group on our left flank and south of it, confronting our neighbours, the Second and Fourth Ukrainian fronts.

I cannot, therefore, say that the telephone call from GHQ about this still unsolved problem took me unawares.

The question was:

"Who, do you think, will be taking Prague?"

Knowing the situation and realising that the troops of the First Ukrainian Front were actually at the gate of Czechoslovakia and would soon be finished with Berlin, I saw that the position of our front could probably be used to advantage.

Despite the bitter fighting and considerable losses, our armies still constituted a powerful striking force and, consequently, could perform a swift manoeuvre from the north to the south and deliver a blow west of Dresden, at Prague. Having considered all this once more, I reported to Stalin that Prague would apparently have to be taken by the First Ukrainian Front.

The fighting for Berlin was not yet over. We had to continue fighting for another three and a half days and do all we could to prevent the Frankfurt-Guben Group from slipping away to the west and, yet, our views concerning the participation of the troops of our front in the forthcoming Prague operation had to be drawn up and sent to GHQ as soon as possible. One operation was far from being finished and another one was already beginning.

After the capture of Berlin and the defeat of the Berlin group I met General Omar Nelson Bradley, the Commander of the American troops in Europe. I should like to tell about this meeting, especially since General Bradley also described our meeting in his *A Soldier's Story.* I see no reason for entering into polemics with him about the interpretation of certain facts in his *Story,* I merely want to give the reader my impression of our visits to each other.

I first met General Bradley, the Commander of the 12th American Army Group, a week after the link-up of the Soviet and American troops on the Elbe. Our meeting took place at my command post, some forty kilometres north-east of Torgau.

Bradley arrived with a retinue of generals and officers and a very large number of correspondents and newspaper photographers; I should even say, too many of them. Present on our side, besides me, were members of the military Council of the Front, A. S. Zhadov, Commander of the 5th Guards Army, and G. V. Baklanov, Commander of the 34th Guards Infantry Corps. It was their troops that had been the first to meet the Americans on the Elbe. We also had representatives of our newspapers, photographers and cameramen, but considerably fewer than the Americans.

Soviet-American relations have fluctuated a good deal; today, too, these relations leave much to be desired, and through no fault of ours either. To be historically exact, I must say that on that day, May 5, 1945, the meeting of two commanders—American and Soviet— took place in an atmosphere of straightforwardness and frankness. Bradley and I were not diplomats, but soldiers, and this left its imprint on both meetings, at once official and friendly.

The General and I examined his map with the positions of the American troops on that day—May 5— marked on it. Bradley briefly explained where and which of his units had reached the fixed line of contact with us. Then he asked me how we intended to take Prague and whether or not Americans should help us to do it.

His question did not surprise me. Although the Soviet troops had not as yet launched an offensive against Schörner's group, the Americans could have had no doubts that the offensive was to be launched in the very near future.

I told Bradley we did not need any help and that any advance of the American troops farther east of the established line of demarcation would only muddle things up and mix up the troops, which was undesirable, I therefore asked him not to do it.

Bradley agreed with me and said that the troops under his command would continue to keep the established line of contact.

During the dinner, in my first official toast, I spoke of the trials and hardships the Soviet Army had endured on its way to victory. I spoke of the important role President Roosevelt had played in creating the anti-Hitler coalition and in all its subsequent actions. Roosevelt's death was still fresh in my memory and I was one of those who were sincerely and deeply affected by that loss. In officially expressing condolences on the occasion of the untimely death of the American President I put my personal feelings into my speech and voiced the hope that the new President would continue the work done by Roosevelt.

Unfortunately, this hope was not realised, and Roosevelt's successor very soon helped to aggravate relations between the Soviet Union and the USA.

Speaking of our common struggle against the Nazi invaders, I noted and appreciated the incontestable merits of the officers and soldiers of the 12th American Army Group.

In his reciprocal toast General Bradley observed the courage of the Soviet soldiers and the valour of the troops of the First Ukrainian Front, whose example, he said, was followed by the American soldiers, officers and generals. Dwelling on Roosevelt's contributions he expressed his regret that the President had not lived to see the happy days of victory and raised a toast to our meeting.

The first official toasts were followed by a friendly conversation interrupted only by, so to speak, local toasts to representatives of our and American staffs, commanders of armies and representatives of various arms of the service. The toasts were cordial and sincere. They showed that we really respected each other and valued the fighting friendship which had formed and gathered strength in the struggle against our common enemy. After dinner I invited Bradley and his companions to a concert given by the Song and Dance Company of the First Ukrainian Front. It should be noted that this company organised by Lidiya Chernyshova in Kiev in 1943 enjoyed great popu-

larity at the front. The company had really excellent musicians, singers and dancers.

When the company sang the American National Anthem the Americans in the hall joined in and when the singing ended, burst into
loud applause. They also applauded when the company sang the
Soviet National Anthem.

That day the company was in particularly high spirits. In addition to Soviet songs they sang the American "There's a Tavern in the
Town" and the English "Tipperary". All this was received by the
guests with great elation. Then they were shown Ukrainian and
Russian folk dances—the best part of our dancers' programme. These
dances generally produce a wonderful impression, but on that occasion the impression was enhanced by the festive, joyous mood of all
who were present.

Bradley thanked me for the concert and announced the decision
of the US Government to decorate me, as the Commander of the
First Ukrainian Front, with the highest American order. He handed
that order to me right there and then and, as is the custom in such
cases, congratulated and embraced me.

Those who were present at the meeting, my comrades-in-arms,
sincerely approved the decoration, rightfully regarding it as our Ally's
high appraisal of the fighting done by the First Ukrainian Front.

After the decoration ceremony Bradley and I left the mansion and
out in the open, in the presence of a rather large audience assembled
on the occasion of the visit of the American guests, I handed to General Bradley, on behalf of the fighting men of the First Ukrainian
Front, a Red Banner as a symbol of our fighting friendship.

I knew that Bradley was going to present me with a jeep especially
brought from HQ by plane. I, too, had prepared a personal present
for him, notably, a horse which had followed me everywhere since
the summer of 1943 when I assumed the command of the Steppe
Front. It was a handsome, well-trained Don stallion, and I presented
it to Bradley with all its harness.

It seemed to me Bradley was sincerely pleased with the present.
Accepting the horse, he presented me with a jeep, which bore the
inscription: "To the Commander of the First Ukrainian Army Group
from the Soldiers of the 12th American Army Group", the American
colours and also an American sub-machine.

A few days later I had to pay General Bradley a return visit.

Numerous staff officers and a still more numerous crowd of
correspondents had assembled near the building we drove up to.

In the main hall of the building Bradley offered us cocktails made, as he told us, according to his recipe. The cocktail was poured from a huge copper kettle into soldiers' mugs with a ladle. I was told that that was a tradition. Well, traditions were traditions.

After the cocktails Bradley took me to his HQ at the other end of the city. A guard of honour, again consisting of all arms of the service, was lined up before the building. We both reviewed the guard. I greeted the men and asked the General to command them to come to attention. When that was done I handed to Bradley, on behalf of the Soviet Government, an Order of Suvorov, First Degree. Bradley is a reserved person, but it seemed to me that at the moment his face betrayed emotion. We embraced in a friendly manner and I congratulated him.

Then we went to the hall where tables were set, and, as usual, it all started with toasts again. The first toast was proposed by the host, the second by me—to our meeting, to Bradley and all his friends and comrades-in-arms seated at the table.

During dinner the subject of war had hardly come up. The only military subject we discussed was Suvorov. On receiving the Order of Suvorov Bradley wanted to know about that historical personality. It turned out that he did not know anything about him, and I told him about the main campaigns of the Russian general, including the Italian campaign and the crossing of the Alps.

When I had finished my story about Suvorov I told Bradley that Suvorov was the most talented military leader in the history of the Russian Army and that the order named after him was primarily one for army leaders, the highest decoration established in our country for generals commanding large formations, and that Marshal Stalin (as was actually the case) had charged me personally to present this order to General Bradley.

Bradley himself impressed me favourably during our meeting both as a man and a soldier.

I formed the impression that he was a soldier in the true sense of the word and a military leader who worthily represented the American troops operating in Europe.

I was also pleased by the fact that in talking to me he repeatedly spoke with affection of the Soviet people and its army, highly and, as it seemed to me, with sincere satisfaction appraised our last operations, and understood all the difficulties of the struggle the Soviet Army had waged against the Hitlerites.

In one of our talks Bradley very frankly said that our army had borne the brunt of the war, that is to say, he stated what many generals in the West, at one time our Allies, later stubbornly passed over in silence or even denied. We also saw eye to eye in our evaluation of the enemy. He considered the German army strong and hardened, capable of fighting stubbornly, very skilfully and staunchly.

Our meeting took place and ended in a free and easy, friendly atmosphere. We were then really on very good terms. I left Bradley in the best of spirits and only on my way back did one small detail somewhat disconcert me.

When we were seating ourselves at the dinner table I had seen a microphone before me. I did not think there was any need to broadcast our table toasts and asked that the microphone should be taken away. Bradley immediately gave orders to that effect. But on my way back to my command post I turned on a radio receiver and heard my voice. The toast which I had raised during dinner at Bradley's had been recorded on tape and was now being broadcast. To be sure, I did not attach any particular importance to it, but I must say that, since we had agreed on it beforehand, such a breach of faith, even in so unimportant a matter, left me with an unpleasant aftertaste, although I admit that it may have been done without Bradley's knowledge and he himself may have been deceived by the correspondents.

I took part in many important events of the war; I saw and knew a good deal, but, even if I were to describe all the four years of war I went through, my story would still comprise but a few pages of the vast annals of the Great Patriotic War.

Vassily Subbotin
(b. 1921)

A poet, prose writer and translator, Vassily Subbotin was born in Siberia. His father came from a family of farmers. Both the father and the son went to the front in 1941.

Subbotin's father was killed in action on the 1st Ukrainian Front, while Vassily, then a twenty-four-year-old lieutenant, fought his way with the army into Berlin and took part in the assault of the Reichstag. It was there, during respites in the fighting, that he wrote the first sketches of his future book, *How Wars End.* It took him, in fact, twenty years to complete the work.

Included in this edition are several stories from Subbotin's book.

How Wars End

THE ROAD

It was a dark night and we were moving fast.

Snowflakes were whirling in the beam of the headlights.

Above us was the night. A keen wind was driving the snow, and it was draughty in the back of the lorry, where we were standing in short army sheepskins with our collars turned up.

The lorry bounced along and the lifeless, frozen earth rang under our wheels.

I don't remember now if there were any lights about. The villages were strangely silent. Just snow and snowdrifts. Dim outlines of hills. And on we went, muffling ourselves against the wind, across those bare, snow-swept fields. We thought we had a long way to go that hard, starry road and we were glad to be going fast.

Suddenly there was an explosion. Right under the front wheels.

Flares floated slowly into the sky. Two lines of coloured tracer bullets coursed across it. Pandemonium broke loose.

Machine-guns began to chatter in the distance.

Nearby, perhaps behind us, another machine-gun opened up in our defence.

We had landed in trouble.

But a minute later we were racing back.

The mine had shaken, but not crippled, our lorry and the driver had managed to swing it round. Before we realised what had happened, he was driving us back as hard as he could go, cursing our youth and inexperience.

We had nearly driven straight into an enemy trench.

I can still picture that road and the trench cutting across it.

When I close my eyes I can see them now.

The road is just a straight country track across the fields. Seemingly endless. Leading away into the distance... And suddenly it breaks off, as though at a barrier.

Beyond is the frontline. A tangle of rusty barbed wire.

Since then I have always remembered the war as a road blocked by a trench.

THE GREY BUILDING

When dawn came, everyone in Himmler's house went to the windows in the hope of seeing the Reichstag. But they were disappointed; there was a building in the way.

Battalion Commander Neustroyev was also staring over a window-sill in the basement. It was high in the wall and he could not see much. On the right were the trees of a park, still bare and black. The damp of April, of last year's rotted leaves was in the air. On the left was a deep defence ditch. Moisture was dripping from the roof. The building Neustroyev saw ahead of him was not very high, rectangular, partly screened by trees. It did not seem very large, although it did have a dome and small towers at each corner, but there was nothing special about it.

The men who had gathered at the window with him were puzzled. They, too, had expected to see the Reichstag, yet there seemed to be no sign of it.

But another Battalion Commander, Davydov, said there was not much of a view from the basement and took the officers upstairs to have a look round. From up there they would be able to see the way ahead.

They climbed two floors and looked cautiously out of a window, keeping well out of sight. Mist was still drifting up from the Spree. The sodden park was deserted. It was quiet. But from here they saw what they had not been able to see from the basement—that the square was ribboned with trenches. They saw the pillboxes on the corners. The tanks. The self-propelled guns in the park. A circular billboard. Something else that looked like a transformer shed and was probably fortified. Besides the ditch there was also a canal, full of water. And this building with the towers at the corners looked more impressive from above than it had looked from the basement, with only its top showing.

A messenger arrived. It was for Neustroyev. Division Commander Shatilov wanted to know why he wasn't advancing.

"Comrade 77! There is a grey building in the way."

"What did you say? What building?"

"Straight ahead of us! I shall go round it on the right."

Neustroyev, lying by the telephone in a corner of the basement, and the division commander at his observation post in Moabit, both leaned over their maps...

Zinchenko, the Regimental Commander, came into the observation post. He had set up his headquarters across the river, next to the

Swiss Embassy.

"What's the matter? Give me the map." They made various reckonings. Moltke Bridge ... the Spree ... Himmler's house...

"Neustroyev! That *is* the Reichstag! "

It had never occurred to him that this grey, rectangular building right in front of the windows, so close to him, was actually the Reichstag that he had been straining every nerve to reach.

Above its ribbed dome there was a platform with a spire. The front of the building was lined with trees, just about to burst into leaf, still not torn or scorched.

But not many people saw it like this, only those who were there early that morning. One hour later the artillery went into action. Rocket mortars and shells were pumped into the Reichstag at long and short range and it soon acquired the appearance we know so well from photographs taken after the war.

IT IS NOT GENERALLY KNOWN

It is not generally known that after we had mounted our flag on the Reichstag the fighting continued in the building for another two days and two nights.

One thousand five hundred Germans, brought in from the Baltic area during the actual assault on Berlin, had installed themselves in the cellars of the Reichstag. They pounded us with faustpatronen, a powerful anti-tank weapon of which they had plenty. And when they realised the Reichstag could not be recaptured, they set fire to it. Or it may have caught fire itself from the faustpatronen.

It burned as any building does, and there was plenty to burn there—the furniture, the paint on the walls. The parquet flooring bulged and blazed, first smoke, then flames belched from the windows and the shell-holes in the walls. A handful of our men—not more than three hundred—fought in the blazing building.

But this was not the only dramatic feature of the situation.

On the morning of May 1st, the 1410th day of the war, it was stated in a Soviet Information Bureau communiqué that Soviet troops had occupied the German Reichstag in the centre of Berlin and mounted the Banner of Victory there. This was also stated by Stalin in his May Day order.

Thanksgiving services were being held in Paris, London and New York. You had only to switch on the radio to hear the peal of bells. But even while the bells of victory rang, our men were standing in a narrow corridor of the blazing Reichstag, driven back to the wall by the flames and shielding eyes with their arms.

The battalion commander was told he could bring his men out. "Come out of the Reichstag, take up all-round defensive positions and, as soon as the building burns out, you will start taking it again."

But there was no way out. Some of the men gathered in a small room, half choking from the smoke, put on their respirators—the few that had them—and lay on the floor. The flames were already creeping into the room.

Then something gave way with a crash. Yellowish smoke poured in through a gap in the wall. But it was not a new danger; it was a way of escape.

Through this unexpected loophole the men made their way into the neighbouring room, which had already burnt out.

The Germans failed in their object. The banner escaped the flames and remained flying over the Reichstag, only slightly darkened by smoke.

When the fire began to die down, all the exits from the cellars were again blocked.

The morning of May 2nd began to break.

ACROSS THE KÖNIGSPLATZ

"Entrance. Entrance. Entrance," the girl telephonist repeated steadily.

There was no reply.

Ten men who had gone out that day to repair the line had failed to return. Some had died on the way to the break, others on the way back.

Then the telephone started working again.

"Entrance receiving. Over."

Neustroyev grabbed the receiver. Ilya Syanov, commander of an assault company, was reporting to his battalion commander. The enemy was mustering for an attack from the direction of the Branden-burg Gate. Syanov wanted the artillery to pound the main road.

Again that familiar screech was heard and heavy mortar bombs crashed down on the road ahead.

All through that long day—one of the most intense of the whole war—the fighting continued on the square in front of the Reichstag. Some of the attackers were crouching near the entrance. They had tried to charge but it was no use. The defence was still alive and active. In some places there were as many as two firing points to a window, besides the pillboxes at every corner and the self-propelled guns lurking in the park...

Across this large square, where so much fire was now concentrated, there ran a barely perceptible red wire. This was the thread that linked the men crouching in front of the Reichstag with the command and observation post, with those who were directing the fire of the batteries. With every fresh artillery onslaught that thin wire was slashed by splinters, but always some invisible hand, out there on the square that separated the command post from the Reichstag, would repair the break and communication would be restored.

When the telephone came on again, Syanov reported that German tanks had appeared to the right of the Reichstag.

The Soviet batteries opened fire again and two tanks were hit. (They were still standing there when it was all over, and figure in several post-war photographs.) The other tanks withdrew round corner.

When the building was eventually taken and most of the defenders had been driven down into the cellars there was a lull in the fighting. During this lull a soldier arrived at the battalion command post, which had by now been transferred from the bank of the Spree to a small room in the Reichstag itself.

His eyes were bloodshot, his tunic was torn.

Vera Abramovna, the battalion telephonist, gasped at the sight of him. Signaller Alexei Melnikov had gone out with the others when the fighting had been at its height.

Now the battalion commander watched him as he walked quietly to the telephones in the corner of the room, knelt down and started turning their handles.

"Entrance?" (The call signs had not yet been changed.) "This is a test..."

Obviously Melnikov had no intention of telling his story. He was not going to say how he had taken cover in shell-holes, or how hard it had been for him to find the broken line on that shell-pitted square, or how he had ducked behind upturned cobblestones while he joined the broken line, or anything else about the vigil of that interminably long day.

The biggest problem had been getting across the canal. It was spanned by a sagging length of rail—all that was left of the demolished bridge. He had straddled the rail and edged his way forward, supporting himself with his hands to prevent himself from falling into the water... After mending the break, he switched on to check the line and listened, then went on again "line-crawling".

His eyes were bloodshot because he hadn't slept for days.
The commander put the receiver aside for a moment.
"Was it you who mended the line?"
"Yes."

"COLONEL" BEREST

A white flag suddenly appeared at the entrance to one of the cellars.

At the bottom of the stairs was an officer, his greatcoat thrown open, a parabellum in his hand. He announced that the German command was prepared to begin negotiations. But only with a high-ranking officer.

The man who went down the stairs to meet the Germans was Berest, the Battalion Commander's Political Deputy, a lieutenant. He had been that only a few days; the promotion order had come through just as we were entering Berlin. Until then Berest had been only a junior lieutenant, although for several months he had been acting as Neustroyev's deputy. How they had managed to work together, I don't know. They were both very strong and contrasting characters.

Alexei Berest was twenty.

It was he who went down to the cellars.

The choice fell on him. Probably he himself said he would go.

A soldier poured water on his hands from a flask and he washed the grime off his face. He had always looked smart. Even after the two nights of the assault his collar still peeped whitely over the high neck of his tunic. Yesterday on the square he had been lying in the same shell-hole as his men. With two scouts, Kantaria and Yegorov, he had mounted the banner on the Reichstag. For the past twenty-four hours he had been at the command post with the others.

Berest put on someone else's long leather jacket over his tunic. Captain Matveyev, of the political department, gave him his peaked cap, a new one, with a crimson band.

Neustroyev went with him after merely throwing off his padded jacket, so that his medal ribbons could be seen. Berest had few decorations, but Neustroyev had plenty—let them have their effect!

The third man in their party was a Russian prisoner-of-war who had recently been liberated on the Oder. He knew German.

Down in the cellar the Germans were waiting for them. There was plenty of light—from blazing torches. The Germans surrounded them immediately, pistols in hand. They still had camouflage nets on their helmets.

A German came up to Berest and his companions. Berest looked at him closely—an Oberst! A colonel. With him were two sailors. Cadets. And an interpreter—a woman in a yellow jacket.

The German soldiers made way for them.

The colonel held out his hand. But Berest raised his to his cap and said: "Colonel Berest."

He stood there in his black leather jacket, tall, young, head erect. The second-in-command—a commissar. Impressive, broad-shouldered, self-assured. One of the Germans said: "Very young for a colonel! "

They hardly looked at Neustroyev. He was quite inconspicuous but for the gleam of his medals. The Germans occasionally glanced at his chest. (Compared to Berest the stocky Neustroyev seemed even shorter than he really was.) When Berest spoke to him, the battalion commander conscientiously came to attention.

"I propose that you surrender! " Berest said to the Germans. "You are trapped here, in the cellars. Your position is hopeless."

But the reply was:

"It is yet to be seen who is whose prisoner. There are three hundred of you in here. When you were attacking, we counted you. There are ten times as many of us."

"Lay down your arms," Berest said. "We shan't let you out of here." And he glanced at his watch, indicating that he wished to end the conversation.

The Germans' representative again tried to prove to Berest that he, Berest, was in the Germans' "clutches", and suddenly demanded they should be allowed to withdraw by way of the Brandenburg Gate.

Berest strove to control his anger. He was young—only twenty—and he forgot that he was a diplomat.

"Why d'you think we came to Berlin?" he said. "To let you escape? If you don't surrender, we'll wipe out the lot of you."

The German colonel protested.

"That is not the way to talk to truce envoys, Colonel! "

Berest refused to listen.

The sailors maintained a grim silence; the yellow-jacketed interpreter showed signs of nervousness.

Suddenly the German colonel broke into Russian, and reasonably good Russian at that.

"We know the position we're in and we wish to surrender. But your soldiers are in a dangerous mood. You must withdraw them from their positions and form them up. We shan't come out otherwise."

"No! "Berest replied. "We haven't come all the way from Moscow to Berlin to parade our men in front of you. Even if there were two thousand of you to our two hundred."

"Very well," said the German. "I shall report that you propose we pass through your fighting lines."

There was no point in staying longer. Berest saluted. So did Neustroyev.

As the interpreter and Neustroyev mounted the stairs behind Berest, they heard "Colonel" Berest muttering to himself, "The swine! The swine! "

The Germans who had taken refuge in the cellars of the Reichstag surrendered that night. Or rather, in the early hours of the next morning.

This time the negotiations were conducted by Senior Sergeant Syanov.

ENCOUNTER

The fighting had died down and we were beginning to make ourselves at home in the Reichstag and find our way about its endless stairs and passages. In the great domed conference chamber it was light. The dome had been pierced and there was only sky above it. Below was a great pile of fallen masonry, bricks and balconies. To cross it was like climbing a mountain.

Later I passed along a dark corridor lined with knights in armour into another part of the building that had escaped the fire. It was in better condition, although even here the walls had been breached and the whole place reeked of fumes. In a luxurious leather armchair there sat an elderly submachine-gunner.

His face was no longer young and he had a heavy moustache.

He had been sleeping off the exertions of the past few days and was still dirty and unshaven. Only his tommy-gun propped against the chair was clean. But the way he sat! In his mouth was a thick cigarette he had made himself, designed to last for hours.

At the sight of him lounging in that armchair I could not help asking how he was finding life.

"I'm sitting pretty in the Reichstag," he replied.

He looked at me with a sly grin, fully aware how significant it was that he should be sitting in this famous building and what kind of figure he cut in his sweat-pickled field service cap and faded uniform lounging in that luxurious armchair.

"Just sitting here," he said and again gave a little smirk that was full of hidden meaning.

I recognised him. It was Garkusha, the company clerk. An old acquaintance of mine. Eighteen months ago, in the winter of '44, when we were still back in the Kalinin Region, he had taken part in an attack and burst into a dug-out full of Germans. There are such clerks! And he, I could see, had recognised me. Yes, this was Garkusha. Grigory Garkusha, the very same.

So he, too, was in the Reichstag.

I went out into the square. It was a warm, sunny morning. The lime-trees near the main entrance were torn and twisted, but they were coming back to life.

The banner was flying over the dome of the Reichstag.

THE FORGOTTEN SOLDIER

The name Pyatnitsky is not among the names of those officers and men who took the Reichstag. Pyotr Pyatnitsky.

And yet it was he who was the first to leap through the window of Himmler's house when the first attack was launched. At the canal, when the assault companies were pinned down by enemy fire, a soldier with a red flag—he had waited until this moment to unfurl it—rose and led his comrades forward. That soldier was Pyotr Pyatnitsky.

Watchers from the house saw our men reach the entrance and run up the steps, and again that red banner flashed among them, then the man with the banner fell.

That, too, was Pyatnitsky.

His banner was mounted on the Reichstag along with the others. But what about him? Men live and die in different ways. His way was exceptional.

Towards evening, when the attack was renewed after further shelling and the men of his battalion closed in on the Reichstag, Pyatnitsky was lying before the entrance, still holding the flag. So that he should not be trampled on someone picked him and laid him beside one of the columns. Then they forgot about him. And when they remembered him again, he had already been buried somewhere, in a common grave. Probably in the Tiergarten.

He fell with his banner just in front of the steps.

Pyotr Pyatnitsky, just an ordinary soldier, although, as far as his commander can remember, he had recently been promoted to the

Marshal Konev (*right*) at a command post. 1944

Soviet bombers attacking enemy positions north of Warsaw

The first units of the Polish Army
marching into liberated Warsaw,
January 1945

May 1945. The population of Bucharest welcomes the Soviet
liberating troops

At the battle positions: Supreme Commander of the National-
Liberation Army of Yugoslavia, Iosip Broz Tito
Yugoslav partisans on the streets of Belgrade

Long live the great fraternal people! Welcoming Soviet troops
in Bulgaria

Hungary. Fighting on the banks of the Danube

Soviet tank forces moning up to help the people of Prague wha had risen against the Nazi occupiers

Ludwig Swoboda, commander of the 1st Czechoslovak Corps

The people of Prague welcome Soviet troops and soldiers of the 1st Czechoslovak Corps

The Auschwitz death camp after its liberation by the Soviet Army.
Soviet doctors and Red Cross representatives with children who were
the camp's inmates

The bones and ashes of more than 200,000 innocent people murdered in the Maidanek death camp

Maidanek. Funeral service to commemorate the victims of fascism

rank of junior sergeant. He was the battalion commander's messenger.

We wrote about him after the assault in the divisional newspaper, but it never went any further than that. Then his name began to be mentioned less frequently.

He is dead and knows nothing of what has happened since. But his widow Yevdokia Pyatnitskaya and his son, now grown-up, live in a village in the Bryansk Region and for many years, as I learnt quite recently, all they knew was their father had been reported "missing".

He joined our division not long before the attack across the Vistula. When the Schneidemühl formation tried to break out at night and the Germans were desperately forcing their way down the road behind their tanks with their tommy-guns at hip-level, it was Pyatnitsky who mounted his machine-gun at the crossroads and broke up their tight column. Much could be written about that and about the way he inspired the men who were crouching under fire on the edge of the canal near the Königsplatz. But I write only of how he ran across the square and how he died, so that you shall know who this soldier was that fell with his flag at the entrance to the Reichstag.

We, who knew him, now speak of him more and more often and can't stop thinking of him.

Let us not forget our dead. They share the glory with the living.

WITH THE FLAG

The Banner of Victory was mounted on the dome by Yegorov and Kantaria.

But there were other flags and banners as well. And although I wrote about them at the time, I want to write again of two daring men—not from Neustroyev's battalion, in which Kantaria and Yegorov served, but from Vassily Davydov's battalion—and of the flag they carried and planted on the Reichstag.

The two were alone together—enemy fire had cut them off from the rest. Using the cover provided by the low embankment of the canal, they crawled under the bridge. It was not far to the Reichstag. They could see the massive columns and steps of the main entrance, but this was as far as they could go. Their red banner, wrapped in dark paper (black-out paper torn from a window), was concealed under Koshkarbayev's jersey. Even here they could not lift their heads. The Germans were firing down from the upper floors and the attackers had to take what cover they could find behind kerbstones and upturned asphalt. Shells tore up chunks of paving; bullets snicked across the cobbles. The buildings behind them were ablaze. Little Bulatov, rather scared, still only a boy—his tunic was a little too long, and even his cap was too big—was scrambling about almost under Koshkarbayev's arm.

"What do we do now?" Bulatov kept asking.

(Koshkarbayev was the platoon commander. Bulatov was one of his men, Lieutenant Rakhimshan Koshkarbayev was a Kazakh; Bulatov was a Russian, from Vyatka.)

Koshkarbayev said: "At least we'll try to fix our banner on the steps of the Reichstag—if we can't get any further."

They called it a "banner", although it was simply an assault flag, just a strip of strong, coarse cloth, like the one mounted by Yegorov and Kantaria.

They decided to sign it. With an indelible pencil they scrawled their names on the banner, and the number "674" beneath. The number of their regiment.

Towards evening, when it began to grow dark and a fresh attack was launched (the first, led by Pyatnitsky, had failed and his group had been wiped out), companies from two other battalions joined up with Syanov's advanced group. Koshkarbayev and Bulatov slipped out of their refuge and made a dash for the entrance. They reached the front wall with its sightless, bricked-up windows. Others joined them...

Bulatov and Koshkarbayev fastened their flag to the central column and later, when the left-hand part of the building had been cleared, they hung it out of a window on the first floor.

Their banner was eventually mounted on the roof, not actually on the dome, like the one mounted by Yegorov and Kantaria, but from above the cornice, near one of the towers.

THE HIGH CLIMB

At the time I asked Yegorov and Kantaria a lot of questions about what had happened and what it had felt like, but somehow I just couldn't get anything out of them except their names and a few biographical details. And the following:

When they reached the canal bordering the square they were thirty metres ahead of the infantry, and in the Reichstag, when they were looking for the way on to the roof, the Battalion's Second-in-Command, Berest, was with them. The banner was mounted at such and such a time. They seemed to think details were superfluous and out of keeping with the triumphant act of mounting the Banner of Victory.

But, perhaps, I can tell the story for them.

They were in a building where fighting was still going on; above them, on the upper floors, and below them, on the ground floor. It was hard to find their bearings; the windows were blocked up. It was dark. They had no idea what passage led where. And where were they to mount the banner? No one had told them that. They couldn't just put it anywhere. It had to be high. So that people could see it.

But here was a staircase. It seemed to be what they needed. And then another one, leading up from the landing. Straight on to the roof. How light it was up here! It had been dark as night inside. Shell fragments were whistling around. Good thing the roof was flat. Where could they fix the flag? Over the cornice there was a bronze figure on horseback. No, that wouldn't do. It would look as if he was carrying the banner. More fragments slashed across the roof. They must hurry. What about putting it up there, on the dome. The ladder had been hit and was hanging loose. They would have to climb the dome itself. How far apart these iron ribs were! And all the windows knocked out. But it was better not to look down through them. The conference hall yawned beneath, like a mountain gorge. And the roofing itself was thin and rusty. It made your flesh creep... What was that? Another shell splinter? No harm done, not wounded. And they had climbed a lot of roof. From the dome they scrambled up to the platform. Higher still. Dizzily high, and they weren't spidermen. The platform at last. Yes, this was the place for it. But don't look down. And here they fixed the banner, making it firm with their belts, and firmer still with the sheath. All without a word spoken. A good, sound job. Now they must get down as fast as possible and back to their own men.

At the time they didn't know they were mounting the Banner of Victory.

SHCHERBINA

I still have an old snapshot of a group of men just after they had come out of battle, standing on the steps of the Reichstag.

In front, and a little lower than the others, stands a soldier with a white bandage round his head.

There are both officers and men in the group. They are all wearing equally tattered, equally filthy uniforms, and scorched greatcoats over their shoulders, and you can't tell officers from men.

This young one with the dark eyebrows is standing one step lower than the rest. He is wearing puttees and holding a submachine-gun. The long sleeves of his tunic are rolled up at the cuffs. His head bandage is fresh and clean. It almost gleams in the sunshine. Evidently he has only just had the wound dressed.

I think this is one of the most authentic pictures of the war. They are standing on the steps of the Reichstag with everything still burning inside.

Who are these men? Who is that particular soldier? I only spoke with him once—in the Reichstag on the following day. I had never met him before the Reichstag was captured.

When I saw this picture I at once remembered his name. The name of yet another of our soldiers—Shcherbina.

When I sought him out in the Reichstag that day he was so tired of talking to newspapermen that he would willingly have gone away and hid himself. He had had no sleep ... after a week of continuous fighting. Still, we did sit down together on the square, opposite the main entrance, near where the photograph had been taken. Not far from that circular billboard, now ripped to pieces, I jotted down what he told me.

Shcherbina, Pyotr Dorofeyevich. Born 1926. That meant he was either 18 or 19 when he was in the Reichstag. His home address was: Zaporozhye Region, Skelka Village... In Berlin, when they reached the Spree, he was wounded in the head. But he refused to go for treatment and stayed with his battalion.

This is what he had to say about the fighting:

"We slipped out of the windows of Himmler's house one after another. Pyatnitsky went first. It was getting dark when we ran across the bridge. Rudnev and Novikov were with me when we crossed the square. And Prokhozhy, too. The fire was very heavy. I had never seen anything like it before. We reached the front steps and dashed up to them.

"We forced our way into a big room. The Germans were potting at us from the cellars and it was a good thing we thought of blocking the exits. The cellars turned out to be packed with Germans. Grenades and fausts kept coming up at us from below and chunks of plaster fell on us from the ceiling. But we stood by the exits and entrances and fought back with grenades.

"We had a tough time when the archives started burning. The whole place was full of smoke and the fire soon reached us. We just couldn't stay in that corridor any longer, so we climbed through a window into another room. Then we found a passage through the attic and followed it to a part of the building that was not on fire...

"But we didn't leave the Reichstag. When the fire had burnt itself out we again attacked the cellars."

And that was all. Either I didn't put it all down, or that was all he told me.

In fact, the situation was much more dramatic, as can be seen from the accounts by others who took part in the fighting.

Yes, Shcherbina was with Pyatnitsky. Shcherbina's squad was the first to reach the entrance to the Reichstag and engage the enemy in the entrance hall. When the rooms began to fill with smoke and the Germans launched a counterattack through a gap in the wall, our men fell back.

"Stay where you are! " Shcherbina shouted. The men took cover and returned the fire, lobbing grenades at the Germans when they appeared through the gap.

Shielding their mouths from the smoke, they stumbled in semi-darkness through a maze of corridors and rooms.

The acrid fumes stung their eyes and made them dizzy. It was impossible to stay there any longer.

Something, probably a faust, hit one of the walls with a crash and it collapsed right in front of them, nearly burying them all.

Shcherbina made his way over the rubble on to a staircase leading to one of the upper floors, probably the first.

"Follow me! " he shouted.

He had also swallowed a lot of smoke and felt he was choking. He led his men on, though he had very little idea where he was going, and they followed him. They followed that white bandage showing through the smoke. He took the lead because he believed he would find a way out.

He still had his head bandage when I talked with him.

Pursued by the fire, they made their way from one room to another until they found themselves in a part of the building where there was less smoke.

I have not yet mentioned the fact that when Kantaria and Yegorov were looking for the way on to the roof to put up the banner, it was Shcherbina and some of his men who guarded their rear on the staircase.

On the square in front of the Reichstag Pyotr Shcherbina was decorated with the Order of the Red Banner.

I should also mention the fighting on the bridge across the Spree and for Himmler's house, and the fact that when Pyotr Pyatnitsky had been killed it was Pyotr Shcherbina who picked up his flag.

Pyotr Shcherbina and Pyotr Pyatnitsky. Two brother soldiers, two heroes. A short but close friendship. Pyatnitsky was over thirty, the father of a family, but Shcherbina was still a mere boy, young and unmarried. At home he had a mother. And it was he who had mounted Pyatnitsky's flag.

So, that's who he is, the young soldier, wounded, with his head bandaged, standing on the steps of the Reichstag.

THE BATTALION COMMANDER

The commander of the 1st Battalion stood for a while in the entrance, then walked with me down on to the square.

After several sleepless nights he still had not had time to make up for lost sleep and return to normal; he was reticent. But he did want to show me the places where the men of his battalion had fought.

We made our way across the square. It was strewn with masonry, slabs of asphalt and splintered branches.

From the embankment along the Spree the Reichstag seemed even more battered. The walls were breached and charred. The columns looked like gnawed tethering posts.

I had known Neustroyev for a long time and I knew him well. Seeing him here, on the broad steps leading up from the square across which his men had advanced, I thought of the little village of Poplavy, lost in the snows of the Kalinin Region...

The fighting round Poplavy started back in the autumn of 1943. But the Germans threw in fresh reserves and our offensive soon came to a halt.

But two months later, in winter, the artillery again went into action near Poplavy. As I approached the frontline, I heard a long drawnout cheer from the other side of the white hills—the voices of charging infantry.

In the half-ruined dug-out—there were several of them at the bottom of the ravine—the colonel in command of the regiment was sitting with his back to me at a radio set and reporting.

"Captain Neustroyev's battalion has broken through the defences and is now fighting in the third line of trenches."

That day I didn't succeed in meeting Captain Neustroyev. A month later I heard his name again, this time in connection with the fighting for the village of Staiki.

By that time I knew all the battalion commanders in the division and was friendly with many of them. Only he eluded me.

One day, however, the division was withdrawn from the fighting line to build defences on the River Velikaya.

The snow had melted and the first blades of grass were sprouting from under the fallen leaves of last year.

A shortish man in a tight tunic, his boots plastered with red clay, was tramping along the line of trenches. I saw him stop at one of them and point out something to a man whose head was only just showing above the parapet. Then he went on from one sector to the next, inspecting the new trenches, bunkers and machine-gun emplacements. He was very busy and very quick.

This was Neustroyev.

After that we began to see each other more often. But not very often. He was not anxious to meet newspapermen; I realised that later.

During a smoke-break we lay on one of the hills above the River Velikaya, in a wood, and he became a little more talkative.

He had grown up in a city in the Urals. His people still lived there, mother, father and sisters...

Then the fighting started again. We tramped many roads and captured many heights before we arrived in Latvia.

Poland, Pomerania, The Oder...

Neustroyev was wounded five times and badly shell-shocked. When a shell hit the dug-out he was in, everyone else was killed but he survived, though badly knocked about.

The five medals on his worn tunic told me where he had fought. All the way from Staraya Russa to Germany.

I recalled these things as we scrambled over the rubble on the square.

"LAY DOWN YOUR ARMS"

Of soldiers like Ilya Syanov—there were not so many of them about at the end of the war—we used to say they had been with us "since the division was born". He was from Kustanai, and it was there that our 150th Division had been formed. Unlike many of us, he was not so young even then. Back in the thirties he had studied at the Workers' Faculty and the Soviet and Party School. Before the war Ilya Syanov had been an accountant.

During the assault on the Reichstag Senior Sergeant Syanov, the company's Party organiser, had to take command of the company.

That was in the morning, in Himmler's house. He arrived back in his company from the medical battalion, just when the men attacking across the square under fire from the upper floors were pinned down and didn't dare raise their heads.

I talked to him later but in the confusion of those days no one thought of asking him how he had gone out and negotiated with the whole group of Germans who had been driven into cellars and the tunnels of the Underground.

Now I can add these few pages on the basis of what I was told many years later.

It is not my story, it is his. This is what he told later, exactly as I wrote it down.

"My company command post was on some crates near the columns in the middle of the central hall. On my right was the main entrance to the cellars. From the columns we had a good allround view.

"It was after midnight on May 2nd. By that time we had got the run of the Reichstag and occupied it right up to the second floor. The fire had not yet died down. There were Germans in the cellars.

"At about 2 a.m. Neustroyev told me to hand over my sector to Lieutenants Antonov and Pavel Gribov, and get some sleep. Antonov was a young man. We had been together before, but he had tasted action only in Germany.

"I told them what the situation was. We went all round the Reichstag. I showed them the entrances to the cellars and the rooms from which we were still being shot at. We were still under fire from both sides.

"The ceiling had not burnt through and the oak veneer was peeling off in charred strips.

"At about 3 a.m. I went for supper. There was a real spread, even wine. Although the square was still under fire, they had managed to bring us everything.

"Sergeant-Major Maltsev reported to me that the company had formed up. Of the eighty-three men I had been given in Himmler's house there were only twenty-six left. There had been times when we had been unable to drag out our wounded, so those who couldn't move had burned to death. That was why there were more dead than wounded. Men just disappeared and I never saw them again. I noticed that Yakimovich, Gusev, Ishchanov and very many other new men were missing. More than half my company had been reserves. I had not even had time to get to know them.

"The men were a terrible sight. Faces burned, blood-stained, bruised, smoke-grimed. Their greatcoats were falling to pieces. There was not a sound pair of boots among them; they all had their soles burnt and their toes and bits of footcloths were sticking out. I was the same. When I tried to wipe my face with the hem of my tunic, the cloth just fell apart.

"They all had a wary, wolfish look in their eyes. They were still tensed up from the fighting. No one spoke. Anyway it was all over now because fresh units had arrived to replace us. Everyone felt that.

"I led the men out of the building and we all lay down to sleep right there, at the entrance. The air was still smoky in the Reichstag but there was a breeze outside. I gave orders that the men should lie behind the columns, up against the wall, so that no one would get hit if there was any shooting.

"Suddenly I was waken by someone shaking my shoulder. I jumped up and was just about to shout 'Company, to arms! '. But the messenger put his hand over my mouth and said they wanted me at the observation post alone. It was about four o'clock. So I had only had about one hour's sleep. There was still a crackle of firing coming from the square and the flanks, but the Reichstag was quiet when I entered.

"I went into the room on the left. Quite a small room, like this one of yours ... but full of people. About twenty officers. And some new people I hadn't seen before. Gusev was among them, and Prelov, too. He smiled at me.

" 'What's up?' I asked.

"Gusev, our chief of staff, said: 'We want to dress you up a bit.'

"And then I saw the battalion commander's orderly coming forward with a new greatcoat and boots for me.

"I couldn't understand what it was all about.

"Major Sokolovsky, I remember, cracked a joke about wanting to marry me off, then said there was a job for me to do.

"Sokolovsky told me the German command had requested by radio that truce envoys should be sent to negotiate on the surrender of German troops in Berlin. They had asked for a truce envoy with the rank of general. 'But at the moment we don't feel that's necessary,' he said. 'So we're sending you. Try to manage it in the allotted time.'

"And Gusev told me: 'We're sending an interpreter with you (his name was Duzhinsky, Victor Borislavovich, a senior sergeant) and another man as your messenger. There'll be a cease-fire from four till six in the morning. Negotiations will be held. The procedure,' he said, 'will be this. Your escort will carry the white flag (the flag had been prepared already). And this is for you,' Gusev said to me, and gave me a big electric torch. 'You will use it to light up the flag. And our interpreter must repeat loudly in Russian and German all the way:

'Russian and German soldiers, don't shoot—truce envoys passing.'

" 'But what terms am I to offer?' I asked.

" 'Unconditional surrender. Unconditional surrender based on the decisions of the Yalta Conference. You will say that officers will be allowed to keep their swords.'

"I also asked what form the surrender would take. Let them march out in formation, I was told, with illuminated white flags.

"I pulled on my new boots and greatcoat and washed my hands and face. I hung the torch on my chest. Then they shook hands with us and we left by the main entrance.

"We went out into the square. Or rather, not quite into the square. We turned left from the main entrance in the direction of the Brandenburg Gate. It had been agreed by radio that the Germans would meet the envoys at the entrance to the Underground. My escort with the flag was on my left and the interpreter, on my right. He shouted, 'Truce envoys passing! ' but as soon as the escort raised the flag and I shone my torch on it there was a burst from a machine-gun. But the bullets went over our heads and hit the wall. We dropped the flag and crawled on a little way. We were a bit confused. But there was no help for it—we had to go on. We talked it over and decided to go round the north side of the building, where there was a brick-lined trench. We jumped down into that and made some good headway. Our infantry had now taken over the German trenches all along the wall.

"From the trench I got a view of the burning city. It' a terrible sight, when such a huge city is burning...

"The men in the trenches were probably from our 171st Division. 'Grab Hitler, grab Goebbels! ' they shouted to us. Ahead there were overturned tramcars and crippled tanks. As we went on the interpreter kept shouting, 'Russian and German soldiers, don't shoot! Truce envoys passing! '

"But the trenches came to an end. Near the entrance to the Underground we saw a group of about fifteen people. Before we reached them, they shouted to us in Russian to stop. We stopped. Then they walked a few paces towards us and I shouted, 'Lower your guns! ' We hadn't raised our submachine-guns but one of the Germans, the Hitlerite, was coming towards us with his parabellum at the ready. He lowered it straight away but said we should all have to leave our weapons at the entrance to the Underground. 'Envoys don't come armed.'

"There was a burnt-out tank near by. We piled our submachine-guns and grenades against it. I put my parabellum in one of the tracks.

Until we had fastened our belts again, the Germans kept at a distance, then they came up and the senior officer said, 'Follow us! '

"We went down into the Underground. Three of them led the way, the rest followed behind. The whole place was packed. The ones ahead kept shouting, 'Make way... Make way! ' There were people of all kinds there, military and civilians. A lot of women! Two well-dressed fellows pushed forward to meet us and said, 'We're Russians. We were driven away to forced labour.' But I didn't believe them. They didn't look as if that had happened to them.

"We went on for about two and a half kilometers like this. We were pretty scared. And the further we went the more scared we got. We saw pretty nasty faces among the soldiers and officers and some nasty looks both at us and those who were escorting us. But they didn't reflect the general mood which was quite different. More and more people kept joining with us. There were colonels among them, and even two generals. They had a man with them who understood Russian, and they went along with us, observing correct order of rank.

"For some reason there were no rails. The light was rather dim and there were some very dark corners. The further we went the less people there were in the tunnel, except for the dense crowd around us. No one asked about our rank. But it was obvious that we were expected. They all wanted to talk to us. They asked what would happen after the surrender. Would anyone be shot? They seemed to think they would all be shot on the spot...

"I stated our terms and, on my own behalf, I said that if they surrendered honourably everyone would be able to go home. This question was put to us in all kinds of ways. Another question they asked was where they would be assembled. One of the Germans asked, 'Who is here? Who are your commanders?' I named them. I tried to mention as many names as possible, to make it sound impressive. Everyone I could remember. The marshals—Rokossovsky, Konev, Zhukov; the generals—Berzarin, Shatilov.

"We came into a large room. It must have been the hall of one of the stations. On the right there was a door into a tunnel. And here we were stopped.

"The two generals went down the tunnel and several guards followed them.

"Meanwhile one of the Germans asked, 'Is Stalin here too?' So, I said, 'Yes, Stalin is here too! ' This made a big impression on them. They all started talking and shifting around and passing on what I had said.

"One of them asked, 'Is General Chuikov with you?'

"That made me laugh. 'Why?' I said. 'Did you have a taste of the Stalingrad mixture?'

"And he laughed too. 'No,' he said. 'We were withdrawn one week before it happened. That's why I'm still alive.'

"We stood there near the door. It was heavily guarded. There were two sentries at the door, and we still had a crowd of Germans round us, officers and men. I watched their faces. I was afraid. Five, ten minutes went past and still the generals didn't come back. I must admit we were pretty worried about our safety. We didn't know what they would do to us. The sentries at the door were just there for show, I reckoned. They weren't the real guard. Among themselves they were saying they ought to have held negotiations back in Stalingrad.

"But we were worried, particularly my escort. He kept nudging me.

"At last the generals came out, leaving the door open behind them. The interpreter told me what they said: 'Our command is not here. We don't know where it is.' Again my escort nudged me, as much as to say, this is a trap.

"I got really angry."

(Later it turned out that the commander of the defence of Berlin, General Weidling, and the commandant of Berlin had given up waiting for a representative of our command and, since they were afraid of the SS, had themselves set out for Chuikov's headquarters to negotiate the surrender.)

"So I asked them, 'What does this mean? You asked for truce envoys and now your own commanders have disappeared.'

"They said there was no one there.

" 'What's this—a game?' I said.

"I gesticulate when I talk. They thought I was holding out my hand for a cigarette and a dozen cigarette cases were offered to me at once. But I took one of their German cigarettes out of my own pocket and the interpreter gave me a light.

" 'What is this,' I repeated, 'a game? I don't think it'll get you very far.'

"One of the sentries said, 'You can go inside and have a look— there's no one there.'

"The officers were standing on one side, arguing about something.

"I went up to them.

" 'All right, you don't know where your command is,' I said. 'But you are commanders yourselves. If you want to surrender, come out yourselves with your units."

"But they replied that they had no right to do anything without orders.

"It shook us when we realised that the negotiations we had expected were not going to take place. What if all this is just a trap, I thought. That's what they were up to when Berest went down into the cellars of the Reichstag. They were playing for time, so that they could muster fresh forces and break out of the encirclement. 'What are you counting on,' I told them. 'There's nothing left of the new army you say is approaching Berlin.'

"Then I told them I was leaving and demanded an escort.

" 'If you can't and won't surrender, give us escorts.'

"That was a tense moment for us. We didn't know what to expect.

"At last, one of the generals gave orders, that we should be escorted back. 'You will have two escorts,' he said.

"We turned round and walked back. I was keeping an eye on the time because I was afraid of exceeding the truce period. My watch showed nearly six o'clock. We had to hurry. The Germans—there was still a whole group of them following us—began to drop behind. They started talking and arguing among themselves again. The road back seemed even longer. 'How much further?' I kept asking. 'Not far,' they said. But it was already three minutes to six. We were back in the crowded part of the tunnel, and quite near the exit, when we heard a shout: 'Stop! .. Halt! ' Soldiers barred our path. We stopped and decided we were just going to get a bullet in the back! But several officers ran up to us with the two generals following close behind. They hurriedly explained that they had decided to surrender with their units. I said they must leave their weapons behind and come out on to the square with white flags and wait.

" 'We'll all be shot if we're alone,' someone said. 'We request you to wait and we shall go together.'

"There was shouting from the tunnels, then a crash and a few shots. Some officers had committed suicide.

"The German troops started piling their arms on the concrete floor.

"This meant we had to wait, and our time was up already.

"It was seven minutes past six when we started mounting the stairs. By that time a column had formed up, and we came out of the Underground with this long column trailing after us. My watch showed twenty minutes past six and a self-propelled gun fired one last shot. That created a panic.

"But there was no more shooting.

"Gusev and Sokolovsky were waiting for us. Sokolovsky had been wounded by a splinter while we were going and his head was bandaged. Gusev seemed very worried. He said he had been afraid they had done away with us.

"When the column appeared and the self-propelled gun fired on it there was some confusion. We, the Germans escorting us and their generals ran into the Reichstag from the other side. Gradually, however, the rest of the Germans were marched out on to the square. They came out of various exits. The officers who had dashed into the Reichstag with us told me that Hitler and Goebbels had committed suicide.

"Later they began coming out of the Reichstag cellars as well. The wounded were taken off to hospital straight away...

"Germans were surrendering all over Berlin."

Translated by Robert Daglish

Vsevolod Vishnevsky
(1900-1951)

Vsevolod Vishnevsky lived an exciting life. He became a ship's boy at the age of fifteen, took part in the First World War, and received the St. George Cross of All Classes, the highest award for bravery in the old Russian army.

During the Civil War he served in a combined revolutionary sailors' detachment of the Navy, and fought in the ranks of Budyonny's Cavalry.

Vishnevsky's first book appeared in 1923. Of particular renown are the film, *We Are From Kronstadt* (1933), for which he wrote the script, and the play, *An Optimistic Tragedy* (1933).

Vishnevsky took part in many battles of the Great Patriotic War, and attended the negotiations on the surrender of Berlin. He described the last days of the war in his *Berlin Surrenders*, which is published in this edition in an abridged form.

Berlin Surrenders

(From a wartime diary)

April 30th, 1945

May Day tomorrow!

How everyone would like it to be that day Moscow saluted the fall of Berlin!

We're going back. They say part of the Reichstag is definitely in our hands.

Pravda, April 29, states the 8th Guards Army has captured fifteen blocks in Berlin.

Soon we'll be on our way to Moscow! Complete victory near. Wonderful, light-hearted feeling! And I'm putting everything into the work.

Order on Berlin expected by 4 a.m.
Chuikov* wants us at once!
Historic event! We're on our way...

May 1st, 1945

0230 hrs.

We arrive at Chuikov's. He tells us to wait. We pace up and down. Nervously. I talk to Chuikov. Surrender expected at 4 a.m.

0355 hrs.

Representatives of the German Army will be here any moment. We draw up reports.

Infantry General Krebs comes in. He is the new Chief of the General Staff of Germany's Land Forces.

KREBS. What I am going to say is absolutely secret. You are the first foreigner I have informed that on April 30th Hitler committed suicide.

CHUIKOV. We know that.

KREBS. The Führer's will states... (*He reads out Hitler's will and a statement by Dr. Goebbels.*) The purpose of this statement is to

---

*Commander of the 8th Guards Army of the First Byelorussian Front.

find a satisfactory way out for the nations who have suffered most from the war. This document may be passed on to your high command.

CHUIKOV. Does this document refer to Berlin or the whole of Germany?

KREBS. I am authorised to speak on behalf of the whole German Army. Authorised by Goebbels.

CHUIKOV. I shall report that to Marshal Zhukov.

KREBS. My first question—will the guns be firing during negotiations?

(He is authorised to order a temporary cease-fire and repeats that he has not yet informed anyone of Hitler's death.)

CHUIKOV *(picks up the telephone)*. Put me through to Marshal Zhukov. Chuikov reporting. Infantry General Krebs has just arrived here. He is authorised by the German authorities to negotiate with us. He confirms that Hitler has committed suicide. Please report to Comrade Stalin that Goebbels, Bormann and Admiral Doenitz, in accordance with Hitler's will, have assumed power. Krebs is authorised to negotiate an armistice with us. He proposes calling a cease-fire while negotiations are on. Wait a minute, I'll ask him. *(To Krebs.)* When did Hitler kill himself?

KREBS. Today, at 1550 hrs. I'm sorry, I mean yesterday...

CHUIKOV *(repeating)*. Yesterday, at 1550 hrs. About peace? No, he hasn't mentioned that yet. I'll ask him now. Yes, I see, right *(To Krebs.)* Marshal Zhukov asks you if you intend to surrender.

KREBS. No. There are other possibilities.

CHUIKOV *(passing this on to the Marshal)*. He says there are other possibilities of establishing peace. No. That is the other government that has applied to the Allies and wants to find other ways. Does Krebs know about this? I haven't yet found out. *(Krebs looks up alertly.)* They have no contact with the Allies. Krebs is authorised to negotiate only with the USSR *(Chuikov listens to the Marshal's instructions.)* Yes... Very good... He is authorised by Goebbels, now Reichschancellor, and Bormann is still chairman of the party. He says we are the first people he has told about Hitler's death and about his will. You, Comrade Marshal, and I. *(A pause.)* Will you ask Moscow? I'll hold the line. I see. Krebs is not authorised to do that, but he can discuss the matter. Very good. *(I am sitting on Chuikov's right, putting everything down in his note pad.)* Yes, Comrade Marshal. I'll ask him. And with others? Yes, I see. *(To Krebs.)* We can hold negotiations with you only if there is complete surrender to the USSR and the United States and Britain.

KREBS. I request a temporary cease-fire to be able to discuss your terms.

(Talk between Chuikov and Krebs.)

CHUIKOV *(into the telephone)*. He can't discuss complete sur-render until he has found out what the general situation is within Germany's new government. When he has done that, he will inform us. He is authorised only to hold negotiations. Yes. I'll ask him. *(To Krebs.)* Will you surrender now?

KREBS. I must consult my government. A new government may appear in the south. The only government at present is in Berlin. We request an armistice.

CHUIKOV *(into the telephone)*. They request an armistice—for nego-tiations. There may be a government representing all Germany. *(Sound of Zhukov's voice in the receiver.)* Yes, I see. All right... I understand... How? Very good. *(To Krebs.)* The question of an armistice can be decided only on the basis of a general surrender.

KREBS. Then you will take over the area where the German Go-vernment is and destroy all the Germans.

CHUIKOV. We have not come to destroy the German people.

KREBS *(attempting to argue)*. The Germans will be unable to work...

CHUIKOV. The Germans are already working with us.

KREBS *(repeating)*. We request that the German Government be recognised until there is complete surrender, that you make contact with it and enable us to communicate with your govern-ment...

CHUIKOV. Our sole condition is general surrender.

KREBS. But we believe that the USSR will have some regard for the new legal German Government. That will be useful and convenient for both sides.

0440 hrs.

The General again asks for a cease-fire.

KREBS. Only a temporary one. *(Krebs, a German, speaks Russian.)* I am not empowered to carry on any other kind of negotia-tions. It is in your interests to conduct them with the new government of Germany. I am only a representative, gentle-men, I cannot answer for my government.

CHUIKOV. My proposal is clear.

KREBS. The German Government says "pass". *(Laughter.)* You

are strong. We know it, and you believe it.

CHUIKOV. We know it, and you ought to know it. You will fight in vain and lose a lot of men. I put the question to you: what sense is there in your fighting?

KREBS. We shall fight to the last.

CHUIKOV. I expect complete surrender.

KREBS. No.

(The calm Soviet generals, Krebs, a young German officer, his interpreter, and I are the only people present. On the table there is a huge map of Berlin.)

KREBS. In the event of complete surrender we shall, in law, cease to exist as a government.

CHUIKOV. Where is General Kleist?

KREBS. He is no more.

(A pause... We wait...)

CHUIKOV *(picks up another telephone)*. How are things? Without resistance? I see. Have the truce envoys arrived? Wait. Certainly. That's right. Good. *(To Krebs.)* I think your garrison is surrendering.

KREBS. Where?

CHUIKOV. Everywhere.

KREBS. Withour orders?

CHUIKOV. Our men are attacking, yours are giving themselves up.

(There is no sound of firing.)

KREBS. In isolated cases perhaps?

CHUIKOV. I think not.

(Krebs asks to be briefed on the general situation. Today's paper is brought in, Chuikov reads out the Reuter report on Himmler's betrayal.)

KREBS. Ja-a-a!

(Chuikov reads on about the Allies' reply and its confirmation by the Soviet Government.)

KREBS. Himmler was not authorised to do that, but we were afraid he would. Himmler doesn't know Hitler has committed suicide.

CHUIKOV. But the German transmitters must have been working? *(Krebs looks surprised.)* Himmler named the rendezvous for negotiations with the Allies by radio.

KREBS. He did that on his own initiative and for his own reasons.

(A German leaflet is brought in. Chuikov reads out a report that Hitler is in the Tiergarten.)

KREBS. That's a lie.

CHUIKOV. There's no smoke without a fire.

(A grim pause.)

CHUIKOV. I don't know what your reply will be, but my opinion is that it's not worth shedding any more blood.

(The German General once again asks for a cease-fire and contact with the Allies.)

CHUIKOV. That doesn't depend on me.

KREBS. But if there is complete surrender we shall not be able to elect our own government.

INTERPRETER. Berlin decides for all Germany.

KREBS *(interrupting him)*. I speak Russian myself. I am afraid another government that will be against Hitler's decisions is being organised. I have only heard Stockholm Radio but it seemed to me that Himmler's negotiations with the Allies had gone a long way.

CHUIKOV. No. The United States and British governments are acting in co-ordination with us. Himmler's was an unsuccessful attempt at diplomatic blackmail.

KREBS. Are you interested in the setting up of a new German Government?

CHUIKOV. What are you hoping to set up? The most popular government would be one that agreed to surrender.

KREBS. Our task is to preserve a government and make peace. Particularly with a victor-power *(the USSR!)*.

CHUIKOV. Do you realise that we and the Allies demand total surrender?

(A pause.)

CHUIKOV. In my view the population of Germany has had enough of the bombing. They are all wearing white armbands. *(Krebs started learning Russian during the First World War. He was in Moscow in 1939. Chuikov asks him about Guderian.)*

KREBS. He has been ill since March 15th. I was his deputy. *(I go on taking notes. My hand is tired... A pause... They are waiting for a telephone call to come through. The atmosphere is tense. So this is how things happen in history: in a strange house, at a stranger's table negotiations are held between the victors and the defeated enemy. It's hard to believe. Krebs gets nowhere with his attempts to "make conversation". We are waiting for a call from Marshal Zhukov.)*

CHUIKOV. Have you been at GHQ all the time?

KREBS. I used to be in charge of battle training. I was in Moscow right up to May 1941, as acting military attaché. After that I was chief of staff of an army group in the East.

CHUIKOV. Where were you during the Stalingrad operation?

KREBS. I was on the Central Front, at Rzhev.

CHUIKOV. On the whole, Stalingrad turned out to be "unpleasant".

KREBS. Yes, terribly. That was the beginning of our misfortunes. You were in command of a corps at Stalingrad, weren't you?

CHUIKOV. No, I was in command of an army.

KREBS. I have read a book about Stalingrad. Who are you?

CHUIKOV. Chuikov.

KREBS. Ach, Chui-kov?

(A long pause.)

CHUIKOV. Why did Hitler commit suicide?

KREBS. Military defeat... The German people's hopes for the future have been dashed. The Führer realised how much the people had sacrificed.

CHUIKOV. He realised it too late.

(Fresh reports are brought in. Chuikov is pleased.)

CHUIKOV. What about this for a solution? We'll give you a telephone line. From you to Doctor Goebbels.

KREBS. I should be very glad. Jawohl! You, too, will be able to speak with Doctor Goebbels. I agree... I hope this will help, while there is still no decision.

(The phone rings.)

CHUIKOV *(at the phone)*. Hullo. Yes. Hullo, speaking. Yes. *(Puts on his glasses and notes something down.)* Yes, I see.

(To Krebs). The Marshal wants to know more about the details of your proposals.

KREBS *(in Russian)*. My document is signed by Goebbels.

CHUIKOV *(once again he reads out the document to the Marshal)*. "We authorise General Hans Krebs within the following terms of reference... *(List of the terms of reference.)* We hereby inform the leader of the Soviet people that today at 1550 hrs. the Führer committed suicide. On the basis of his legal right the Führer in his will handed down all his power to Doenitz, myself and Bormann. I have been authorised by Bormann to establish contact with the leader of the Soviet people. This contact is necessary for peace negotiations between the powers who have suffered the greatest losses. Signed: Goebbels." *(Screeching of "Katyusha" rocket mortars.)*

KREBS. Himmler is a traitor. He was working against the Führer; for a long time he has wanted to conclude a separate peace with the Western Powers and disunite us. The Führer got to know about his intentions and this was one of the causes of his suicide. The Führer valued the devotion of his comrades-in-arms. Before he died he was seeking a way out—he wanted to make peace, above all with Russia.

CHUIKOV. So, Himmler is a traitor?

KREBS. Yes. In accordance with Hitler's will Himmler has been expelled from the party. Himmler is outside Berlin. He is in Mecklenburg.

CHUIKOV. Did you know about Himmler's proposals of total surrender to the United States and Britain?

KREBS. As you know, we suspected him but it was Reuter's report that finally convinced me. We were not kept informed by Himmler. The Führer allowed him to remain outside Berlin,so that he should send all the available armed forces in Germany to aid the capital. But he deceived the Führer and did nothing of the kind. He is a traitor; he wanted to make peace without the Führer's knowledge. Himmler has acted against Germany's interests. I was with the Führer all the time. I was his direct adviser on matters of war. But the GHQ was outside Berlin, in Mecklenburg. The Führer sent them orders direct from Berlin. I was responsible for the Eastern Front.

CHUIKOV. Who is Commander-in-Chief at present?

KREBS. According to the will, Doenitz. Schörner is the new commander of land forces; von Grein is in charge of naval forces. Goering is ill. Guderian is ill.

CHUIKOV. Where is Ribbentrop?

KREBS. In Mecklenburg. His place has been taken by Seyss-Inquart.

CHUIKOV. So there has been a complete reshuffle?

KREBS. Yes.

CHUIKOV. Who will be authorised to conduct the final negotiations with the Soviet Union and the Allies?

KREBS. Goebbels and Bormann who are in Berlin, and are the sole representatives of Germany.

CHUIKOV. What will the other members of the Government do?

KREBS. They will carry out the Führer's order.

CHUIKOV. Will this government be recognised by the troops?

KREBS. If it is possible to inform the army quickly of the contents of the Führer's will, the troops will do as he commands. It would be better to do that before another government is set up.

CHUIKOV. Are you afraid there may be other governments?

KREBS. Himmler has betrayed us and may set up a new government. Himmler still does not know of the Führer's death or about his will.

(The phone rings. Pozharsky says something quietly to Chuikov.)
CHUIKOV. So a government has been formed to work on the territo-
ry of Germany, to rally all forces and continue the war?
KREBS. No, in order to start negotiations and end the war.
CHUIKOV. But perhaps end the war, and then start negotiations?
KREBS. Only my government, not I, can reply to that.

0637hrs.
It has gone on like this all night. The phone rings... A crash
of firing... The phone rings again...
CHUIKOV *(on the phone)*. I am waiting for him. Who will meet
him? We shall. What else? It shall be done. *(He addresses every-
one present)*. Listen to this—Marshal Zhukov wants Goebbels's
statement and the other documents delivered to him personally.
KREBS. There is also an appendix showing the composition of the go-
vernment I have told you about. *(He holds out another sheet.)*
CHUIKOV. Deliver them to the Marshal at once. *(To Krebs.)* Is the
aim of your visit negotiations only with the USSR?
KREBS. Only with you.
CHUIKOV. But with the other Allies through us?
KREBS. If I am given wider powers I shall negotiate with them too.
CHUIKOV. And that depends on your government's decision?
KREBS. When it *assembles*—that is the chief aim.
CHUIKOV. Where is your government to assemble?
KREBS. That has not yet been decided. The best place would be
Berlin.
CHUIKOV. I don't understand this!
KREBS. I am prepared to explain in detail.
CHUIKOV. Your government will not assemble until the Berlin
garrison has unconditionally surrendered.
KREBS. But I am quite sure that if the Berlin garrison surrenders,
our government will never assemble. That will be a failure to
carry out the Führer's will. I believe that total surrender cannot
be decided upon until the new government has been recognised
by all parties.
CHUIKOV. So your government is functioning and does not surrender?
KREBS. I am here to resolve all these problems and convey certain
German assurances. The question of total surrender can be
decided a few hours after the cease-fire and recognition of the
new government.

CHUIKOV. That means you want to fight to the last! Do you know the terms of total surrender?

KREBS. Yes, but who will conduct these negotiations?

CHUIKOV. There is Reichschancellor Goebbels. He has the authority, has he not?

KREBS. He cannot take any final decision.

CHUIKOV. Who takes the final decision? Bormann and Goebbels?

KREBS. It is impossible to take a decision on total surrender without informing Doenitz* on all matters. The only transmitter is in Himmler's hands. The only receiving station left in Berlin, Doenitz's, has been bombed down.

CHUIKOV. Broadcast the Führer's will over the radio. We'll provide the facilities.

KREBS. That would be awkward. It would be unexpected news for Doenitz. He does not yet know about the will. We have made an attempt to interest the USSR. We don't want an *illegal* government that would agree to a separate treaty with the United States and Britain. We prefer to negotiate with Russia.

CHUIKOV. That is how I understand your "move".

KREBS. I am afraid the Allies will nevertheless conduct separate negotiations with Himmler.

CHUIKOV. Don't be afraid.

KREBS. We don't refuse to negotiate with your Allies, but to do so we need the help of the Soviet Government.

CHUIKOV. As a soldier, I am interested in only one thing—finishing off the enemy's troops. We propose total surrender.

KREBS. If the Berlin garrison is destroyed there will be no legal government of Germany.

CHUIKOV. It doesn't make sense.

KREBS. I have informed you of my mission. I have no other.

CHUIKOV. I have told you the one and final condition: *unconditional surrender.*

KREBS (*angrily*). Complete and actual surrender can be decided upon only by a legal government.

CHUIKOV. We shall use force.

KREBS. That will be a take-over!

CHUIKOV. Occupation? That is one of the things we *are talking about.*

KREBS. It is in the interests of the peoples that Germany should have a government.

*Doenitz was in Mecklenburg at the time.

CHUIKOV. It depends what kind! (*The cold answer of the victor!*)
KREBS. If Goebbels has no agreement with you, what will be the result? You should prefer a legal government to one organised by a traitor. The war issue is already decided. The results must be settled with the government indicated by the Führer.
CHUIKOV. Announce the will of your Führer.
KREBS (*agitatedly in Russian*). The betrayer and traitor Himmler may destroy the members of the new government. (*What terrors!*)
CHUIKOV. No. Himmler hasn't enough forces to oppose the Allies.
KREBS. May I send a colonel to the German zone?

Morning. It is sunny. We all look tired. The Germans are quietly conferring with one another. Chuikov is telephoning the units to check on the situation. Army General Sokolovsky arrives. He is told about Hitler's suicide, about the will, about Doenitz, Bormann, etc.

CHUIKOV (*telephones Marshal Zhukov*). This is the situation: Krebs insists on his point of view. So we must wait? He won't do anything without Doenitz, and Doenitz, he claims, knows nothing about events. Krebs requests that he be informed of all this. Then, so he says, a decision will follow. Should a colonel or some other person be sent to Goebbels, and then, perhaps, someone be sent to Doenitz? It's 200 kilometres to Mecklenburg and back by car. Should we send one of our officers for him—Doenitz could be waiting for him on the frontline? (*Artillery fire is heard... A pause. There are fourteen of us in the room; three are Germans.*)
CHUIKOV (*still on the phone*). The colonel had better go. Very good! (*Krebs writes something down rapidly in his notebook.*)
KREBS. May I talk with the colonel?
CHUIKOV. Certainly.
(*Krebs and Colonel von Dufwing leave the room. They soon return.*)
CHUIKOV (*picks up the receiver*). I order you to contact our battalion in the forward area with a German battalion and put Goebbels in touch with us.
KREBS. The government of Germany must be authoritative.
CHUIKOV. And you believe that with Germany completely defeated

Hitler's authority has still been preserved?

KREBS. You see our sufferings. The Führer's authority may be a little less, but it is still great. What he has done can never be changed. New people, new governments will base themselves on Hitler's authority.

(The man is a fanatic! He speaks quite seriously. On his uniform he wears the red and gold tabs of a general, narrow shoulder straps, a medal ribbon for the winter of 1941, a Knight's Cross, various orders, and Iron Cross... He is quite bald.)

KREBS *(continuing)*. Perhaps the basis will be broader, more democratic. I admit that possibility. But we want to retain our identity. And if Britain and France dictate to us the formulae of the capitalist system, we shall fare badly. *(What a line he's taking now!*)

CHUIKOV. We do not wish to destroy the German people, but we shall not allow fascism. We do not intend to murder the members of the National-Socialist Party, but that organisation must be dissolved. The new German government must be formed on a *new* basis.

KREBS. I believe, I am confident that there is only one leader who does not want Germany to be destroyed. And that is Stalin. He said that the Soviet Union could not be destroyed, and that Germany could not be destroyed either. That is clear to us but we fear the British-American plans for the destruction of Germany. If they are given a free hand with us, it will be terrible.

CHUIKOV. What about Himmler?

KREBS. May I speak frankly? Himmler believes the German forces can still operate against the East. He has reported this to your Allies. That is clear, absolutely clear to us.

CHUIKOV. In that case, Herr General, I completely fail to understand your insistence. Fighting in Berlin means useless bloodshed.

KREBS. Clausewitz says that shameful surrender is worse than dying in battle. Hitler committed suicide in order to retain the respect of the German people.

(Tragicomic logic!)

1015 hrs.

We are desperately tired.

The phone rings. The Soviet Government gives its final answer: general surrender or the surrender of *Berlin*. In the event of refusal, we begin a fresh artillery bombardment of the city at 1015hrs.

Lieut.-Gen. DUKHANOV. I shall give the command.

KREBS. I have no authority. We shall have to go on fighting and the end will be terrible. The surrender of Berlin is also impossible. Goebbels cannot consent without Doenitz.

(The phone rings... It is reported that the colonel sent by the general is under fire and cannot cross the frontline.)

KREBS. This is a great misfortune. May I speak with the interpreter? I did ask for a pause.

CHUIKOV. We are not shooting—it's the Germans.

(Krebs is nervous. Our artillery softening-up has begun. Aircraft fly overhead... The interpreter returns.)

INTERPRETER. As we were going along, I kept shouting: "Don't shoot! We are truce envoys! " We raised our hands. The Germans didn't reply. A Russian major was winding out the telephone line after us. At the corner of Prinz-Albertstrasse he was fired on from the German side, perhaps from another sector, more to the right. I shouted to them, then went on with the line. The major was wounded in the head. The colonel was following behind. Then he took off his greatcoat and weapons and went ahead with a white flag. He went on under fire from the German side. There were some Russians there and some of the men were wounded and also their company commander. They were waiting for contact. It hasn't been made yet. The Russian end is switched on, but the Germans haven't tried to make contact yet. I suppose the German task force has not been informed. What shall we do now? Wait for contact or for the colonel to come back? The Russians said that for their part the colonel would be guaranteed a safe return without being fired upon.

KREBS. Go back and see that the colonel returns safely. Everything is set out on the map. Who fired?

INTERPRETER. It must have been a German sniper. The Russian major will probably die. It's a pity.

(They say they're sorry but it was the Germans who fired. We examine Prinz-Albertstrasse on the map.)

INTERPRETER. That's the Excelsior Hotel. That's where we shouted. That's where the sniper fired. The Russians didn't fire a shot throughout the whole sector. (The general marks off all three blocks on the map. A phone call from our battalion: the German colonel has reached the German side but there is still no contact.)

We go in to breakfast... A cold room, everything very formal. Brandy, a few snacks.

Chuikov receives a call from Marshal Zhukov.

A member of the Military Council enters:

"Our terms are not only the surrender of Berlin but of all units."

I am back in the conference hall. The negotiations continue. General Krebs asks for all clauses in the surrender demanded by the Soviet command to be stated exactly. He is now talking to his command (they have been linked up by phone), and stating the special point that Himmler's betrayal will be announced over the radio. Goebbels replies that he demands the return of General Krebs, and then he will talk the whole thing over with him personally. We give our consent.

KREBS (*reading out his transcript of our terms*).

1. Surrender of Berlin.
2. All who surrender must give up their arms.
3. Officers and men are, on general grounds, granted their lives.
4. The wounded are to be given aid.
5. There will be an opportunity of talking with the Allies by radio.

CHUIKOV (*returning after a telephone conversation*). Your government will be given the opportunity to announce that Hitler is dead, and that Himmler is a traitor, and to announce to the three governments—the USSR, USA and Britain—your *total surrender*. In this way we partially satisfy your request. Shall we help you to form a government? *No!* But we shall grant you the right to submit a list of persons whom you do not wish to see as prisoners-of-war. We grant you the right after the surrender to make a statement to the United Nations. The future of your government will rest with them.

KREBS. The list of persons in Berlin that we give you will not be regarded as a list of prisoners-of-war?

CHUIKOV. That is assured. We shall allow officers to keep their ranks, decorations and side arms. We grant the right to get in touch wich Doenitz, etc. But this will be *after the surrender*.

KREBS. For the purpose of forming a legal government of Germany?
(*The question is put squarely. A pause.*)

CHUIKOV. Only for the purpose of making statement and contacting the governments of the countries represented in the United

Nations. I repeat to you: it is their business to decide how things will go in the future. The military command gives no guarantee of further developments.

(Both I and the German general, each in his own way, write everything down.)

KREBS. So, after the surrender the Soviet radio will broadcast an announcement on the death of Hitler, on the new government and on Himmler's betrayal?

(He says he will try to reach agreement on all points as quickly as possible. With whom?)

1325 hrs.

Krebs was putting out feelers. He wanted to bluff us. We'll bear that in mind: they're spinning their web for all they're worth. Perhaps this is the last attempt to cause a split between us and the Allies? Very soon we shall learn what Goebbels and Co. are thinking of.

CHUIKOV *(on the phone)*. We have taken Potsdam Station (block 13). Fighting is at present going on in the 28th block. Exactly. The Germans are holding firm in the Zoo. That's not my sector. I'm advancing in my own direction. Nth corps is advancing across the canals. The left flank is in the Zoo, in the centre... The enemy is resisting: small arms, machine-gun and faust fire. On the whole, things are going well. That's all I have to report.

(We make our comments and jokes. The first ten minutes' relaxation after a whole 24 hours of continual tension. Generals Chuikov, Sokolovsky and Pozharsky and I are in the room together.)

CHUIKOV *(into the phone)*. Pour in the fausts* and the shells. And done with it. Get on with the assault! *(Our terms are clear: Berlin must surrender! The 161st block has been taken!)*

CHUIKOV *(on the phone)*. Capture the Scharlottenburger Schaussee. Then turn right and attack *the government buildings from all sides.* How are you getting on there?

(An enormous colonel has just arrived from Konev... The fighting is now for the 94th and 93rd blocks. That is on the other side of the Spree. We are pressing on steadily. May Day battle! Now they're taking the Gestapo— 152nd block.)

CHUIKOV *(on the phone)*. Objective 5 taken, objective 154 taken. We're fighting on the Sieges-Allee—Victory Avenue. Got that?

*That had been captured from the Germans— *Author.*

There are Germans on the right. That's your sector. Do you feel my spearhead? (*Into another phone.*) You haven't had a delegation arrive, have you? Report in 15 minutes. (*He goes on with his interrupted conversation.*) Never mind, carry on. Good luck!

(*Our troops are slowly but steadily advancing. General Berzarin's Assault Army and General Chuikov's Guards Army will soon link up.*)

CHUIKOV. After that I'll throw everything into Scharlottenburg to mop the place up.

(*I ask Chuikov if he has eaten anything. "So what?" He still hasn't had anything. We go in for "breakfast". I chat with Chuikov. A report comes in that Krebs has crossed the frontline safely.*)

It is now 2220 hrs.

(Same room... Evening.... Night... Tired faces, ash-trays full of butts; phone calls. Chuikov has his feet up on the sofa. It's quiet. The member of the Military Council is dozing in his chair. The phone rings.)

CHUIKOV (*wakes up and takes the receiver*). Comrade Ryzhov, mount a strong guard... Fine... That's all. (*This terseness is the style in our forces.*) Has the 561st been taken? Completely? Right! Haven't you sent anyone out to meet Bogdanov? I see. (*To me*). Our men are in the region of Scharlottenburg, north of the Zoo. They've taken the Swedish Embassy and the people there are asking for protection. They're delighted with the courage of the Red Army and have sent a message to the Soviet Union. They're in a shelter and pleased with everything. So the corps commander reports. They dropped a hint that they, the Swedes, protected Soviet citizens...

2355 hrs.

CHUIKOV. We've forgotten all about the truce envoys, haven't we? To hell with them! I shan't even talk to them now. That was a political reconnaissance!

(*The phone rings. Chuikov speaks on the phone, then paces up and down in silence. He's a big man, and about the same age as myself... Another phone call.*)

CHUIKOV *(into the phone)*. Reassure the Swedes. We have had instructions from the centre. Absolute courtesy. That's right. Now carry on! Get the job done and link up with your neighbour. That's all! *(To me.)* We should be through by tomorrow, eh?

May 2nd, 1945

0600 hrs.

Phone call: "Delegation from Goebbels on its way." *(A delegation of four people arrives.)*

"Bring them in."

(Three men in plain clothes, two in grey overcoats, one in a jacket—how well-groomed they are—and a soldier in a helmet, carrying a white flag.)

CHUIKOV. The soldier can wait outside. What can I do for you? *Was wollen Sie?*

"*Berlin retten.* To save Berlin".

(The delegation hands over a letter in a pink folder. Chuikov reads it. Silence. Other comrades present are Pozharsky, Vainrub, Tkachenko and myself.)

CHUIKOV. When did Doctor Goebbels commit suicide?

"Yesterday evening, in the Ministry of Propaganda."

CHUIKOV. Where is the body?

"It has been burnt."

CHUIKOV. That seems suspicious to us.

"Goebbels killed himself. His body was burnt by his personal adjuntant and his chauffeur."

CHUIKOV. Where is Chief of the General Staff Krebs. who negotiated with us yesterday on Goebbels' authorisation?

"We don't know. We know the new chief –General Einsdorf."

CHUIKOV. Do you know our terms—unconditional surrender?

"Yes, we do. That is what we propose."

CHUIKOV. Good. Can you bring Herr Fritzsche here?

"I will go back and bring Doctor Fritzsche and General Einsdorf here in person."

(He asks for a transmitter to announce the surrender publicly.)

(The phone rings.)

CHUIKOV *(picking up the receiver)*. Comrade Varenikov! A delegation has arrived from Doctor Fritzsche with a letter addressed to the Marshal stating that Goebbels is no longer among the living, that the Commander of the 56th Tank Corps, General

Weidling, has begun the surrender. I am waiting for him to arrive here. Fritzsche wants to make a statement over the radio to the people of Germany and Berlin. (*Pause.*) Comrade Marshal, this is Chuikov reporting. A delegation has just arrived here with a letter for Marshal Zhukov. I'll read it out: "As you have been informed by General Krebs, the former Reichschancellor Goering cannot be reached. Doctor Goebbels is no longer among the living. I, as one of those who are still alive, ask you to take Berlin under your protection. My name is well known." He asks permission to speak over the radio. He asks for mercy on behalf of the people and the opportunity to work for the benefit of humanity. Signed: "Director of the Ministry of Propaganda, Doctor Fritzsche." And General Weidling is also surrendering. I have completely lost my voice. I'll give the phone to Pozharsky.

(Pozharsky again reads out Doctor Fritzsche's letter to the Marshal. The member of the Military Council comes in.)

CHUIKOV (*taking the phone*). Where is General Krebs?

There are rumours he has also committed suicide. Who is their commandant of Berlin? General Weidling. He should be coming to see me. As a prisoner-of-war. (*To the Germans.*) Who else, beside Fritzsche, is in the administration?

"None of the higher officials are there."

CHUIKOV. Where is Bormann?

"He is supposed to be in Hitler's Chancellery, but there has been a gas explosion there. Goebbels's family was killed there, too."

CHUIKOV. General Weidling will soon be here. Shall I send for Fritzsche? I see. Yes. Right. Take the city and the prisoners under my protection? Very good. I see. May I tell them that? I shall act on that. Yes. Very good. I am taking action now.

0645 hrs.

CHUIKOV (*To the Germans*). Marshal Zhukov accepts the surrender of Berlin and is giving orders to stop the fighting. That's the first point. Second: announce to the soldiers, officers, and the population that all military property, buildings and public property must be kept in order. And there must be no demolition! Particularly military property! Third point: you will go with our officer to fetch Herr Fritzsche and he will broadcast over the radio, and then be brought here. Fourth point: I add this—we guarantee the lives of the soldiers, officers and generals and medical aid for the wounded. Fifth: there must be no provocatory shots or other acts of sabotage.

(The Germans ask for protection for the officials of the Ministry of Propaganda.)

CHUIKOV. Not a hair on their heads will be touched.

"I don't know what your rank is."

CHUIKOV. I am Colonel-General Chuikov. (*He picks up the phone.*) Headquarters? Give orders for a cease-fire.

CHUIKOV (*on the phone*). What? Are the families of any of the prominent officials in Berlin? Take them under our protection? (*He speaks to the delegates, then to the Marshal.*) They say Goebbels's family was killed in a gas explosion. In the opinion of Fritzsche's representatives, the families of the others are in South Germany. If we find out, we'll tell you exactly. I see. I'll do that. Yes. I'll propose that to General Weidling. (*To the Germans.*) Marshal Zhukov demands the immediate demining of all buildings, and that we be given maps of all the mined areas so as to avoid any accidents.

(Colonel Vaigachov, political deputy head of reconnaissance at Chuikov's Army HQ, comes in.)

CHUIKOV (*to Vaigachov*). You will go to Doctor Hans Fritzsche. Let this Hans Fritzsche order the troops in the name of their government to give themselves up in proper order with all their arms and equipment.

COLONEL. Very good! (*Makes a note.*)

CHUIKOV. Report that Marshal Zhukov has accepted the offer of surrender and is taking Berlin and the whole garrison under his protection. On this basis Fritzsche must announce over the radio what I said. He and his closest associates must report here. We shall talk here about what is to happen next. Is that clear?

COLONEL. Quite clear.

(I read Fritzsche's letter. It is clearly written.)

CHUIKOV *(on the phone)*. I have ordered a cease-fire.

(Artillery General Weidling arrives. He is wearing spectacles... He makes the fascist salute... His documents are checked.)

CHUIKOV. Are you in command of the Berlin garrison?

WEIDLING. Yes, I am the Commander of the 56th Tank Corps.

CHUIKOV. Where is Krebs? What does he say?

WEIDLING. I saw him yesterday in the Imperial Chancellery. I supposed he would commit suicide. At first he reproached me because the surrender was (*unofficially*) begun yesterday. Today the order to surrender has been issued to all troops. Krebs, Goebbels and Bormann had rejected the idea of surrender, but soon Krebs realised himself how complete the encirclement was and decided—in spite of Goebbels—to put a stop to the senseless bloodshed. I repeat: I have ordered my corps to surrender.

CHUIKOV. What about the whole garrison? Does your authority extend to them?

WEIDLING. Yesterday I gave everyone the order to defend themselves, but later on I gave another.

CHUIKOV. Write the order for complete surrender and your conscience will be clear.

(Weidling drafts the order. Silence. Our people talk in low tones.)

0757 hrs.

Weidling's statement:

"On April 30th the Führer committed suicide and, in so doing, left us, who had sworn our loyalty to him, alone. According to the Führer's order you, German troops, were to go on fighting for Berlin despite the fact that all ammunition is exhausted and the general situation makes further resistance pointless.

"I hereby order: cease all resistance immediately.

"Signed: Weidling, Artillery General, former commandant of the Berlin defence district."

CHUIKOV. No need to put "former", you are still the commandant.

POZHARSKY. Is that formulation about the oath of loyalty necessary?

CHUIKOV. No need for rewording—it's his own order. Type it out and add the date.

WEIDLING. *Jawohl...* Oh, yes—how should it be headed: appeal or order?

CHUIKOV. Order.

INTERPRETER. How many copies?

CHUIKOV. Twelve.

WEIDLING. I have a large staff. I have two chiefs of staff and two more generals, besides, who were retired but came and placed themselves at my disposal. They will help to organise the surrender.

CHUIKOV. I understand.

(Sound of a typewriter.)

WEIDLING. I left my greatcoat in the Imperial Chancellery. Can it be sent for?

CHUIKOV. Certainly. (*Weidling thanks him*). Tea–this way.
(*Sokolovsky, Chuikov, Skosyrev, Tkachenko, Pronin, Vainrub, Semyonov, Pozharsky and I.*)

0915 hrs. Moscow Time.
A grey, chilly morning. We are talking about Stalingrad, joking, smoking.

The order is now quite ready. It will be transmitted by radio and other means (*we fix the points on the map*). One of the German officers is particularly gloomy.

0935 hrs.
I ask Colonel von Dufwing whether there will be any protests in the German units.

Von Dufwing:

"In some. When I was on my way here yesterday I was shot at."

Have been giving breakfast to two German generals and Colonel von Dufwing. "Where are your generals?" they asked me. "They are resting." I sit with them alone, offering them food. It's all rather awkward and constrained. We say nothing. I observe them with great curiosity.

A stir at HQ. Yet another German general arrived. I invited him to the table. Also an official from the Ministry of Propaganda. Naturally, the conversation drags somewhat. The Germans are conscious of their unequal status–in effect, they are prisoners. We talk about the food situation in Berlin, about the sowing campaign that started in Germany while the fighting was still on. The conversation brightens up a little... The Germans sometimes talk quietly among themselves, discussing what might have happened to Krebs.

...They ask about Marshal Zhukov, about Chuikov–I tell them what they ought to know. We talk about Heroes of the Soviet Union, badges of rank, but everyone has an inward train of thought of his own. We are all becoming more profoundly aware of the significance of events.

The Germans speak of the tremendous destruction in the centre of Berlin.

We tell them how quickly Leningrad and Stalingrad are being restored, about the general economic development of the USSR; about the link-up with the Allies.

21*

We compared the losses of the USSR and Germany. I tell them about the "dead zones", about the questions the soldiers ask, "Why did the Germans attack us?" One of the Germans replies: "We needed territory." "Well, here's your territory in the USSR." We close the discussions.

The German generals are escorted to the nearest house. Let them live there for the time being, *under guard.*

Chuikov is asleep. We pace up and down the room. "Is the war really over? It seems strange..."

It is reported that Germans in various sectors are not shooting but will not allow anyone to approach them. "No order".

We chat about the homeland, about going home... We're all incredibly tired... My hand aches.

A phone call: our men are occupying the centre! ! Prisoners are being counted.

1130 hrs.

The adjutant reports that Fritzsche has arrived on a self-propelled gun. We stand in a group to meet him.

Fritzsche enters in a grey overcoat, wearing spectacles. He is reading papers as he walks. He sits down in silence. An interpreter at his side... They wait... Our people are busy receiving reports from the intelligence department.

SOKOLOVSKY (*to Fritzsche*). It's in our interests that life in Berlin should proceed calmly. We can provide protection for people who fear for their lives.

FRITZSCHE. As the last responsible representative of the government I wrote you a letter. I wrote it in order to prevent bloodshed.

SOKOLOVSKY. We understand the gesture you were compelled to make.

FRITZSCHE. I should like to expand the document and should like to get in touch with Doenitz.

SOKOLOVSKY. Your document has been sent to Marshal Zhukov. We have no authorisation for anything further, particularly putting you in touch with Doenitz. There will be an answer from Marshal Zhukov and you may be invited for a talk. Who of the high officials is still in Berlin?

FRITZSCHE. I don't know.

SOKOLOVSKY. Then, as far as we are concerned, that is all.

FRITZSCHE. Where am I to stay?

SOKOLOVSKY. Here. Wait for Marshal Zhukov's reply. *(Fritzsche is led away. We are all obviously suspicious. Perhaps this man is just a stooge? Chuikov comes in: "Well, where's that Fusche or whatever his name is?" Sokolovsky relates his conversation with Fritzsche.)*

CHUIKOV. Our men are guarding the government offices. At ten in the morning Doenitz appealed to the army and the people: he is taking over the leadership and will fight to the finish against Bolshevism, and also against the British and Americans if they get in the way. But we aren't worried about him—he's too weak in the guts! *(Laughs.)* Doenitz has declared Himmler is a traitor. So that means Berlin has surrendered separately. Perhaps Hitler has gone underground? On the whole, we've beaten them to a frazzle. What a state of chaos and political confusion they must be in if Goebbels was leaning towards us! *(Laughter.)* *(Chuikov phones up to find out whether the Reichstag has been taken.)*

CHUIKOV *(to us).* They're still shooting in the centre. The Germans have set fire to the Reichstag.

(He checks up on how things are going at the Imperial Chancellery. Belyavsky comes in.)

SOKOLOVSKY. Who set fire to the Reichstag?

BELYAVSKY. There was fighting there—not everyone surrendered at once.

(Phone call: units of Chuikov's Guards Army have linked up with Kuznetsov's Assault Army.)

GALADZHEV. The war is coming to an end.

CHUIKOV. Yes, we'll soon be lighting the pipe of peace.

Well, the salute they'll fire in Moscow today will be something quite out of the ordinary!

What rejoicing there will be in the USSR! There are undoubtedly isolated centres of resistance, but Breslau and other cities will also fall after surrender of Berlin. Weidling's document must be widely published as soon as possible for the Germans.

How simple it all is... Such a strange feeling that the war is all over and done with. There is *none* of the special atmosphere of triumph that we expected from the capture of Berlin, from victory. The road was too long and hard.

We shall immediately be faced with the enormously difficult task of getting everything in order, back to normal.

Chuikov goes off to have a shave. Galadzhev, Pronin, Semyonov and Skosyrev talk of the work to be done in the units and the need to give people a chance to relax.

Chuikov comes in:

"Where's Blanter? I wish he'd play the Guards March! "

The generals recall April 15th, the beginning of the battle for Berlin, and discuss what impression the fall of the German capital will produce on the world.

Shouts from the soldiers:

"The war is over! "

"What about a trip round Berlin?"

The strain is terrific—only willpower and nerves keep me going. My hand aches, it's sending great spasms up my arm. I've been writing constantly for two whole days.

Berlin is taken. I wonder how to describe it. I ought to do a feature for *Pravda*, but what can you squeeze into six or seven pages?

I say good-bye to my friends and thank them for the honour they have shown me.

Translated by Robert Daglish

Yelena Rzhevskaya
(b. 1919)

Four Springs in a Greatcoat is the title of one of Yelena Rzhevskaya's books and could also be called part of her biography. When the war broke out in 1941, she was a student of the Institute of Philosophy, Literature and History. Upon finishing a course for military interpreters she went to the front, where she was involved in the battles to liberate Rzhev, Riga and Warsaw, and, finally, the battle for Berlin (hence four springs in a greatcoat). She is also the author of the books, *Berlin, May 1945; Earth's Gravitation, From Home to Front;* and *Years After.*

This edition contains documentary stories from *Berlin, May 1945.*

Berlin, May 1945

BEYOND WARSAW

At the end of 1944, the 3rd Assault Army, to which I was attached as a headquarters interpreter, was transferred to Poland. It was the first time in the whole war that our army had travelled by rail. When we went through Siedlce the doors of our boxcar were open and I noticed a lighted window with a fir tree on the windowsill. It was Christmas.

For three years we had been plodding across the war-ravaged country where there had been nothing but war. But in the small uncurtained window I caught a glimpse of a different, domestic life. It may have been oppressed, downtrodden, ridden with shortages, but it was a life in which there were homes and families, and it excited and tempted us with thoughts of peace.

After the fighting for Warsaw the troops pressed on. We sped along past old roadside crosses and posters of a soldier adjusting his footcloths over the words: "On to Berlin! "

While we were en route, an order came through that we were to spend a day in N—(I don't remember the name of the place). All I recall is the black appearance of those squat shell-torn houses, a metal signboard from a baker's shop dangling from a telegraph wire, doors wrenched off their hinges and the crunch of rubble and glass underfoot.

Six days after the liberation of Warsaw, the 3rd Army captured the town of Bydgoszcz (Bromberg) and pressed on in pursuit of the retreating enemy. The streets were alive with people. The whole Polish population had turned out. People were hugging each other, weeping and laughing. They all wore national red-and-white flags in their button-holes. Children were dashing about squealing and shouting for all they were worth and taking a delight in the noise they were making. Many of them had never realised their voices possessed such marvellous abilities, while others, the older ones, had almost forgotten how to use them in the five grim years of oppression, tyranny and fear, when it had been forbidden ever to raise one's voice. Any Russian who appeared in the street was at once surrounded by a crowd. What with the milling throngs and the ring of children's voices the town seemed springlike despite the January cold and the falling snow.

Soon prisoners-of-war from the Nazi camps began streaming into Bydgoszcz. There were Frenchmen and tall, thin Englishmen in khaki. The Italians, who had been allies of the Germans until they suddenly found themselves behind barbed wire, hung back at first but were soon drawn into the rejoicing stream.

Russian and Polish soldiers, arm in arm with liberated prisoners of a dozen different nationalities, strolled in the streets, heedless of the traffic. People burst into song. An old man with a two-coloured Polish flag on his tall Astrakhan hat and the yellow-and-black arm-band of the blind tapped his way along the pavement, craning his neck to catch the sounds of the street. A Polish soldier, flushed with wine, was marching along arm in arm with two French sergeants. An American pilot, hatless, in olive-coloured uniform, kept stopping everyone who passed him and laughing with sheer joy.

Down a narrow gloomy side-street leading off the main square a straggling line of people were making their way with their belongings on their backs or in carts and sledges. These were German farmers who had left their homes and were roaming the roads as fugitives. Now a young Polish lad on skates had barred their path and an elderly German woman with a thick shawl round her head and shoulders was trying to explain something to him, but he was beating the pile of chattels furiously with a stick and shouting: "Why can't you speak Polish?" I took him by the shoulder. "Let them alone! " He looked up at me, his eyes filled with angry tears, and, seeing my army sheep-skin and the star on my cap, skated away. But he went on observing us alertly from a distance. It seemed quite intolerable to him that *today* the Germans should be allowed to walk freely about the streets *after all that had happened.*

Upon leaving Bydgoszcz after the German counterattack had been repulsed, we drove for the last time through its narrow, cosy streets between the old grey-stone houses. The tall spires of the churches stood out black in the whitish light of an early winter's morning.

A party of men ahead were clearing snow off the pavement. As we drove nearer we saw they had swastikas chalked on the lapels of their overcoats. It had been decided by the municipal authorities that *after all that had happened the Germans* would have to go out and clear the streets.

It was not hard for us to understand the bitterness of the Poles. The compulsory Germanisation of Poland had meant the closing of Polish schools, eviction of Poles from their homes, their being allowed to ride only in the rear car of a tram, and much else. It had meant the attempted destruction of a nation by humiliation, starvation and the death camps. We could understand their feeling. We, who had gone through so much terrible hardship, through death and destruction, who had seen the ghastly trail of nazi atrocities.

How many times had we told ourselves, "Surely this must be avenged? Won't your hatred be satisfied by revenge?"

But these drab, melancholy figures, these identification marks chalked on people's clothes—I remember to this day how depressing that was. I believe that municipal regulation lasted only one day. So much the better! To hell with that kind of satisfaction! To hell with it!

POZNAN

The road to Poznan. A flat, snowless expanse; a dead German soldier, bootless, frozen into the earth; fallen horses; a white sprinkling of leaflets we had dropped before the offensive; soldiers' helmets, a steely blue on the battlefield. Prisoners under escort. The mounting roar of artillery. Soviet troops on the march. Banners sheathed. Lorries, carts, carriages, and people on foot, people on foot all the time... The whole population was in motion, roaming the roads of Poland. There was an old man sitting shivering on a chair in the back of a lorry. A Pole kissing a woman's hand at the edge of the road, oblivious of the traffic. Two nuns with huge white, starched headdresses plodding along together. A woman in mourning leading a small boy by the hand.

There is only an occasional patch of snow. But it is cold. Trees with whitewashed trunks line the road.

In the town of Gnezno an electrician's family showed me a letter secretly delivered from Breslau: "Are the Russians coming? We shall die otherwise."

Yes, Russia was coming, coming to rid Polish soil of the Nazi occupation.

Today, February 9th, our army newspaper ran the headline: "Tremble, Germany—Russia is Advancing on Berlin! "

About a year previously Governor-General Frank had stated: "If I were to come to the Führer and say to him: 'My Führer, I have to report that I have again exterminated 150,000 Poles,' he would say, 'Splendid, if it was necessary.'

"The Führer has stressed once again that the Poles must have only one master—the Germans. There could not, and should not, be two masters existing side by side; all representatives of the Polish intelligentsia must, therefore, be destroyed. It sounds cruel, but it is the law of life.

"The area ruled by the Governor-General is a Polish reservation, a large Polish labour camp... If the Poles rise to a higher stage of development, they will cease to provide the labour force that we need."

The pace of the offensive mounted day by day as the forces of the First Byelorussian Front tore apart the enemy defences. Tanks ploughed into the deeply fortified defence lines and pushed on, leaving it to the infantry to consolidate their gains. While the main assault forces pursued the enemy, more troops avalanched into the breach and expanded the front of the offensive. Outfought and outspaced, the enemy was forced to abandon town after town without destroying it and sometimes even leaving a bridge undemolished. But resistance stiffened as we neared the German frontier.

In 1939, Poznan was one of the first Polish cities to be captured by the Germans. Thousands of businessmen and party officials followed in the wake of the German divisions to take over the "Wartegau Province". The Poles were evicted from all but the worst flats. Their factories, their shops, their schools and personal belongings were confiscated. Their streets were renamed, their language forbidden, their monuments pulled down and their churches desecrated.

This was how national-socialism celebrated its victory in Poland.

Soviet troops who had learned their street fighting at Stalingrad battled for every house, every staircase in Poznan. They were helped by the artillery, but the issue was usually decided by an infantry charge and hand-to-hand fighting. A pall of smoke hung over the city. The Germans blew up or set fire to the buildings in the centre as they retreated. Soon only the ancient Poznan citadel remained in their hands. It towered over the city, surrounded by a massive wall and nearly two square kilometres of trenches and earthworks.

But the rest of the city had been cleared of occupation forces and in honour of the Red Army the Poznan bakers, tailors and butchers brought out the banners of their guilds that they had kept for more than five years at the risk of their lives.

School children squeezed themselves into their old uniforms and, although the sleeves were far too short and the buttons would not fasten, they were proud to be wearing them, for any uniform of the old Poland had been banned by the Germans.

Amateur bands came out to play in the streets and struck up national tunes. They were cheered lustily for their performances,

but even more for the fact that they still existed. They had been forbidden to play under the occupation because the authorities were
afraid of the unity that patriotic music could arouse; penalties for
infringement had been severe. But the quartets and quintets had kept
going like tiny underground organisations.

The municipal authorities set to work. Polish schools and institutions were reopened, the shops began to function again. And all
this while in the citadel there was still a force of ten thousand Germans, the remnants of the Poznan group. Their occasional attempts
to shell the city were crushed by Soviet artillery. It was rumoured
that German soldiers were making their way into the central streets
by way of underground passages, murdering civilians and changing
into their clothes. The siege was accordingly strengthened.

People soon began to forget about the enemy in the citadel altogether; there were too many other things to be done in the liberated
city. The army assigned units for the assault on the citadel and moved
on. Soviet forces were already beyond the frontiers of Brandenburg
and Pomerania.

The town of Poznan was now far in the rear of the advancing
army. The Oder had been forced. The armies of the First Byelorussian
Front under the command of Marshal Zhukov had advanced 400 kilometres in two weeks.

ENCIRCLED

For three days Berlin had been completely surrounded. Colonel-
General Kuznetzov's 3rd Assault Army, Colonel-General Berzarin's
5th Assault Army and Colonel-General Chuikov's 8th Guards Army
broke through in the direction of the Tiergarten, the Unter den
Linden, the government offices. General Berzarin, the Soviet Commandant of Berlin, had already decreed the dissolution of the National-Socialist Party and banned its activities.

The people of Berlin were huddled together in cellars under the
blazing, collapsing buildings. There was little water and even less food.

At ground level the firing and the crash of bursting shells was continuous. The air was filled with smoke, fumes and flying masonry.
It was terrible for civil population.

There could be no doubt as to the final outcome and further
resistance was a crime.

But Goebbels' "bulletins" with their concoctions of lies, provocation, flattery and threats were still being dropped on the surrounded German troops.

Here is one of the last, dated April 27th, of Goebbels' "Berlin Frontline Bulletins", nicknamed in the German army "armoured bears" (in the centre of the coat-of-arms of Berlin is a bear).

"Bravo, Berliners!

"Berlin will stay German! The Führer has announced this to the world, and you, Berliners, will see to it that his promise is kept. Bravo, Berliners! Your conduct is exemplary! Continue with the same courage, the same determination, without mercy or relenting, and then the storm waves of Bolsheviks will break even as they strike you... You will endure, Berliners. Help is on the way! "

This "bulletin" came into our hands on April 29th not far from Potsdam Square.

THE FINAL TASK

On signposts, on tanks, on shells for the guns, on gun barrels there was only one message, painted in red: "To the Reichstag! " It was our one thought in those Berlin days. This was the helm of the German state. The seat of the supreme legislative body.

It had been the scene of one of the vilest acts of provocation known to history—the Reichstag fire of 1933.

To capture the Reichstag, to mount the red flag over its dome meant announcing to the world that victory over fascism, over Hitler, had been won.

On April 29th Colonel-General Kuznetsov's forces reached the Königsplatz, over which rises the six-columned frontage of the grey-stone Reichstag.

But the forward patrols were concentrating not on the Reichstag. Their objective was the Imperial Chancellery. Theirs was the last task of the war—to capture Hitler.

Hitler's headquarters was in an air-raid shelter under the Imperial Chancellery. The shelter contained more than fifty rooms, though most of them were mere cubicles. There was also a communication centre, a food store and a kitchen. The shelter was linked with an underground garage. Access to the shelter could be had from the inner courtyard of the Imperial Chancellery and from the entrance hall, from which a fairly broad and gently sloping staircase led down to the cellars. At the bottom, one immediately came into a long corridor with numerous doors on each side. To reach Hitler's refuge one had to take a rather long and confusing route. But from the inner courtyard the entrance led straight to the "Führerbunker", as it was called by the staff.

The two-level "Führerbunker" was situated at a greater depth than the shelter under the Chancellery, and its reinforced concrete roof was much thicker. (The chief of Hitler's bodyguard, Hans Ratten-huber, in a statement written while he was a prisoner in Russia des-cribes the bunker as follows: "Hitler's new air-raid shelter was the safest in Germany—the reinforced concrete roof was as much as eight metres thick."

As the man responsible for Hitler's life, he must have known.)

In the courtyard near the entrance to the bunker stood a concrete mixer; the roof of the shelter had recently been strengthened—probably after a direct hit.

We were to learn all these details only later, however, when the assault groups broke through the final defence ring and burst into the Imperial Chancellery.

There was a skirmish with those of the bodyguard that had not already fled. Then, down the staircase. Military and civilian personnel started coming out of their cubicles with their hands up. Wounded were sitting or lying on the floor of the corridors. Groans could be heard all round.

Here, in the cellars, and upstairs, in the Chancellery, firing broke out again and again. The attackers had to find their bearings instantly and block all exits, then go on with the search.

Assistants were hard to find among the odd collection of people who lived in the cellars; assistants, that is, who knew something of what had happened to Hitler and who could act as guides through the maze of corridors.

We did our first hurried questioning.

This was of the boilerman, a rather wretched-looking civilian. With his help Lieutenant-Colonel Ivan Klimenko and Major Boris Bystrov found their way to Hitler's bunker along dark corridors and side-passages, where at every step they could have run into a bullet.

Hitler's quarters were empty. On one wall hung a portrait of Fre-derick the Great. One of Hitler's tunics was in the wardrobe; another, dark-grey, was hanging over the back of a chair.

The little boilerman said that when he had been in the corridor he had seen two bodies wrapped in grey blankets being carried out of the rooms towards the exit from the shelter. This was the limit of his observations, which at the time seemed to bear little resemblance to the truth. Klimenko and Bystrov came out into the shell-torn garden of the Imperial Chancellery. What should they do now? If Hitler really was dead and his body had been burnt, perhaps it had been burnt somewhere here in the garden?

We began to realise that we should have to look for the "place of burning" as soon as we found Karl Schneider, one of the garage hands, a burly, thickset man of about forty.

On April 28th or 29th, he could not be sure, the duty telephonist at Hitler's secretariat had passed instructions to him to send all the available petrol from the garage to the Führer bunker. Schneider sent eight petrol cans, each containing twenty litres. On the same day, a few hours later, he received from the duty telephonist an additional order—for fire torches. He had sent the eight torches that were available.

Schneider himself had not seen Hitler and did not know whether he was in Berlin or not. But on May 1st he had heard from the head of the garage and from Hitler's personal chauffeur, Erich Kempka, that the Führer was dead. Rumours of his suicide were current among the bodyguard too. There was talk that his body had been burnt.

Comparing these rumours with the orders he had received, Karl Schneider assumed that the petrol he had sent had been required for burning the Führer's body.

But on the evening of May 1st there was another call from the duty telephonist, again demanding that all the available petrol should be sent to the Führer's bunker. Schneider siphoned off what petrol there was in the car tanks and sent another four cans.

What did this fresh call mean? Who was the petrol needed for this time? Major Bystrov, Lieutenant-Colonel Klimenko and Major Khazin went out into the garden with Schneider and Lange the cook.

Churned-up earth, twisted trees, charred branches, smoke-blackened lawns, broken glass and rubble everywhere. Where was the place of which one could say without having any additional information that this was where the body had been burnt?

They began an inspection of the garden. Two metres from the exit from the "Führerbunker" they discovered the charred bodies of Goebbels and his wife. That was what some of the petrol had been needed for. The bodies, fire-scarred but easily recognisable, were so close to the entrance that the Red Army men who had charged headlong down into the bunker during the attack might easily have trampled them underfoot.

GOEBBELS' DIARY

The Berlin sky was still ablaze. Smoke was drifting over the Imperial Chancellery. The ventilators were out of action and the shelter was stuffy, damp and forbidding.

It was my task in those days to go through the papers and documents that were left in the Chancellery.

Reports on the street fighting, communiqués from the local nazi chiefs on the hopelessness of the situation, the shortage of ammunition, the demoralisation of the troops, Bormann's correspondence. Hitler's personal papers.

These papers carried one back into the history of the war that was just ending. They could provide material for a socio-psychological portrait of the leaders and ideologists of Nazism.

One of the most important of our discoveries was Goebbels' diary.

Ten thick notebooks filled with close, upright handwriting that was almost illegible. The first of them deal with 1932, the year before the Nazis had come to power, the last ended in the middle of 1941.

I was extremely sorry I had no opportunity at the time to study these diaries, which did not make easy reading. They would have required days of earnest study and we had not a minute to spare. Our immediate task was to establish what had happened to Hitler, and, if he was still alive, to find him.

We kept on discovering fresh documents. When I had read them, I wrote summaries, which I sent to Front HQ.

In later days, when I remembered Goebbels' diary, I was afraid that it had been lost among the mass of other documents that had poured into Front HQ in those days from all sectors of the front.

But now, after many years, I have been able to read the diary, which reached the archives safely and remained there.

Goebbels' diary deals with his everyday affairs as Minister of Propaganda of the Third Reich. In May-June 1941 he was busy with preparations for the attack on the Soviet Union.

Goebbels was one of the few people who had been initiated into the "Barbarossa Plan", and was one of its chief proponents.

"I am quivering with excitement", he wrote on June 5th. "I can't wait for the day when the storm will break."

The first hints regarding the attack that was under preparation appear in the entry for May 24th. Goebbels sent his representative to Rosenberg, who had been designated for the post of Minister for Affairs of the Occupied Eastern Territories, to co-ordinate their activities in the forthcoming operation.

"R. (Russia—*Ed.*) must be broken down into its components... We cannot tolerate the existence of such a colossal state in the East.

"...The weather is splendid but there is no time for a holiday. The constantly ringing telephone brings more and more fresh news. A life of intense excitement. One will be sorry when it ends.

"The 'Barbarossa' Operation is coming on. We are beginning our first big camouflage job. The whole state and military apparatus is being mobilised. Only a few people have been informed on the real course of affairs. I have had to put the whole ministry on a false track at the risk of losing my own prestige in the event of failure.

"To work! "

June 15th, Sunday. The last Sunday before the terrible war in the East.

A secret conference of the plotters.

"After dinner the Führer summoned me to the Imperial Chancellery. I had to go in through the back door to avoid being seen. The journalists are keeping Wilhelmstrasse under constant observations, so one has to be careful. The Führer looks splendid and received me with great warmth. My article gave him tremendous pleasure. It had again provided us with a certain breathing-space in our feverish preparations. The Führer explained the situation to me in detail. The attack on Russia will begin as soon as our forces have been fully deployed. This will be in about one week from now.

"...The Führer counts on completing this operation in about four months. I imagine it will be less. Bolshevism will collapse like a pack of cards.

"When Russia has been conquered, we shall be able to demobilise some age groups, and then build, arm ourselves and prepare. Only after that can we launch an attack on Britain from the air on a grand scale. Sea-borne invasion of Britain is probably impossible, all things considered. We must create other guarantees of victory.

"The Führer says we must win by hook or by crook. It is the only way and it is the right way, both morally and in terms of necessity. And when we are victorious, who will ask us about our methods? We have so much on our conscience already that we must win, otherwise our people and we ourselves at the head of everything we hold dear, will be wiped off the face of the earth. So to work! "

June 22 nd.

"...Outside my window on the Wilhelmplatz all is quiet and deserted. Berlin is asleep, the empire is asleep, I have half an hour to spare, but I can't sleep. I pace anxiously about the room. I can hear the breathing of history.

"The great, wonderful time of the birth of a new empire. It will conquer its pain and see the light.

"A new fanfare sounds. Powerful, resounding, magnificent. I broadcast on all German stations the Führer's appeal to the German people. It is a solemn moment for me, too.

"...A few more urgent matters, then I go off to Schwanenwerder. The sunrise is wonderful.

"Birds are twittering in the garden.

"I fell on the bed and slept for two hours.

"Deep, healthy sleep."

June 23rd.

"The Russians are arraying their forces as the French did in 1870. And they will suffer similar disaster... We shall dispose of them quickly. We must dispose of them quickly. The people's mood is one of slight depression. They want peace, not a shameful one, to be sure, but every new theatre of military operations means grief and anxieties."

Having overreached themselves, these adventurers now place their hopes on military victories. They are alarmed by the general discontent caused by the food shortages to which they have condemned their country and the whole fascist coalition.

The purpose of the war is to tone down all the internal contradictions of fascism.

But no matter how much Goebbels exults over the results of the surprise attack, a new and unexpected note creeps into his record of events.

At first it has a ring of perplexity. "The enemy is fighting well," is his verdict as early as June 24th (as usual, he writes of the past day). In his reflections he looks for some advantage in this new fact.

"The Russians are defending themselves bravely. There have been no retreats. Good. It will come all the sooner in the future. They are losing countless tanks and aircraft. This is a precondition of victory."

But the tone of anxiety grows more and more insistent. The southern front is "resisting desperately and has good commanders. The position is not dangerous, but we have our hands full".

A yawning gap appeared in the nazi doctrine on the weakness of the Red Army. A corresponding gap appears in Goebbels' psychology. A typical gambler, he exults in success and falls into despair at the first signs of resistance and failure. But only the first days of the Eastern war figure in the notebook, which ends on July 8th*. The nazi armies had not then experienced their first defeats. And yet the shadow of disaster hovers even over these pages...

"On the whole, the fighting is very heavy and bitter. This is certainly no picnic. The Red regime has mobilised the people. In addition to this there is the Russians' fantastic doggedness. Our soldiers are hardly able to cope. But up to now everything is going according to plan. The situation is not critical, but it is serious and demands an all-out effort".

The war had not solved the vital problems. In the Balkans "there is real starvation. Particularly in Greece. Discontent is being expressed in Italy. Mussolini is not being energetic enough. In Rumania our popularity has waned. There is trouble wherever one turns."

"France and Belgium are near the starvation level. Hence the general mood there".

But whatever worries or hardships the German people are forced to endure, none of these things prevent him from enriching himself and adding to his personal comfort. The war goes on but in addition to the recently completed castle in Schwanenwerder, where he spends quite a lot of his time, and the residence in Lanke, also outside Berlin, and other rural retreats, "a new Norwegian cottage is being built. It will be in extremely idyllic surroundings". "I have looked over our new blockhouse, which is very fine. It stands in a forest and has facilities for the period of peace which will, of course, come."

Only one thing was lacking—the defeat of the Russians. "We must act quickly. The operation on the Eastern Front must not be allowed to drag on. The Führer is seeing to this."

The same phrases, the same assurances but there is a flaw somewhere.

"The British are trying everything to make use of this postponement of their execution. But it will not, let us hope, be long in coming."

"Smolensk is being heavily raided. Nearer and nearer to Moscow."

"We shall not rest until we achieve the downfall of the Reds... We did it in 1933. We shall do it again today...

"Surrender! That is our watchword."

*On that day, July 8th, Hitler signed the following order: "Moscow and Leningrad are to be razed to the ground, so that we may rid ourselves completely of the population of these cities and not have to feed them during the winter..."

ON THE EVENING OF MAY, 1945

But now war had come to Berlin. "Surrender! " was not a watch-word but a reality.

It was evening, on May 2nd. Several hours had passed since the Berlin garrison had ceased resisting. The surrendering of arms, which had begun at 3 p.m., was still in progress. The square in front of the City Hall was piled high with submachine-guns, rifles and machine-guns. The streets were littered with abandoned German artillery, muzzles pointing to the ground. Rain was falling.

German units that had been shattered on the Volga, Dnieper, Danube, Vistula and Oder were tramping despondently under the triumphal arch of the Brandenburg Gate, now crowned with a red flag. The helmets many of them still wore looked absurd. Exhausted, deceived, haggard, the prisoners tramped along, some of them bowed with grief, others obviously relieved, but most of them in a state of utter depression and indifference.

Marshal Zhukov's Army was in total possession of the German capital.

Goebbels' body had been carried out into one of the streets. A charred face. The Nazi uniform, dark serge trousers and a light-brown tunic, scorched and tattered. But what stuck in my mind was the yellow tie stirring occasionally in the breeze—a silk yellow noose round the black, charred neck, pinned with a round metal swastika badge.

Berliners emerging from their cellars paused to stare at one of the men who were to blame for the disaster that had overtaken them. He was photographed for the latest newsreel and for the historical records. It was he who had lighted the first bonfire of books, and the flames of that bonfire had blazed so fiercely that eventually they had threatened to consume Germany herself. As commissar for the defence of Berlin, he had treacherously doomed his fellow citizens to destruction. He had lied to the last breath: "Wenck's Army is coming to the aid of Berlin! " On his orders officers and men had been hanged for retreating.

Goebbels had given instructions that after his death he was to be burned to ashes. But our assault groups arrived too soon. Beside the body of Magda Goebbels lay a gold party badge with a single-digit number that had fallen from her burnt dress, and a scorched gold cigarette case with Hitler's facsimile on it.

The wheel of murder turned its full circle. Before he died Goebbels destroyed his own children. Poison and fire had been well tested in the concentration camps. These were his instruments.

The report reads: "On May 2, 1945, in the centre of Berlin, on the premises of the Imperial Chancellery air-raid shelter, a few metres from the entrance, Lieutenant-Colonel Klimenko and Majors Bystrov and Khazin in the presence of citizens of Berlin, the Germans Wilhelm Lange, cook to the Imperial Chancellery, and Karl Schneider, garage mechanic of the Imperial Chancellery, at 17.00 hrs. discovered the charred bodies of a man and a woman; the man's body was short and the right foot twisted (clubfoot), with scorched metal artificial limb, the charred remains of a NSDAP uniform, a gold badge, half-burnt..."

The Walter pistol found beside them had not been used.

Lieutenant-Colonel Klimenko was still a young man at the time, 31 years of age, a regular army officer. I did not know Major Khazin. Major Bystrov had a Master's degree in biology. His home was in Siberia and he had enlisted during the war.

In the long years of fighting the three of us had travelled the scorched, blastered lands of Kalinin Region, Smolensk Region, Byelorussia and Poland.

We had seen the results of Goebbels' propaganda: the devastated lands, the death camps, the ditches full of people who had been done to death, the "new civilisation" in which man was an executioner unto man.

The road of war had brought us to the Imperial Chancellery.

Now, many years later, I am sometimes asked whether I was not frightened by the sight of these charred corpses. My feeling was one of awe, rather than fear. And not merely because we had seen much horror in the four years of war, but rather because these charred remains seemed satanic rather than human.

But the dead children *were* terrifying. No matter whose they were.

They were lying in their beds wrapped in blankets. Six children, five girls and a boy, killed by their own parents.

Was this the terrible form in which Retribution had been destined to appear?

"Whose are these children?" Bystrov asked Vice-Admiral Voss, whom he had just brought down into the shelter. Voss, chief naval liaison officer at Hitler's HQ, had been assigned the task of reaching Admiral Doenitz to confer upon him the supreme power willed to him by Hitler and to pass on the Führer's order to continue the war at all costs. No surrender on any terms!

With the remnants of Monke's brigade, which had defended the Imperial Chancellery, Voss had tried to break through the ring near Friedrichstrasse but had been taken prisoner.

"Did you know these children?" Major Bystrov asked. Voss nodded and, having first asked permission, slumped down defeatedly on to a chair.

"I saw them only yesterday. That is Heidi." He pointed to the youngest girl.

Before coming to this room he had identified Goebbels and his wife. Goebbels with a suite of journalists had in the summer of 1942 visited the battle cruiser *Prinz Eugen,* which Voss had commanded. He had Goebbels to thank for his promotion. Driven underground by the course of events, they had met in the air-raid shelter as old acquaintances.

Major Bystrov and Voss stood alone together in this damp, terrifying room of the shelter, where the dead children lay under their blankets.

Voss was shattered, drained of all feeling. He sat hunched in despair. Neither of them spoke.

The children had been discovered in one of the rooms of the shelter by Senior Lieutenant Ilyin on May 3rd.

They were lying in their beds in long nightdresses or pyjamas, all of which were made of white flannel with thin blue stripes. Their faces bore a dark flush—the effect of potassium cyanide.

In the hospital of the Imperial Chancellery we found a doctor, Helmut Kuntz, who had been involved in the killing of the children. He had been employed in the medical department of the Berlin SS. On April 23rd, when the department was disbanded, he was sent to the Imperial Chancellery.

Hollow-eyed, unshaven, in SS uniform, he punctuated his story with sighs and wringing of hands. He was, perhaps, the only person in the shelter who had not lost all sensitivity, all the power of reacting to what he saw. He told Bystrov his story:

"On April 27th before supper, between eight and nine in the evening, I met Goebbels' wife in the corridor at the entrance to Hitler's bunker. She told me she had something very special to talk to me about, and added at once that the times were such that we should have to kill her children. I gave my consent."

On May 1st he was at the hospital about 500 metres from the bunker, when he received a telephone call summoning him urgently to Goebbels' office. There the reason for the summons was explained to him. He advised Goebbels to place his children and his wife under the protection of the Red Cross, and to poison himself. Goebbels replied: "That would be no use. They will still be Goebbels' children."

Kuntz gave the six children morphia. "After that I again went out to the front room and told Frau Goebbels that she must wait about ten minutes for the children to go to sleep. I looked at my watch—it was 20.40 hrs."

Since Kuntz had told her that he would probably not be able to muster sufficient resolution to administer poison to the children, Magda Goebbels asked him to find and send to her Stumpfegger, Hitler's personal doctor. She and Stumpfegger forced open the children's mouths, placed the ampoules between their jaws and closed them. Stumpfegger left and Kuntz went down with Goebbels' wife to his office. Goebbels was pacing up and down the room in a wildly agitated state. "It's all over with the children, now we must think about ourselves," his wife told him. He responded hastily: "Hurry then, we have very little time."

Kuntz returned to the hospital.

Goebbels' wife had told him that she had obtained morphia and a syringe from Stumpfegger. Where she had obtained the poison ampoules, he did not know.

They might have been given to her by Hitler. We afterwards learned that he distributed poison to some of his associates at the end of April.

Vice-Admiral Voss, Doctor Kuntz, Lange the cook, Schneider the garage mechanic, Ekkold, head of Goebbels' bodyguard, engineer Tzim, the works manager of the building of the Imperial Chancellery, and many others identified Goebbels. He was of distinctive appearance. His head was disproportionately large for his puny body and noticeably flattened at the sides. His right leg was lame. It was shorter than the left and he had a clubfoot. The right leg had not been touched by the fire and the special orthopaedic shoe and artificial limb were intact.

"During the autopsy a smell of bitter almonds was detected and pieces of an ampoule were found in the mouth," reads the medical report.

When the results of the chemical analysis were received, a final judgement was arrived at:

"Chemical analysis of the internal organs and the blood reveals the presence of cyanide compounds. It must, therefore, be concluded that death ... occurred as the result of cyanide poisoning."

I don't remember that we managed to establish who had burnt his body. It was obvious that this had been done in extreme haste and the cremators had fled without completing their task.

"NOTHING CONFIRMED"

Early morning on May 4th. A pinkish mist was rising from the Alexanderplatz. It was chilly. The square was like a vagabonds' camp, the "vagabonds" being the remnants of the Berlin garrison. Some were sleeping on the pavements wrapped in their army blankets. Others had woken up and were sitting with the blankets round their heads and shoulders. Nurses in dark jackets and white kerchiefs were attending to the wounded.

The square was fringed on all sides with ruins. Gaping walls. Crumbling heaps of rubble.

A hand cart loaded with bundles clattered over the cobbles, pushed by two women. Evidently they were returning from the suburbs. The rattle of the cart invaded the numb silence of the ruined buildings.

Once again we were in the Imperial Chancellery.

Who had seen Hitler last? Was there anyone among the shelter survivors who had seen Hitler? What was known of his fate? Karl Schneider, the garage mechanic, said: "I don't know whether Hitler was even in Berlin up to May 1st. I never saw him here."

But on May 1st, as he had already said, he had heard of Hitler's suicide in the garage of the Imperial Chancellery from Hitler's chauffeur Erich Kempka, and from the garage chief. "That was only hearsay," he explained. "Everyone spoke of it but no one knew for sure." Comparing the rumour with the order he had received from Hitler's secretariat about sending petrol to the bunker he had drawn the obvious conclusion.

Wilhelm Lange, a man of fifty, who introduced himself officially as the Führer's household chef in the Imperial Chancellery, stated:

"I last saw Hitler in the early days of April 1945, in the garden of the Imperial Chancellery, where he was walking his dog, a German Alsatian called Blondie."

What did he know of Hitler's fate?

"Nothing reliable... On the evening of April 30th, Hitler's household vet, Tornow, came to me in the kitchen for food for the puppies. He was upset and said to me: 'The Führer is dead and there is nothing left of his body.' Rumours were circulating among the staff of the Chancellery that Hitler had either poisoned or shot himself, and his body had been burnt. Whether this was so in reality, I don't know."

Wilhelm Tzim, works manager of the Imperial Chancellery:

"I last saw Hitler at noon on April 29th, when I was called to the Führer's bunker to mend one of the fans. While I was working, I caught a glimpse of Hitler through the open door of his office."

What did he know of Hitler's fate?

"At 6 p.m. on April 30th the workmen Wernika, a plumber, and Gunner, an electrician, returned from work in the Führer's bunker and said they had heard the Führer was dead. They gave no further details."

Vice-Admiral Voss had taken part in the conference held in Hitler's presence in the shelter. He had heard of Hitler's death from Goebbels. That was all we had discovered by morning on May 4th.

"Nothing reliable", as Lange the chef would have said. But even this information had been sifted from other reports which, though sometimes contradictory, we could not at that stage afford to discount. It had been suggested, for instance, that Hitler had flown out of Berlin with the woman pilot Hanna Reitsch three days before the city fell, and that his death had been staged. Another version was that Hitler had escaped by underground passages and was hiding in an "inaccessible" fortress in the South Tyrol.

In the complex situation of the early days of May 1945, the work of the intelligence officers had to be co-ordinated and a clear sense of direction given to the search. This task was undertaken by Colonel Vassily Gorbushin.

On the morning of May 4th that quiet, domesticated, extremely civilian person, the little boilerman, whom no one in the Chancellery had paid much attention to, was sitting in front of me.

He had told us before that while he had been in the corridor he had seen what he described as the bodies of Hitler and Eva Braun wrapped in grey blankets being carried out of the Führer's apartment; Eva Braun, he said, had been wearing a black dress.

He had not insisted; he had simply related what he had seen. Amid the chorus of louder and more confident voices the voice of truth was ignored. The boilerman himself was so modest and unpretentious that it was hard to relate him to the scale of these events.

Vice-Admiral Voss seemed a far more likely figure, but he possessed no exact evidence.

The boilerman was the first German to tell me about Hitler's marriage. In those days, when the smoke of fires and battle had scarcely cleared in Berlin, this tale seemed to me pure fantasy. I looked at this unpretentious little man who was calmly sorting out in his memory the bizarre scenes of the past three or four days as though they were something from the distant past. And indeed, it was not merely days but a whole epoch that was passing into history.

I don't remember the boilerman's name. He popped up out of a volume of history like a nameless bookmark inserted at the right page. But we were too sceptical and too careless to take much notice of it.

Doctor Kuntz was in too bad a state of nerves to detach himself from what had happened. He had been in the Imperial Chancellery almost by chance and was unnerved by his part in the killing of the children. On the first day it had been the only thing he could talk about. But on May 4th, sighing, jumping to his feet, mixing up dates, he began to recall haphazardly the events of the past few days.

As confirmation of the fact that the marriage of Hitler and Eva Braun actually had taken place he related the following: in his presence Eva Braun had told Professor Haase, the head of the Imperial Chancellery hospital, that Goebbels' children had addressed her that day, as usual, as "Aunt Braun", to which she had replied that they should now call her "Aunt Hitler".

Later he remembered that in the evening he had been sitting in the casino over the Führer bunker with Professor Haase and two of Hitler's secretaries, Frau Junge and Frau Khristian. Eva Braun had come into the casino and invited the four of them into a separate room for coffee. She had then told them that the Führer had written a will which had been sent out of Berlin. He was now waiting for confirmation that it has arrived, then he would die. She had said: "They have all betrayed us, both Goering and Himmler." After which she had added: "It won't be so hard to die because the poison had been tested on the dog."

Doctor Kuntz was certain that this conversation in the casino had taken place on the evening of April 30th, whereas according to other information Hitler was dead by that time.

At every step we ran into contradictions. But we could not afford to ignore a single chance remark of Doctor Kuntz's. He said that when Goebbels' wife told him of Hitler's suicide she gave no details of how it was done. "There were rumours," he added,"that his corpse was to be burnt in the garden of the Imperial Chancellery."

"Who did you hear that from?" Colonel Gorbushin asked. "From Rattenhuber, the SS Obergruppenführer responsible for security at the Führer's headquarters. He said, 'The Führer had abandoned us and now we have to carry his dead body upstairs! ' "

On that day, May 4th, we still had no more authoritative evidence than what the chief of Hitler's bodyguard had said, as reported by Doctor Kuntz.

As on the first day, the garden of the Imperial Chancellery became the chief target of investigation.

TWO MORE BODIES

...In the garden of the Imperial Chancellery one of Lieutenant-Colonel Klimenko's men, Churakov, was attracted by a bomb crater that was on the left of the Führerbunker as one approached the entrance. Churakov had been alerted by the fact that the soil at the bottom of the crater was soft and friable; an unused faust had rolled down into it, and there was something sticking out of the soil that looked like the hem of a grey blanket. When he jumped into the crater, the soldier found himself treading on the half-burned bodies of a man and a woman, which had been sprinkled with earth. The soldier called for help and four men lifted the bodies out.

The names of those who made the discovery are recorded in the official report compiled on the following day.

REPORT

"May 5th, 1945.

"I, Guards Senior Lieutenant Panasov, Alexei Alexandrovich, and privates Churakov Ivan Dmitriyevich, Oleinik, Yevgeny Stepanovich, and Seroukh, Ilya Yefremovich, in the city of Berlin, in the area of Hitler's Imperial Chancellery near the place where the bodies of Goebbels and his wife were discovered, near Hitler's personal air-raid shelter, discovered and unearthed two burned bodies, one a woman, the other a man.

"The bodies are badly burned and in the absence of any further information cannot be identified.

"The bodies were lying in a bomb crater, three metres from the entrance to Hitler's shelter, and were sprinkled with soil."

Later the soil at the bottom of the crater was turned over and two dead dogs, an Alsatian and a puppy, were discovered.

The dogs were easily identified. The Alsatian, "Hitler's dog", as one of the reports described it, was "tall and had long ears".

The faces of the man and the woman were unrecognisable. However, a close examination of the bodies revealed that in all probability they were those of Hitler and Eva Braun; the bodies bore certain distinctive marks.

Our subsequent investigation of all the available information confirmed the fact that it was Hitler and Eva Braun who had been hastily buried in the bomb crater.

In those days we were able to establish a lot of facts and appreciate the actual atmosphere of events. But now as I go through the valuable material that has been preserved in the archives I can gain a fuller picture of events.

THE BREAK-THROUGH ON THE ODER

On April 16th, the Red Army began a new offensive. The piercing of the Oder fortifications, which had been considered impregnable, threw Hitler's HQ into panic. Berlin officialdom piled into their cars and fled to Munich. The Berlin-Munich road with its jam of fleeing vehicles was nicknamed by Berliners the "Reich refugee road". The Berliners themselves were left behind, while the tanks and infantry of the Red Army raced towards the capital.

After the Soviet breakthrough on the Oder Hitler and his staff considered moving to the castle at Berchtesgaden (Obersalzberg). Orders were given to prepare for take-off.

Bormann wrote in his diary:

"Friday, April 20th.

"The Führer's birthday, but no one is in the mood to celebrate, unfortunately. The advance party has been ordered to take off."

In Bormann's papers, which I went through in the shelter just after the surrender in May—they are before me again now—there are radio messages to Hummel and Frank with instructions on the preparation of quarters. A reply from Hummel on April 21st outlines his plan for the distribution of the various services and departments already partly completed, and requests approval of the plan.

Certain services, part of Hitler's archives, one of his secretaries, his personal doctor Morell—Hitler had for long been unable to do without the doctor's powerful stimulants—had already been sent to Berchtesgaden.

Hitler's intention to move to Berchtesgaden is further confirmed by his appointment of Doenitz as commander of all forces in the northern zone (Nordraum). But no commander was appointed to the southern zone, evidently because Hitler had left this post for himself.

Everything was in readiness for departure.

But on April 21st, Soviet artillery began shelling the centre of Berlin and Hitler gave orders to launch a counterattack. On April 22nd, Hitler heard from his generals that the counterattack commanded by SS General Steiner had failed, and that Berlin could not hold out for long, he should therefore leave the capital in order to allow the troops the opportunity of retreating. It would be senseless for Hitler, as Commander-in-Chief, to remain in encircled Berlin, from which no effective command could be exercised.

Hitler responded with hysterics, accusing both the SS and the army of treachery and threatening the generals that he would commit suicide. He then fell into a state of depression and withdrew to his quarters with Bormann and Keitel. What they conferred about is not known. When he returned, he listlessly informed the generals that he would remain in Berlin.

On April 22nd radio messages flew back and forth between Bormann, Hummel and Frank. Frantic instructions were given to prepare for the Führer's arrival. The day's exchange ended, however, with the following message:

"22.4.45.

"From Berlin.

"To Hummel, Obersalzberg.

"Send immediately with today's aircraft as much mineral water, vegetables and apple juice as possible, and my correspondence.

"Reichsleiter Bormann"

The departure from Berlin did not take place.

But now British and American forces were within striking distance of Munich; from there it was a stone's throw to Berchtesgaden. Hitler had realized how weak his bargaining position would be if he allowed himself to fall into British or American hands after fleeing from a surrendered capital.

His decision to remain in Berlin was regarded by the generals as admission of his inability to continue in command.

THE "FUHRERBUNKER"

The high command, Gross-Admiral Doenitz, General Field Marshal Keitel, Chief of Staff of the Armed Forces, Colonel-General Jodl, Head of Operations Divisions, and General of the Air Force Koller with their staffs, all left Berlin. Hitler's adjutant Günsche wrote in his testimony of May 14th, 1945, that no further contact was established with them and no information was received concerning their whereabouts.

Meanwhile Red Army tank and infantry divisions, overcoming desperate resistance at each successive defence ring, fought their way towards the centre of Berlin.

Russian shells were pounding the Imperial Chancellery and only the enormously thick concrete of the bunker saved Hitler from the results of a direct hit. The radio mast collapsed; underground cables were damaged.

Germans were dying in the streets of Berlin. The reports from the Nazi local authorities—they were in Bormann's file along with the radio messages to his adjutants and have been preserved in the archives—describe the hopeless position of those fighting in the streets and the hardships endured by the civilian population.

Reporting that the enemy was advancing about the Schönhouser-allee up to the Stargarderstrasse and could not be stopped in this sector, district leader Herzog wrote:

"Question: what are we to do about the population? People cannot even leave the cellars. They have no water and cannot cook anything."

Similar reports must have reached Goebbels, Berlin's defence commissar and party leader. But they fell on deaf ears. They were not even considered. There is no evidence, not a single line, to show that at this moment of supreme disaster those who were to blame for the German people's misfortunes thought for one moment of what people were suffering or felt any responsibility for them.

But the scale of the disaster was already indescribable. The city had been left to its fate. No evacuation had been organised, not even for the children. The city was without bread or water.

The reports to Bormann from the local Nazi chiefs at this time have little to contribute but the usual backbiting that was part of the struggle for party power.

Hitler skulked in his shelter, surrounded by his closest associates. Eva Braun; Manziali, the Führer's vegetarian cook, Goebbels, who had spent most of his life aping Hitler's tricks and foibles: Bormann, whom Goebbels reffered to in his diary for June 14th, 1941, as "behind-the-scenes operator", hated even by the Nazi upper crust. Bormann sat in a corner drinking brandy and "recording for history" Hitler's pronouncements.

How they all longed to go down in history! But great thoughts were not forthcoming. The only phrase that absolutely everyone who saw Hitler in those days remembers was, "What was that? What calibre?" Every time a shell-burst in the vicinity brought him to the door of his office with these words on his lips.

When generals from the fighting areas managed to reach the shelter, they would find Hitler poring over a map and moving the buttons that represented German troops. Now and then he would draw an arrow to indicate a counterattack.

Every general knew that it might cost him his life to report that an army which still existed in Hitler's imagination had been destroyed; Hitler could not and would not face the facts. He would go into a frenzy at every hint of defeat, accuse his generals of treachery and ruthlessly send them out to be shot.

If he was lucky, the commander who had got through to ask for help or instructions would find himself listening to assurances that a miracle was about to happen, that Wenck's army was hastening to the relief of the capital after which the officer with a fresh medal on his chest would be sent back upstairs into battle.

On learning that the 56th Tank Corps commanded by General Weidling had been defeated and had retreated from Küstrin, Hitler screamed that Weidling must be shot. When Weidling appeared in the shelter, however, Hitler quite obliviously began to initiate him into his new defence plan, in which a key part was to be played by Wenck's and Weidling's forces. Wenck's army was powerless because it was hemmed in by the Soviet forces, and only a few badly battered units of Weidling's corps still survived. Weidling went away expecting to be shot, but was soon recalled and, in accordance with the tyrant's fresh whim, appointed commandant of Berlin, an appointment that Weidling himself believed to be the equivalent of a death sentence.

"His contradictory and erratic orders completely disoriented the already confused German commanders," writes SS Obergruppenführer and police Lieutenant-General Rattenhuber, chief of Hitler's bodyguard, in his unpublished manuscript.

After the attempt on Hitler's life at his East Prussian headquarters, on July 20th, 1944, "Hitler was seized by fear and suspicion and the hysterical elements that were part of his character began to assert themselves".

Now "he was literally a wreck, his face was a mask of fear and confusion. The wavering stare of a maniac. A barely audible voice, shaking head, unsteady walk and trembling hands."

Lange, the cook, was the last to see him at ground level in the early part of April.

While the men Hitler had tricked and deceived died in the streets of Berlin, the inmates of the shelter relied on a miracle, on horoscopes and the Führer's instinct. The atmosphere was one of intrigue and agitated bewilderment, for which there was food in plenty.

Goering had abandoned Berlin and started negotiations with the British and Americans on conclusion of a separate peace and his treachery occupied the inmates of the shelter to the exclusion of all that was going on overhead.

Bormann wrote in his diary: "Wednesday, April 25th. Goering has been expelled from the party! First mass attack on Obersalzberg. Berlin surrounded! "

When arrested by the SS, Goering withdrew his claims. Hitler had sent him a telegram stating that he would be granted his life if he renounced all his ranks and titles. A radio message was promptly received in the Imperial Chancellery declaring that Goering was offering his resignation on account of "heart trouble".

Going through the archives, I discovered a letter to Wenck signed by Bormann and Krebs. It was sent to him by messenger on the night of April 28th. I regard this letter as a very important document.

It reached our military commandant's office at Spandau on May 7th, 1945, in the following manner.

A certain Josef Brichzi, aged seventeen, who had been training as an electrician and been called up for the Volkssturm in February 1945, was serving in anti-tank squad defending the government district.

On the night of April 28th he and another lad, of sixteen, were summoned from barracks in Wilhelmstrasse and escorted to the Imperial Chancellery.

Here they were informed by Bormann that they had been chosen for a responsible mission. They must break through the encirclement and deliver a letter to General Wenck, the Commander of the 12th Army. Bormann then handed each of them a packet.

It is not known what happened to the other boy, but Brichzi managed to get out of Berlin on the morning of April 29th on a motorcycle. He had been told he would find General Wenck in the village of Ferch, north-west of Potsdam. When he reached Potsdam, Brichzi discovered that none of the military there had any idea of the whereabouts of Wenck's headquarters. Brichzi then decided to ride to Spandau, where his uncle lived. His uncle advised him not to go anywhere else and to hand in the packet to the Soviet military commandant's office. After some time Brichzi brought it to the commandant's office on May 7th.

Here is the text:

"Dear General Wenck,

"From the enclosed messages you will see that SS Reichsführer Himmler has made the Anglo Americans a proposal that places our people unconditionally in the hands of the plutocrats.

"This can be reversed only by the Führer in person, only by him!

"The precondition for this is the immediate establishment of communication between Wenck's army and us, so that the Führer shall have internal and external political freedom to carry on negotiations.

"Yours   "Heil Hitler!
Krebs,
Chief of the General Staff"   "Yours, M. Bormann."

THE ODOUR OF BITTER ALMONDS

Hitler's life had never held any real inspiration besides the lust for power, or any real aim besides personal aggrandisement, for which the German people were to provide the means, his last days showed what a sordid sham his life had been.

While he still breathed, he killed. The courtyard of the Imperial Chancellery became a place of execution, where people were shot out of hand.

But in spite of Hitler's threats the betrayals multiplied.

Hitler's associates testify that General Weidling, as commandant of Berlin, begged Hitler to leave the city, so that it could stop fighting and avoid complete destruction. Hitler was defeated, crushed, dead, but even in death he dragged the whole country after him. Let them all perish. "The Allies will find in Germany nothing but ruins, rats, starvation and death," he declared.

The local Nazi bosses were terrified of Bormann, but the reports he kept in his file reveal even their growing despair. Their messages became shorter, more strident. The shelling was unbearable, losses were too great, ammunition was running out, no one could stop the Russian advance. But all this passed unheeded.

On April 29th, the rumour finally reached the Chancellery that Wenck's army had ceased to exist.

"This shattered all our hopes of salvation," writes Rattenhuber. "The attempt to break through to Berlin had failed. The drama of the situation was intensified by the fact that Hitler received all these messages with heavy Russian shells bursting in the grounds of the Chancellery. Hitler was really frightening to watch that day."

The long-expected but ill-fated General Wenck had disappeared into thin air. Back on April 21st, Hitler had withdrawn the forces from the Elbe, thus offering the Americans free entry into Berlin; but they were still far away. To delay the hour of doom a little longer Hitler gave orders to blow up the canal and flood the Berlin Underground, by way of which Red Army assault units were making for the government district. Hitler gave the order in the full knowledge that thousands of his fellow countrymen, wounded, women and children who had taken refuge in the tunnels of the Underground, would be drowned in the deluge.

On April 30th, it was reported that the Russians were 200 metres from the Wilhelmstrasse entrance to the Imperial Chancellery, once besieged by the journalists Goebbels had taken such pains to avoid four years ago, when he entered by the back door to attend the Führer's secret invasion conference. The only remedy now was the poison ampoule. Death is death and the bodyguards carried the body out through the emergency exit to burn it, as Hitler had commanded.

"Hitler summoned me, Linge and Günsche," Rattenhuber wrote, "and in a barely audible voice told me that his body and Eva Braun's must be burnt. 'I don't want the enemy to exhibit my body in a museum.' "

Two weeks later adjutant Günsche testified: "After the bodies had had petrol poured over them and been set fire to, the door of the shelter had to be closed because of the fierce flames and smoke. Everyone present went to the anteroom... The door into the Führer's private rooms was half open and from it came a strong odour of bitter almonds..."

The deaths of Hitler and Eva Braun were recorded in Bormann's diary on April 30th, 1945.

The entry for May 1st, evidently after the return of Krebs from preliminary negotiations with the Russians, consists of one sentence:

"Attempt to break out of the encirclement! "

Here the diary ends.

"Corks popped in the bar," Rattenhuber writes, "and the SS men braced themselves with alcohol before the desperate getaway under Russian fire."

Only those who had less fear of retribution remained behind. All the others fled.

When tyrants die there is a moment of general confusion. Can it be that they, too, are compounded of mortal molecules?

But soon the circumstances of their death, if these are in the least doubtful, become embroidered with legends. There was ample scope for this in Hitler's case.

And yet, things did not go as Gross-Admiral Doenitz on whom Hitler had conferred supreme power wished them to go, although the admiral in his official communiqué told the deliberate lie that Hitler had fallen in battle, while commanding the defenders of the capital of the German Reich.

Nor did they go as Reichsführer Axmann, leader of the Hitler Jugend, wished, when he claimed that he had taken away Hitler's ashes. All that he had taken was a pistol.

Nor did they go as Hitler's chauffeur described them in his sensational book *I Burned Hitler.*

Nor did they go as his servant Linge described them.

Nor did they go as they are summarised by the British historian Trevor-Roper in his serious study: "Whatever the explanation, Hitler achieved his last ambition. Like Alaric, buried secretly under the river-bed of Busento, the modern destroyer of mankind is now immune from discovery."

After four years of incessant, intensive fighting the Red Army reached Berlin and rid the world of Hitler.

The people whose task it was to establish the truth about Hitler carried out their task with a keen sense of responsibility. Any lack of clarity might do great harm by giving rise to legends that would facilitate a revival of Nazism.

"Hitler—corpse or legend?" was the title of a Reuter dispatch sent in May 1945. The examination of these human remains, stated the dispatch, forms the culminating point of a whole week of intensive search among the ruins of Berlin.

We hoped that the irrefutable proofs we had collected would very soon be made public. The people who had given everything for victory over fascism had the right to know that the finishing stroke had been delivered. It was also of great consequence to the future of Germany, that an accurate answer should be given to the question whether Hitler was alive or not.

Quite a number of people took part in the various searches and in the first stage of the investigation. But by May 8th reconnaissance men had gone back to the various corps and divisions and Colonel Gorbushin's group had been cut down to the minimum. In fact, there was no one left but Major Bystrov and myself, the interpreter.

We thought that if the proofs we had discovered were not presented to the world now, hot on the heels of events, but to our descendants, at some time in a remote and hazy future, would they then appear sufficiently convincing? Had everything been done to make the fact of Hitler's death and the fact of the discovery of his body unquestionable in years to come?

In these complex circumstances Colonel Gorbushin decided to obtain incontrovertible proofs.

THE DECISIVE ARGUMENT

In Berlin-Buche, on May 8th, the very day the German surrender was signed at Karlshorst, which I did not yet know, Colonel Gorbushin called me in and handed me a box. The box, he said, contained Hitler's jaws and I should answer for their safekeeping with my life.

It was a rather soiled, dark-crimson box with a soft satin lining, the kind that is used for perfume bottles or cheap pieces of jewellery.

Now it contained what was to become the decisive argument, the indisputable proof of Hitler's death. There are no two people in the whole world who have identical teeth. What was more, this proof could be preserved for a very long time.

The box had been entrusted to me because the regimental safe had been left behind in the second echelon and there was no safe place to keep it. I had been charged with its safekeeping because Colonel Gorbushin's group, which was still investigating all the circumstances of Hitler's end had been reduced by this time, as I have said, to three people.

My acquaintances who met me that day in the canteen, or at work with that box, had no idea of its contents. Everything concerned with the work of proving Hitler's death was kept in strict secrecy.

All that day, so full of the expectation of Victory, I had to carry the box about with me and shudder at the thought that I might mislay it. The thought of its contents was depressing.

By this time the historical attributes of the Third Reich had undergone considerable devaluation in my eyes. We had had too much of it. The death of its leaders and all that went with it now seemed something quite commonplace to me.

When I went to bed that evening, on May 8th, I locked my bedroom door and began wondering what to do with the box. The idea of keeping it close to me was repulsive, but I had to put it somewhere within view, so that when I woke up I could see whether it was still there. My bedroom was on the ground floor of a two-storeyed suburban villa. It was a small room and besides my bed and a bedside cabinet contained only a small wardrobe. I put the box on top of the wardrobe. But as soon as I had done so I heard someone calling my name and, grabbing the box, ran upstairs to the floor above.

One of the doors was open. Major Bystrov and Major Picheko were bending eagerly over a radio.

This was what we had all been waiting for but, when it came, we felt numb and confused.

"Signing of the Act of Unconditional Surrender of the German Armed Forces."

The voice of the Soviet radio-announcer came over the air: "To mark the victorious conclusion of the Great Patriotic War..." We shouted something and waved our arms.

The wine was poured in silence. I put the box on the floor. We clinked glasses in a kind of a dazed, subdued excitement as the salute sounded from Moscow.

I walked down the steep staircase, once again clutching the box to my chest. Suddenly it was as though something had pushed me and I had to hold on to the banisters. I was overcome by a feeling I shall never forget.

Was this really happening to me? Was it I who was standing here at the moment of Germany's surrender with a box containing what would probably be the only irrefutable evidence of Hitler's death?

On the morning of May 9th Berlin-Buche was agog. In expectation of something wonderful, of some indescribable triumph and rejoicing to celebrate the long-awaited Victory Day, one or two people were already dancing; some were singing.

Soldiers were strolling in the streets with their arms round each other's shoulders; the army girls were busy washing their tunics.

Colonel Gorbushin and I drove out that morning on a fresh assignment. We had to find Hitler's dentists.

The post-mortem examination stated: "The basic anatomical discovery that can be used to establish identity is the jaws containing a large number of dentures, plates, crowns and stoppings."

The report to which this conclusion referred contained a detailed description of them.

We passed a tractor pulling a gun. On its barrel, as on the side of a passing lorry, were the words, "To Berlin! " The soldiers, the guns, the lorries were still there. Everything was still the same. And yet it has all suddenly changed.

The guns would fire no more; the soldiers would not have to go into an attack. The long-awaited peace had come. Not only those distant battles on the Volga, but even the recent fighting with its incomparable urge and resolve to reach Berlin, had already become part of history.

Our search brought us, at last, to the Charité Clinics of the University. The buildings were oddly camouflaged with green and white stripes. We had been told that one of these clinics—ear, nose and throat—was run by Professor Karl von Eiken, the laryngologist, one of the doctors who had treated Hitler. But we had no idea whether we should find him in Berlin.

We drove into the grounds of the clinic. It was now a hospital, mainly for civilians. The wards were in dimly lighted cellars where wan-faced nurses in grey frocks went about their duties. People were being carried in and out on stretchers.

The fact that most of the wounded in these dark, overcrowded cellars were civilians brought home the cruelty of the war that had just ended.

Professor Eiken, a tall, lean old man, was there. Despite the terrible conditions, he had stayed at his post in those grim days; many had tried to persuade him to flee from Berlin on the eve of the surrender but he had refused, and the whole staff had followed his example. He took us into the camouflaged building of the clinic, which was still empty. In his surgery we had a long and unhurried conversation.

Yes, he had once been asked to treat Hitler for a throat disease. But that had been a long time ago, before Hitler came to power.

Eiken named the doctors who had been in attendance on Hitler to the last, including Professor Blaschke, Hitler's personal dentist. How could we find him? Eiken sent for a student on practical work at the clinic who had been studying under Blaschke.

The student, wearing a black autumn overcoat, hatless, with dark wavy hair and a round, gentle face, was cordial and quite willing to talk. He drove with us to show us the way.

We drove into the fashionable Kurfürstendamm. It was in just as bad a state as the other streets. But house No 213, or rather the part of it containing Professor Blaschke's surgery, was still standing. As we entered, a man came out wearing no overcoat and with a red ribbon in the buttonhole of his dark jacket. This was unusual, the predominant colour in the Berlin of those days was white for surrender; red signified friendship and solidarity with the Russians. He introduced himself as Dr. Bruck.

On hearing that we were looking for Professor Blaschke he told us that the professor was not in Berlin; he had flown out to Berchtesgaden with Hitler's adjutant.

We went to the first floor and Dr. Bruck took us into a spacious dental surgery with large windows.

Bruck, however, had nothing to do with the surgery and Colonel Gorbushin asked him if he knew any of Blaschke's colleagues.

"But of course! " Dr. Bruck exclaimed. "Are you thinking of Fräulein Heusermann? She is at home in her flat, only a few steps from here".

The student volunteered to go and fetch her.

"Pariserstrasse, 39/40. Flat No 1," Bruck told him.

On his invitation we sat down in the well-upholstered armchairs in which the Nazi leaders had so recently reclined. The professor had been Hitler's personal dentist since 1932.

Bruck also sat down in one of the armchairs. He had been a dentist in the provinces and Professor Blaschke's assistant. Kätchen Heusermann, whom the student had gone to fetch, had been one of his students and, afterwards, his assistant. This had been before the Nazis seized power. Later she and her sister had helped him to escape persecution as a Jew and he had been obliged to live under an assumed name.

A tall, slim, attractive woman in a dark-blue overcoat and with fair hair showing from under her headscarf walked into the room.

"Kätchen," Bruck said gently. "These people are Russians. They need you for something."

Before he could go on she burst into tears.

"Kätchen! " Dr. Bruck exclaimed, spreading his arms in confusion. "These are your friends, Kätchen! "

She was a head taller than the doctor, but he took her hand as though she were a child and patted the sleeve of her blue overcoat.

These two people had been at opposite poles of the Nazi regime. She had been in a privileged position, employed in looking after Hitler. He had been an outlaw, but in spite of persecution had found support in her family. Life was far too rich and varied to be squeezed into the pattern framed for it by Nazism.

Colonel Gorbushin told me to ask her whether there was any dental case history referring to Hitler.

Heusermann said there was and at once started looking through the card index. We watched her fingers anxiously as they flicked through the cards. Case histories of Himmler, Ley, Dietrich, Goebbels, his wife, all their children...

At last Hitler's case history was found. That was something! But there were no X-rays.

Heusermann suggested there might be some in another of Blaschke's surgeries, in the Imperial Chancellery itself. In the last days of the regime caps had been made for Hitler's teeth, but there had been no time to fit them on.

The sentry came to attention but would not let us in. He had been told that no one should enter without a special pass from the commandant of Berlin.

Gorbushin eventually had his way and we were admitted. We opened the heavy oak door. On the right was the great hall; the door had been smashed in, chandeliers lay on the floor where they had fallen.

Only Kätchen Heusermann knew her way about the place. She had left this "tomb of the Pharaohs" three days before the fall of Berlin.

She led up to a small cubicle where her chief Professor Blaschke, had had his quarters until he was flown out of Berlin.

The beam of the torch picked out a dentist's chair, a sofa with an adjustable headrest and a tiny desk. Something was lying on the floor—a photograph of Hitler's favourite Alsatian out for a walk with his adjutant. The room was damp and smelt of mildew.

We searched through a card index, the drawers of the desk and a cabinet that was also in the room.

With Heusermann's help we found X-ray pictures of Hitler's teeth and the gold caps that there had been no time to fit. We were lucky, desperately lucky that the tempest which had swept through the bunker only a few days ago had left this little cubby hole untouched.

TELLING IT STRAIGHT

Lovers of detective fiction may be disappointed that there have been no ambushes, no safe-breaking, no shots from lurking criminals. I am afraid I must also disappoint those who prefer fiction to facts— there were not even any doubles.

At this stage we were lucky and, as usual, a lot of unexpected things happened.

With Kätchen Heusermann's help we managed to obtain irrefutable proofs of Hitler's death, proofs that could be preserved for posterity.

Kätchen Heusermann first described Hitler's teeth from memory. This was at Berlin-Buche. Gorbushin and Bystrov talked with her. I interpreted.

After that Heusermann talked with experts and the official report states that in a conversation with the chief forensic expert of the front, Lieutenant-Colonel of the Medical Corps Shkaravsky, which "took place on May 11th, 1945", citizen Heusermann, Kätchen, "described in detail the condition of Hitler's teeth. Her description coincides with the anatomical facts of the oral cavity of the charred body of the unknown male upon whom we performed an autopsy". She also drew from memory a diagram of Hitler's teeth, pointing out all their peculiarities.

On May 10th Heusermann told us:

"In the autumn of 1944 I assisted in extracting the sixth tooth in Hitler's left upper jaw. For this purpose Professor Blaschke and I drove to Hitler's headquarters in the neighbourhood of Rastenburg. In order to extract this tooth Professor Blaschke drilled through the gold plate between the 4th and 5th teeth in the upper left jaw. While he was doing so I held the mirror in Hitler's mouth and followed the whole procedure attentively."

This could be compared with the medical report of May 8th, which stated: "The plate of the upper jaw has been drilled through vertically to the left of the small tooth (4)", and with the whole detailed description of the teeth which figures largely in the report.

But the main thing was the teeth themselves. Heusermann examined them and confirmed that they were Hitler's teeth.

She recalled this fact twenty years later in a West German magazine.

It took place in a house near Berlin, she writes, in the presence of a colonel, a major and a woman interpreter...

"Look closely," the colonel told her, "and tell us what this is, if you know what it is."

She describes how she examined the teeth that were taken out of a box and recognised them: "I held the plate in my hand. I looked for some definite sign, found it immediately, breathed with relief and blurted out: "They are the teeth of Adolf Hitler."

"Showered with words of praise, I went home."

The dental mechanic Fritz Echtmann, who made dentures for Hitler, also first gave a description of Hitler's teeth from memory, and was then shown the exhibit at Berlin-Buche.

Martyn Merzhanov, a *Pravda* correspondent, was present. On May 2nd he had been one of the first to visit the spot where Goebbels' body had been discovered, and had helped to write up the report.

Fritz Echtmann was a shortish pale-faced man, a little over thirty. His straight dark hair hung down over his eyes as though it were wet, and he had to push it back with his hand as he examined the teeth lying on the table in front of him.

He identified them as Hitler's.

This was how one German came face to face with the fact of Hitler's death. Echtmann, who had been obliged to stay in Berlin all the time with his wife and daughter, had been through too much to be surprised at anything. But the sight of Eva Braun's teeth sparked his excitement. My notes of what he said read as follows:

"That design of plate is my own personal invention. I never made a plate like that for anyone else except Eva Braun and in my practice I have never come across teeth fixed in that way. That was in the autumn of 1944. Braun refused my first plate because when she opened her mouth the gold could be seen. So I made her a second plate without that defect. I used an original way..."

The investigation was complete. Hitler's jaws, which with the X-rays and dental records provided incontrovertible proof of his death, were sent to Moscow with the rest of our findings.

TWENTY YEARS AFTER

As I complete these notes I again find myself sitting over Hitler's papers, just as I did twenty years ago.

"Dear Sister," he writes on February 13th, 1932. "With this letter I send you my private secretary Hess." It was Hess' task to obtain "through some competent Austrian government agency" a document clearing Hitler of the charge of desertion from the Austrian army in 1913.

Here is the draft of a letter to President Hindenburg. A typescript corrected in Hitler's hand in black ink. Shameless flattery, expressions of devotion, veneration for Hindenburg's services in the First World War. He describes himself modestly as a "simple soldier".

And here is another letter from Hitler to the old Hindenburg, his rival in the presidential elections of March 1932.

He was gravely disturbed by the fact that Hindenburg's election campaign was presenting him, Hitler, in an unfavourable light abroad.

He complained that the Prussian Minister for Foreign Affairs had called his National-Socialist Party a party hostile to the state. That the Imperial Minister for Internal Affairs had "attributed to Reichstag deputy Dr. Goebbels words that are not recorded in the verbatim report". And that the president of the Berlin police Herr Crzhechinsky had temporarily banned one of his party's newspapers.

Nonetheless, this repressed, pitiful ego shows its obstinacy and arrogance, and eagerly insists that it is on intimate terms with history:

"Considerable responsibility to history has fallen to my lot."

January 30th became the day of the inauguration of the Nazi regime.

It was only a year since Hitler had complained feverishly in his letter to Hindenburg of the violation of democratic procedures in the conduct of the elections, which in the letter he had described as "dangerous, on the one hand, and, in my belief, illegal, on the other."

But now a mere year had passed, Reichschancellor Hitler wrote his appeal to the National-Socialists concerning the forthcoming elections to the Reichstag. The folder contains the typescript of this appeal, corrected by Hitler in pencil and signed by him on February 22nd, 1933.

It reads:

"The enemy that must be overthrown on March 5th is Marxism! All our propaganda and all our electioneering struggle must be concentrated against that.

"If in this struggle the Centre supports Marxism by its attacks on our movement, then I in person shall deal with the Centre at the first opportunity, I shall rebuff it and put an end to this."

How the language of both documents differs. It reflects the path that was travelled, the shortest distance between two points. A straight line from the struggle for power to the seizure of it.

Previously he had appealed to the president for fair treatment as an opponent, in the spirit of the good old bourgeois-democratic traditions. Now his political opponents were to face dictatorship and its language of terrorism and violence.

"The Origins of Adolf Hitler", an extract from the *Monthly Bulletin* published by the Adler Heraldic-Genealogical Society in Vienna in 1932. This is a pedantically objective investigation of Hitler's ancestry undertaken by a certain scholar "in connection with the various reports of his origins" and establishing that Hitler's pedigree consisted "exclusively of German elements".

A folder containing the Führer's most important private papers begins with this work of "scientific" research. It ends with Hitler's heraldic tree in typographical form.

Here are the inventories of the pictures he bought, compiled when they had been crated and were ready for shipment.

The only masterpieces are a sketch by Becklin, and Khodovetsky's portrait of Frederick II. Most of them are works of the naturalistic landscape painters of the Düsseldorf school. There are also some sentimental conversation pieces, while artists of the new fascist school are represented by such pictures as "Mother of the Führer", "The View From Above—Adolf Hitler", "Old Berchtesgaden", "Torch Procession on January 30th, 1933."

Hitler had intended building a picture gallery for this collection in the town of Linz, of which he had childhood memories; he refers to it in his will. While German cities were being bombed to the ground, the Führer, who had once been refused admission to an art school, devoted himself to the design of this gallery.

But Linz did not lose much by not acquiring Hitler's art collection.

The crates containing the pictures are lettered and the inventories show that after letter P there was nothing much in them except a bust of Wagner, a zither, a small picture by an unknown artist, a ceramic stand, two wall plates, and other personal belongings of the Führer; 13 pillows, 18 blankets, 34 tablecloths of various sizes, 1 silver sugar bowl, 3 Turkish towels, 3 dish cloths, 1 bath mat, 1 runner, 1 fruit plate, 1 lace-embroidered eiderdown cover and pillow case to match, 1 wooden bread plate, 1 bookholder, 2 trays, candlesticks, wine glasses, cups, 1 length of lace, 1 set of table linen (12 napkins and 1 tablecloth), 2 damask tablecloths, 1 damask eiderdown cover, and so on.

These inventories which he took with him to his last refuge bear a resemblance to the inventories kept by Magda Goebbels... Just as Goebbels' diary is written in a spirit similar to that of Hitler's papers.

What a nonentity Hitler appears when stripped of the aureole of power and mystification! It is natural enough that the idea of fascism should have been personified by just such a man. But how abominable that such a man should have gained control of Germany and threatened the whole world!

Unrestricted power, megalomania, persecution mania. His chief bodyguard Rattenhüber writes in his manuscript: "He would not even put on underclothes from the laundry until they had been X-rayed... There were numerous alarm signals in his rooms. There was even one in his bed. No one, except his closest associates, was admitted to Hitler's apartments without being searched."

Hitler's papers contain a draft letter to the president of the German Agricultural Council.

It reads in part: "It may be confidently stated that the Prussian idea of the state had already created in the form of the Prussian state an example of the most perfect state socialism of modern history."

So much for the ideal.

And here is the method for achieving this ideal. It is stated in the appeal to the National-Socialists of July 26th, 1933, also contained in the folder:

"At last the goal we have been striving towards for fourteen years has been attained—the young people of the Stahlhelm come under my command as the supreme Führer of the SA... The future of our people does not depend on how many unions stand for this future, but on whether the desires of many can be subordinated to a single will."

To achieve the unthinking subordination of the masses to the single will of the "leader", all individuality had to be trampled on and destroyed.

The banning of thought led to its atrophy. Despotism and tyranny. The appeal to the lower instincts.

Ein Volk, ein Reich, ein Führer! I saw that fascist slogan last autumn in the duty officer's room of a hut in the Oswiecim death camp, the last of a long row of huts, where the torture chambers were and from which there was only one exit—to a wall in front of a firing squad.

What unavoidable logic there is between this slogan and this hut!

Translated by Robert Daglish

Roman Karmen
(1906-1978)

At seventeen Roman Karmen started working as a news photographer. Later he became interested in motion pictures. In 1931, Karmen graduated from the Institute of Cinematography and became absorbed in his work. He filmed the Civil War in Spain and was often seen in the trenches of Guadalajara and among the defenders of Madrid. On the basis of his work, 22 newsreels *Events in Spain* and the full-length film *Spain* were released.

The Second World War found Karmen again at the front line with his camera, taking shots from tanks and from attacking dive-bombers. He was among the cameramen who created the documentary film, *The Rout of the German Troops Near Moscow*. Later, Karmen produced the films *Judgement of the Peoples* about the Nuremberg Trial, and *The Second World War*. He was a winner of the Lenin Prize and was honoured with the title of Hero of Socialist Labour.

Doctor Goebbels on the Phone

One of the toughest stages in the Battle of Berlin was the forcing of the Berlin-Spandau-Schiffahrts Canal. Between the canal and the Spree lies the huge expanse of the Siemens-Werke, which used to supply half of all Germany's electrical appliances.

We were in one of the deserted flats in Siemensstadt, the housing estate adjoining the works, when the sight of a telephone reminded me that if there was still a connection with the city centre any Nazi agent could simply pick up the receiver and supply his defence headquarters with information about our troops, correct the fire of the German artillery, direct planes to the right targets, and so on.

To check this I lifted the receiver and dialed the first Berlin number I came across in the directory lying beside the phone. A woman's voice replied and I rang off. The line to the centre was still in order.

A sudden mischievous thought occurred to me.

"What would happen if we tried to ring up Goebbels?" I asked the other men of the tank crew I was with.

The idea caught on at once and our interpreter Victor Boyev, who spoke fluent German, volunteered to try it out. But how could we get through? We looked up inquiries in the directory and dialed the number. The operator who answered was told that it was a matter of the greatest urgency for the caller to be put through to Dr. Goebbels.

"Who wants to speak to him?" she asked.

"A citizen of Berlin."

"Hold the line."

In fifteen minutes the same voice informed that we should shortly be put through to the office of Reich Minister for Propaganda Doctor Goebbels. Then a man's voice asked who wished to speak to Goebbels. This time Victor Boyev said, "A Russian officer wants to speak to him. Who is that?"

"You're through to Dr. Goebbels," came the reply.

There was a click on the wire and another man's voice said, "Hullo".

The following is an almost verbatim report of what was said.

INTERPRETER VICTOR BOYEV. Who is speaking?

REPLY. Reich Minister for Propaganda Doctor Goebbels.

BOYEV. This is a Russian officer speaking. I should like to ask you a couple of questions.

GOEBBELS. Certainly.

BOYEV. How much longer do you intend to go on fighting? And how much longer will you be able to?

GOEBBELS. Several—*(Boyev missed the rest.)*

BOYEV. What did you say—several weeks?

GOEBBELS. Oh no—months.

BOYEV. One more question: when and in what direction will you be running away from Berlin?

GOEBBELS. I consider that question impudent and out of place.

BOYEV. Remember this, Herr Goebbels. We'll find you anywhere you run, and the scaffold is ready and waiting for you.

The response to this was a kind of moaning sound.

BOYEV. Have you any questions to put to me?

"No! " was the irritable reply, and Goebbels rang off.

Rumours of this amusing conversation flashed round among the tankmen, and Boyev had to tell the story dozens of times of his "heart-to-heart" talk with the Reichskommissar for the defence of Berlin.

"Well, now we are going to have a word with Goebbels, and not over the phone but in person," I heard one of the tankmen say as he climbed his machine.

The air around us was vibrating with the rumble of hundreds of guns. Soviet aircraft streamed overhead as if they were on a conveyor belt. This was how our gunners and airmen continued the "chat" with Doctor Goebbels. Every hour, every minute the iron ring round Berlin tightened. Any clear-headed observer of the situation could see that the final outcome was not a matter of months or weeks but of the next few days.

Forty-eight hours after the telephone conversation Goebbels committed suicide.

TO THE CENTRE OF BERLIN

For the past two days I have been with General Bogdanov's troops. They outflanked Berlin in the north, then swung sharply south and are now thrusting eastwards into the heart of the city. After forcing the Berlin-Spandau-Schiffahrts Canal our tanks yesterday crossed the River Spree and smashed their way into the Scharlottenburg District. Now the Tiergarten and Moabit are under attack.

The streets of Berlin that we have occupied are a fascinating sight. The guns are still thundering a few blocks away and stray bullets are

Soviet dive-bombers over Berlin

At the height of the battles for the Reichstag

Soldiers of Colonel Zinchenko's unit
storming the Reichstag

The Victory Banner over the
Reichstag

Mikhail Kantaria and Mikhail
Yegorov, the men who raised the
Banner of Victory

◄

They fled from retribution

The marble eagle, emblem of nazism, thrown down from the pediment
of the Reich Chancellery

Commanders-in-Chief of the Allied Forces of the anti-Hitler coalition. *Left to right*: Field-Marshal Montgomery, General Eisenhower, Marshal Zhukov and General De Lattre de Tassigny

◄

Berlin. May 1945. Marshal of the Soviet Union Zhukov delivers a speech before signing the act of unconditional surrender by Nazi Germany

Signing the act of unconditional surrender by Nazi Germany

Link-up on the Elbe, April 1945

◄

Field kitchen serving food to the German population

Soviet writers Vsevolod Vishnevsky and Alexander Bezymensky with the first commandant of Berlin, General-Colonel Berzarin (*centre*)

Front Commanders at the final stage of the war.
Sitting left to right: Marshals Ivan Konev, Alexander
Vassilevsky, Georgi Zhukov, Konstantin Rokossovsky and
Kirill Meretskov; *standing*: Marshals Fyodor Tolbukhin,
Rodion Malinovsky and Leonid Govorov, and
Generals Andrei Yeryomenko and Ivan Bagramyan.
1945

The Victory salute

Victory Parade on Red Square in Moscow on 24 June 1945.
Soldiers throwing down the banners of the routed fascist
army at the foot of the Lenin Mausoleum

Muscovites welcoming demobilised soldiers

still flying about but there are lively bunches of Berliners all round us. The Germans surround every Soviet officer and soldier they meet, plying him with questions. The key question is, may they leave the cellars? People can scarcely believe that the bombing is over, and that tonight they will be able to sleep in their own beds and not in an air-raid shelter. The next thing that worries these harassed, half-starved people is bread. In streets where there is as yet no commandant or local authority, where our tanks and guns are still rumbling past, Soviet officers and men readily share their rations with the population. In some districts I have seen army kitchens dishing out hot food to civilians. Colonel-General N. E. Berzarin, commander of the 5th Assault Army, has been appointed military commandant of Berlin. Besides the Berliners themselves there are people from the concentration camps and deportees' barracks—Frenchmen, Italians, Czechs, Russians, Poles, Belgians, Dutchmen.

Our planes roar over the city day and night; there is hardly a German aircraft to be seen. The Germans snarl back with their artillery and mortars. Yesterday we captured the last airfield—Tempelhof—held by the encircled Berlin garrison. Now the only chance the Nazi bosses will have of escaping from Berlin is by using some wide street as a runway.

Our troops attacking from the east yesterday started fighting their way along those famous Berlin streets, the Kurfürstendamm and the Hohenzollerndamm. In the south-east they have only a few blocks to go before they reach the Unter den Linden. Prisoners and deserters speak of the utter demoralisation of the defenders. They all realise that further resistance is futile, but still submit to compulsion.

The cannonade doesn't slacken for a second. Column after column of tanks grinds along the broad thoroughfares of Berlin. The German capital is in its death agony; its days and hours are numbered.

AT THE BRANDENBURG GATE

At dawn on May 1st, the Supreme Commander-in-Chief's May Day order was read out to the units fighting in the streets of the German capital. The heavy artillery and mortars thundered into action and the infantry began the assault of the remaining enemy-held districts. The men went into battle knowing that this was the final thrust, destined to crush the resistance of the enemy. They also know that the enemy's last shots would stop some of them from taking part in the victory celebrations. On May Day our tanks and guns moved forward among the grey, alien city blocks with bright-red flags and streamers draped over them. Gunbarrels were decked with scarlet tulips. The spring festival that we all love is here with us in the capital of Germany.

The Banner of Victory is already flying over the Reichstag. Those who were closing the circle in the south and west spotted it from their distant observation posts. The Germans fought back frantically. They not only fired on the advancing tanks; they shot us in the back from every window. The fighting went on all day without respite. The regiments and divisions, now with the additional title Berlin, will always remember that May Day battle. Sokolov and Vainrub's tanks advanced on the Tiergarten down the broad Berliner and Bismarck streets. That night the fighting flared up afresh. Generals and men alike sensed that it needed only one more blow, one more attack, one more squall of fire to bring the enemy to his knees. No one thought of himself. At dawn the field telephones brought the news to all unit commanders—surrender.

SURRENDER

By evening on May 2nd, the people of Berlin had recovered from their fears and realised that the war in the city was all over. They came out into the streets and carried their belongings up from the cellars to the upper floors. Order was quickly restored. Only now, when Berlin was totally occupied and one could drive freely back and forth across the city, could one see what enormous damage had been done by the bombing. Whole streets had been reduced to rubble. Berliners spoke of the enormous loss of life among the civil population because there were, in fact, no proper shelters in the city.

I have been reading General Berzarin's order to the people of Berlin. It states that the whole population shall observe all regulations and remain where they are, the National-Socialist Party and all its subordinate organisations are dissolved and their activities are banned; all members of the German army, the SS and SA troops who are still in Berlin shall within seventy two hours of publication of this order report for registration; the leading personnel of the Gestapo, the secret police, security troops, prisons and all other state institutions shall report to the district and sector offices of the military commandant; all public utilities—power stations, water supply, sanitation, urban transport, all medical institutions, all food shops and bakeries shall resume their services; all personnel of the above-mentioned organisations shall remain at their posts; food shall be distributed by the shops on the basis of the previous ration system and documents until further notice, the owners and managers of banks shall temporarily cease all financial operations, seal their strong rooms immediately and report to the military commandants' offices on the state of their affairs; all bank employees are categorically forbidden to issue any valuables; the population shall surrender all weapons, ammunition, explosives, motor vehicles, motor cycles and radio apparatus to the military commandants' offices, all printing-shops shall be sealed; the population of the city is warned that it bears responsibility for any hostile attitudes towards the soldiers of the Red Army or their Allies; anyone accused of attacking soldiers of the Red Army and their Allies or of committing acts of sabotage will be court-martialed; units of the Red Army and individual servicemen arriving in the city of Berlin shall take up their quarters only in places designated by the military commandants, soldiers of the Red Army are expressly forbidden to carry out any eviction or moving of the population, confiscation of property, valuables, or to make any searches without the authorisation of the military commandants.

Towards the end of the day I saw many citizens come out into the streets to pull down the barricades. This is not easy work by any means. There are barricades at every step. They are made of brick, trees, tramcars, and concrete. Dug-in tanks and guns stand at many of the crossroads.

THE FIRST PEACEFUL DAY

May 3rd. Only yesterday Berlin was a frontline camp. Today there are signposts at every crossroads indicating the way through the maze of streets of the huge city. The girl traffic controllers wave their flags cheerfully. Those sweet girls! They kept their watch in snowstorms and rain on the shell-torn roads of war. And now this blue-eyed blonde Tanyusha from Ryazan is regulating the traffic on the Frankfurterallee. She may look outwardly stern but the sparks of merriment in her eyes give her away; she, too, is happy to have completed the long journey of war here, on the streets of Berlin.

Today I visited two of Berlin's prisons. The famous Moabit Prison— a model of the application of industrial techniques to the work of burying alive. Its frontage in Altmoabit Strasse looks like any other government building. Only when you are inside do you realise it is a prison. The hundreds of solitary confinement cells where the Gestapo kept its victims are empty today. On April 27, three hundred of the prison's inmates were taken away by Nazi gaolers in an unknown direction. An old hunchbacked news vendor, who was in the prison right up to the last day, has stayed there because he has no other home in Berlin. It was he who showed us over the prison. We saw fetters, of all sorts. There was a steel waist belt to which a man's hands were manacled. There was a combination of manacles and leg-irons joined by an iron rod. We even saw axes with which people were beheaded... Now it is all history, exhibits for a museum where our descendants will study a grim page in the history of Europe.

In the Litzensee Prison, which had been badly damaged by bombing, we saw the death chamber with its guillotine and a scaffold from which several nooses dangled. One wall of the building had collapsed and the whole interior of the prison with its honeycomb of solitary confinement cells was exposed to view.

The streets of Berlin are swarming with people. There is no public transport and what we see is a kind of transmigration. Whole families go along pushing and pulling thousands of carts and wheelbarrows. They intermingle with streams of army vehicles. Our troops do not stay long in Berlin. They are pressing on. Today I paid another visit to the Reichstag. Hundreds of our army lorries pull up there. Everyone wants to see the building with the Banner of our Victory flying proudly from its dome. Today I met Lieutenant Semyon Sorokin, commander of a reconnaissance platoon. On April 30th he and Private Grigory Bulatov fixed a red flag on the pediment of the Reichstag under withering enemy fire.

INTERVIEW WITH COLONEL-GENERAL BERZARIN

General Berzarin received me in his office at the headquarters of the army under his command, which had fought its way from the Vistula to Berlin. He is forty-one, grey-haired but with a young face and a gleaming good humour in his eyes. Berzarin began the war as commander of the Riga garrison. He was badly wounded in the fighting near Vyazma. When he returned to the front he took command of the forces that captured Smolensk, and had a part in the defeat of the Germans at Jassy-Kishinev sector. Now he is commandant of Berlin.

"I assure you," he told me, "that it is far easier to fight than to administer a huge city like Berlin. The city has been bombed out and damaged by fighting. All its vital services, transport, water, gas, sanitation, have been dislocated. The measures we are taking should put life on a normal footing in a very short time."

I quote my questions to the general and his replies.

QUESTION. How big is the population of Berlin at present?

ANSWER. Over two million, but it is growing every day on account of people coming in from other areas.

QUESTION. How about food supplies for the population of Berlin?

ANSWER. Every citizen of Berlin receives a daily ration of 200 grammes of bread, 400 grammes of potatoes, 15 grammes of sugar, 30 grammes of meat and 5 grammes of fat. Berlin's largest mills, bakeries and refrigerators are already in operation. Some of the supplies were in Berlin warehouses, but much has to be brought in from outside. The inhabitants of Berlin have been issued with ration cards, the network of food shops is being expanded to eliminate queues.

QUESTION. Do you consider it possible to start the city transport in this chaos of ruins?

ANSWER. There is a plan for bringing into operation the whole city transport system. Yesterday I had a long talk with the chief director of Berlin's public transport and its chief technical manager. According to this plan the first Underground line should start operating on May 15th. The city tramlines are being repaired. We shall give priority to restoring freight transport. That will help us to put the city in order quickly.

QUESTION. How do matters stand with regard to power, water supply and sanitation?

ANSWER. Berlin's largest power station with a capacity of 730,000 kilowatts is already functioning. Many districts of Berlin now have electricity. Within the next few days it will be restored everywhere and all Berlin will be lighted. Sanitation and water supply are working in three districts. We are forcing the pace to have all damage to water mains and drains repaired. On May 8th I shall hear a detailed report on this matter from managers of enterprises. The first gasworks will come into operation on May 7th and several districts will be supplied with gas.

QUESTION. Don't you encounter acts of sabotage in carrying out all these measures?

ANSWER. On the contrary, I am bound to emphasise that the managers, engineers and workers have set about all these tasks with great zest. They sincerely want to bring the city back to life. All my orders are being fulfilled most energetically.

QUESTION. How is the city administration organised? What part are representatives of the German population playing in matters of administration?

ANSWER. The city has been divided into districts. Each district has a military commandant. We select as commandants well-educated senior officers with administrative experience. In every district there is also a German *Bürgermeister*—the most influential person, whose prestige stands high among the local population. In addition, groups for co-operation with the Red Army have been organised in every district. The groups, which consist of German anti-Nazis, render the *Bürgermeister* and the commandant great assistance in restoring normal life, supplying the population with food, guarding public property and seeing to it that the population carries out all the points in my Order No. 1.

"It seems to me," the general said in conclusion, "that the Germans had such a bad time under the Nazi regime, and were so utterly exhausted by a very long war, that they are entirely sincere in their desire to help us in all measures aimed at restoring normal life in their capital. The Germans are a very well-organised people, they like discipline and order. See how enthusiastically the people of Berlin have set about clearing the streets of rubble and of barricades. In a week's time you won't recognise Berlin. We have one other big worry. In Berlin there are nearly 7,000 wounded German soldiers. They have all been provided with food and treatment. Many of the hospitals which were underground are being moved to good premises in the city and outside it. We have supplied them with medicines. We place very strict demands on our soldiers and officers stationed in Berlin. District commandants as well as unit commanders are held responsible for maintaining the strictest discipline in all units."

I tood my leave of the general. It was late at night when I walked out into the street. The city was quiet. The hum of army lorries and the measured tread of the commandant's night patrols were the only sounds to disturb the stillness of the sleeping city. A torch flashed in the darkness and our car stopped for our papers to be checked. A sergeant with a red armband on his grey coat saluted and said, "Your papers are in order, you may proceed."

As I reread the dispatches I cabled in those days and the record of my interview with General Berzarin I see two Berlins. One is the tragic smoke-wreathed Berlin, battered and burning, of May 1945, the other is the Berlin that is the capital of the German Democratic Republic today.

A new Berlin has risen from the ruins. I have paid it several visits. Every year it improves in appearance and services; every time I go there I find myself admiring new districts of handsome modern buildings. Fresh greenery has replaced the charred tree stumps. As I look round at this new Berlin I cannot help remembering the death agony of a city in which Soviet soldiers counted the last blocks, the last shots, the last bursts of machine-gun fire that lay between them and victory.

Grigory Baklanov
(b. 1923)

Grigory Baklanov has written much about the 1941-45 Great Patriotic War and belongs to the generation of Soviet writers represented by such names as Yuri Bondarev, Vassil Bykov and Vladimir Bogomolov. Having gone to the front right after their school-days, they, as Alexander Tvardovsky once said, "saw the blood and sweat of the war on their field shirts".

Baklanov is the author of novels and novellas, including *Nine Days, An Inch of Land, The Dead Know no Shame* and *Nineteen Forever.* For the latter, the author was awarded the USSR State Prize.

The Cost of War*

It was the month of May, six days after the end of hostilities, and we were stationed in a German village. There were five of us, four reconnaissance scouts and myself, the officer in charge. The village did not resemble our villages in the least: it consisted of twelve sturdy houses, under every house was a well-swept sand-strewn cellar lined with barrels of cold cider, in every yard were hens and pink pigs, in every barn were Dutch cows that kept sighing deeply, and behind every house were carefully cultivated fields of corn. The peaceful sun of spring shone down upon all of this—the little fields, the red tiled roofs, the pink pigs, and the farmers who bowed to us good-naturedly every morning. They instantly accepted a state of peace, without any mental perturbation, as if the only thing required for this was to take off their boots and put on the felt slippers they had exchanged for boots six years before. They avoided discussing the war, limiting their comments to a sad shake of the head and the murmuring of Hitler's name, as much as to say: he's the guilty one, let him answer for it; as for them, they had exchanged their boots for felt slippers.

On the second day of peace we found a German corporal hiding in the fields beyond the village. He was a tall man in a shiny black macintosh with a velvet collar such as German officers wore, and it was the first time that we were at a loss what to do with him. As I looked at his sharp shoulders hunched beneath the shiny macintosh, I was keenly conscious of how relative all human values are. Two days ago he would have been our enemy; now he was neither enemy nor prisoner of war; and yet it was hard for us to let him go.

One day back in July 1941, when we were retreating and had already suffered many losses, we took a German prisoner. As soon as we saw his big calloused hands, the hands of a working man, we slapped him on the back and, as we shared our soup with him, tried to find out how Hitler could have made him take up arms against us. That was at the beginning of the war. Now the war was over, and here was this German corporal whom we had found cringing in the corn, and not one of us was inclined to slap him on the back and speak words of encouragement to him. We could not find it in us to say to

*English translation © Progress Publishers 1981
© Raduga Publishers 1985

each other, as perhaps soldiers had said to each other at the end of other wars: "You're a soldier and I'm a soldier and it is not we who are to blame but those who forced us to shoot one another, let them answer for it." Something else lay between us: the guilt and responsibility of each individual was measured by different standards this time.

But the people of this village and the farmer in whose house we were quartered seemed not to be aware of our feelings. Every morning when I sat down to breakfast, my belt and pistol holster slung over the wooden bedstead, the owner of the farm would appear with his pipe between his teeth to greet "Herr Ofizier". At first he came only to the door, but in a day or two he took a chair beside the table.

There he would sit in the slanting rays of morning sun, his legs crossed, sucking on a pipe whose metal lid was darkly stained with nicotine. He seemed to enjoy watching "Herr Ofizier" eat his breakfast; he had been young once himself and knew that a young man wants a good meal in the morning. His eyes twinkled with good humour. We could hear his wife's quick steps out in the yard and the clank of her enameled milk pail. She had borne him a son at the age of eighteen, and now, at the age of thirty-two, one could hardly believe she was the mother of that tall lanky boy, already half a head taller than his father. At times we thought he must be his son by another wife.

On the very day of our arrival the farmer asked me to allow him and his wife to spend the nights with relatives in the next village. He explained it by saying his wife was still young and there were soldiers about. To allay any suspicions I might have, he promised to leave his son at home. Since he left all his household effects and livestock as well, I had no doubt as to why the boy was left behind.

The farmer and his wife usually went away at sundown, and for a long time after they had gone the rattle of the boy's keys could be heard in the barns and sheds. We paid no attention to him. My scouts would gather in the yard to watch the sunset and sing a two-part song about the Cossack who went to the war, and this song, which we had known from youth, went straight to our hearts here in Germany.

The farmer and his wife would come back in the chill of early morning. He came to say good-morning to "Herr Ofizier", she immediately set about her tasks in the yard, stirring the mush for the pigs with plump hands that were very quick and able.

My scouts lounged lazily in the sun while she rushed from the barn to the house and back again, leaving in her wake the smell of the manger, warm milk, and sweat; she would shoot glances at the boys and try to sweep their knees with her skirts as she ran past. With her hoop-like hips, powerful curves, and the puckered brow of a well-fed infant, she looked like a symbol of Content and Plenty standing at the entrance of the pigsty, her hands on her hips, her bare legs planted wide apart and half-hidden by the hogs swarming and squealing at the feed trough. Her husband was knotted and sinewy, with bony shoulders and big hands and a pipe in his mouth that seemed never to go out. But I thought I could detect a military bearing carefully concealed beneath his rustic appearance and slouchlike walk.

On the morning in question he sat at the table as usual and broached various subjects cautiously. As I glanced at him over the edge of my glass I felt a sudden wave of homesickness, as if we had been quartered in this neat little German village (which by some miracle had been spared the ravages of war) a hundred years instead of only six days. The one bright spot in my life this May morning was that a new motorcycle was waiting for me out in the yard. My scouts had brought it to me early in the morning and I had not yet set eyes on it.

I saw Magda, with her wrinkled, impassive face and steel-like arms, go past the window in thick-soled army boots, clutching a wet oaken tub to her belly. She had been working for our farmer since autumn.

She had had a husband. A Communist. He had been knifed in the back at a meeting. Late in life she had given birth to one child, a son. She had lived only for him. He had been killed on the Russian front in 1944.

Sleepy-eyed Margoslin, one of my scouts, shambled forth in bare feet and unbelted tunic and reached for the tub. She did not let go at first and they had a little tussle. Margoslin won. He lifted it easily to his shoulder and Magda followed in his footsteps, her face an ashen grey even in the sunlight. I watched them until they disappeared behind the shed.

Never had I seen my men offer assistance to the family in whose house we lived—neither to the wife with all her voluptuous attractions, nor to the boy. The only one they felt sorry for, without stopping to analyse why, was old Magda who had lost everything in the war and now had to work for people who had gained rather than lost.

I finished the fried eggs I was eating out of the frying-pan and poured myself out another glass of wine. It was pale and transparent and so cold that the glass remained frosted for a long time after I had emptied it. Then I slipped my strap over my shoulder (the farmer watching my movements respectfully), buckled on my belt, delighting in the feel of my muscles and of the pistol on my hip, pulled my officer's cap to a jaunty angle, and went out into the yard. Judging by the pleasure I took in showing off in front of this German, a man is still very young at the age of twenty-two even if he has been through such a war.

The wine made the sunlight in the yard seem more dazzling than ever, and the motorcycle leaning up against the white wall of the house was a blaze of nickel and black enamel. I wheeled it, shaking and sputtering from the running motor, out of the yard, and as soon as my feet touched the pedals it fairly leaped out from under me and dashed up the steep country road to meet the bright blue wall of the sky. There could be no doubt that the war was over and we were in Germany—were here on behalf of all those who had fallen on the way. I gave my motorcycle as much gas as I could, and felt nothing but the wind on my teeth and a cold thrill of excitement in the pit of my stomach.

Over the hill was another village where Volodya Yakovenko, head of reconnaissance for another of our units, was quartered. He, too, had four scouts with him. When my race up the stony road through the woods brought me to the crest of the hill, I swooped down into the village street with a deafening roar of motor and exhaust. Trees, shutters, porches and front gardens were blurred by tears into two sunny streaks on either side of the road.

In front of me a heap of cobblestones marked a fork in the road. Yakovenko's house was on the right. As I took the turn at high speed, the motorcycle leaning perilously, a puppy ran out in front of me, heading straight under the wheel. It all happened so quickly that my hands worked quicker than my brain. I jammed on the brake and twisted the handle-bar. Instantly I found myself being dragged in the dirt which I clutched at with both hands.

I jumped to my feet. A child of about three was standing in front of the house with the puppy in his arms. He did not run away, he just stood there gazing at me wide-eyed and pressing the puppy to his breast with all his might.

The fall had split my breeches at the knees and lacerated my hands. The twisted motorcycle lay on the heap of cobblestones with its back wheel whirling. I sat down on a stone. My knees were trembling. I spit the dirt out of my mouth. One thought formed vaguely in my mind: I might have been killed ... now ... with the war over. Yakovenko's scouts came running towards me. They took me to their house in pieces: first me, then my cap which one of the boys had found on the other side of the road.

While they pulled off my boots Yakovenko stood beside me with a glass of vodka in his hand.

"Drink it," he said. "No bones broken? Feel his bones, fellows. His skull, too. Does it hurt? Not here, either? You seem to be all right. No reason why you shouldn't drink it."

When the others had gone he sat down beside me on the bed. Only then did I notice how drawn and white he looked, and his breath smelt of vodka.

"I've been to see a concentration camp," he said. "It turns out there'd been a concentration camp here. Three kilometres away. I rode over last night."

He drew a hand across his forehead.

I knew that his father, commissar of a tank battalion, had been lost near Kiev in 1941. Two years later a man came to see his mother and told her he had been in a concentration camp with her husband. The man had escaped and run away from Germany, but Yakovenko's father had been too weak to make the attempt. He had asked the man to tell his family he was still alive. Yakovenko's mother had written him of this, asking him if he thought she dared believe it, dared hope.

Ever since then Yakovenko had cherished the secret hope of finding out something about his father when he got to Germany. The urge grew as the end of the war drew near.

Whenever we met people in striped suits, indicating that they had been freed from concentration camps, he would question them excitedly.

Last night he had seen a concentration camp for the first time. He himself had walked the blood-soaked path from the camp gate to the crematorium, which hundreds of thousands of victims had trod before him. And he knew that if his father's footsteps were among all those others, no one would ever tell him about it.

"I saw a ditch there. Behind the crematorium." He suddenly went even whiter. "Flies swarmed above it. Bluebottles. I didn't understand at first. Then it came to me in a wave of horror. It was the smell, I guess. The ditch was full of human fat. When the bodies were burnt, the fat ran into the ditch."

He rocked back and forth, gripping his knees with his hands.

"There's only one hope: my father was a commissar, and they didn't take commissars prisoner. And then that man said the name was Yakovlev. Not Yakovenko, but Yakovlev. It may not have been my father at all. Mother never saw the man again."

What could I say to him? I assured him that it could easily have been a mistake, that no doubt it was, that I had heard of lots of similar cases. For instance, when our regiment fought its way out of enemy encirclement...

Yakovenko sat there rocking, his eyes closed, the skin paper-white on his cheek-bones, sweat beading his flushed temples and forehead.

That night I woke up and saw an enormous shadow on the ceiling—shoulders reaching from wall to wall and the head bowed between them. Yakovenko was sitting at the table with his head in his hands, his face lighted by two candles burning in a saucer. Seeing that I had waked up, he shuffled over in his bedroom slippers, still in his breeches and unbelted tunic, and set down on the edge of my bed.

"They told me there that the ashes—the ashes of human beings—were carted away. They fertilised the fields with them...."

He rubbed his throat. His lips were dry and his voice hoarse.

"I went back. 'Did you know?' I asked them. *'Nein, nein,'* they said. 'Then come and look,' I said." His neck was red and distended. "They wouldn't come. They didn't want to know. Understand? People were burnt next door to them, their fields were fertilised with the ashes, and they go on eating the corn. I can't bear the sight of them."

He got up, the candles sputtered, the shadow of his arm darted up the wall to the shelf. He took a statuette off it and held it with the trade-mark to the light. "See this?" The trade-mark was French. In the quivering light various objects that were strikingly unlike looked down from the shelves at us. They had been taken from people's homes, and their original owners had probably been killed, had never seen one another before, spoke different tongues. Out in the barnyard were cows brought from Holland, pigs from Denmark. And a few kilometres away was the concentration camp. Perhaps it was there that the people to whom these things had once belonged were killed.

The next day the sight of the fields filled me with revulsion. Fertilised with human ashes. I could not bring myself to believe it, yet I could not drive the thought out of my mind.

We were going down-hill, and the scout held in the horses by pulling on the reins. I was lying on some straw, the sun was shining, and the labouring horses gave off the smell of sweat. Through chinks in the side of the cart I could see the countryside slipping past. Young corn, powdered with dust, rose out of the ash-grey soil. The swelling grains glistened in the sunlight. I could not bear the sight of that earth and that corn.

Pure white clouds were floating across the idyllic blue sky of Germany. Their shadows crept over the earth. Everything was quiet and peaceful. Yet how many people in this new world of peace were to resurrect their dead only to bury them again, while a fortunate few would welcome home those they had thought dead.

We rode down the village street and turned into my yard, then the scout who had driven me over hurried back to join his fellows. I made for the house. None of my boys were about and the farmer and his wife slipped into the barn as soon as they saw me. I could hear them whispering to each other and from time to time I saw them glance at me excitedly. Something had happened in my absence.

I sat down on a bench under a window with my bruised leg outstretched and took out a cigarette. But I was wearing Yakovenko's breeches and had forgotten to put my lighter in the pocket. The farmer came towards me. I licked my finger and pressed down a scratch on my belt.

The farmer was even more polite than usual. Seeing the unlighted cigarette between my fingers he instantly but unhurriedly, like an old friend, offered me a light. Then he sat down beside me with the air of one man chumming with another.

While lighting my cigarette I had noticed the farmer's wife dart into the pig pen. There was an expression of anger on her face, yet she looked cowed and as if ready to humble herself. Her husband had not noticed this. He sat smoking his pipe serenely while the sun shone down on us both where we sat on the bench under the window. Presently his son came over to us with a notebook and pencil in hand. He stopped in front of me and held up the notebook like sheet-music, clearing his throat as if about to sing. I looked up at him. When he began to speak he dropped his shoulders and stretched out his neck. He spoke so fast that I could catch only separate words, but these were repeated over and over. It seems that one of my scouts had shot a pig. "*Erschoss, erschoss!* " he kept saying, showing how it had been done.

Margoslin crossed the yard in a shiny new leather jacket. His slightly rolling gait showed that he was going out to reconnoitre and was filled with a sense of his own importance. The boy did not notice him. He said, his face blotched with excitement:

"It was a fine pig. It weighed thirty kilograms and was still growing. Thirty kilograms of first-class pork, each kilogram worth..."

Kosten was one of the words he kept repeating. I remembered it from childhood, when I had learned the little rhyme:

> *Guten Tag, Frau Maier,*
> *Was kosten die Eier?*
> *Acht Pfennig. Acht Pfennig?*
> *Das ist so teuer!*

Good old Frau Maier! In this war there was a General Maier, a hangman and sadist.

Leaning on his hands, his feet drawn under the bench, the farmer rocked back and forth. His bony shoulders were hunched, his head drawn in. He said not a word, merely listened with eyes closed and jiggled his smoking pipe between his teeth. I glanced at the hands gripping the edge of the bench. They were a labourer's hands, big and rough, and there was dirt in the creases and around the nails. Dirt? Perhaps ashes?

The farmer sat jiggling his pipe while his son went over and over the calculations the whole family had made. It was important that I see they were not cheating me, that they were asking a very modest price for such good pork. The boy was white about the nostrils and his movements were nervous. Jerking the notebook up to his eyes, he read the name of the scout who had killed the pig. "*Soldat* Makarushka." Then he looked at me. I did not at first realise who this "*Soldat* Makarushka" was, the name sounded so foreign in his pronunciation. It was, of course, no other than our Makarushka, the youngest of our scouts.

One day he had come to us, a barefooted ragamuffin whose eyes said he was desperately hungry, and asked us to take him with us. Nobody in the village knew him, he had arrived there in the spring, before the snow had melted, barefooted even then and with blue goose flesh showing through the holes in his trousers. The village women had looked upon him as a half-wit and had fed him from time to time. His reputation as a half-wit had kept him from being sent to Germany.

He immediately felt at home among the scouts, but for a long time called us "The Russians", as the Germans and the people in occupied regions called our army. He was quiet and harmless and, after he had been properly fed, exceedingly strong. I don't remember who first christened him "Makarushka", but the name suited him, shy strong fellow that he was, and nobody remembered his real name. Once when we were on duty together at our look-out post, he told me about himself. He came from a partisan village. Almost all the men, including his father, had taken to the woods, but for some reason the Germans did not immediately punish their families. Then one night there was a round-up. All the inhabitants were driven into the school, the doors were locked and the building set fire to. Those who tried to escape by jumping out of the windows were shot. That is how his mother was killed. In spite of the unexpectedness of the round-up, some mothers had time to hide their children. Some of the population, too, managed to hide. They were searched for in cellars and outhouses and those who were found were taken at night to be shot. Makarushka carried his two-year-old sister in his arms. They were lined up on the edge of a gully. Makarushka could not forgive himself for holding his sister in his arms.

"If I had put her down they might not have noticed her, she was so little and it was dark. But she was scared and hung on to me so tight I couldn't tear her loose. Dug her fingernails into me. Here." He pointed to his neck.

As long as he lives, I thought to myself, he will feel the nails of the two-year-old child whose tiny body was aware of the presence of death.

"It was still growing," the farmer's boy had said about the shot pig that weighed thirty kilograms. It was his pig and nobody had a right to shoot it. And the farmer, sitting on the bench in his felt slippers and jiggling his pipe between his teeth, was pleased with his son.

I glanced up at the boy. He was fourteen years old, his voice was changing, it cracked when he spoke. Makarushka had been just the same age when the Germans led him away with his sister in his arms to be shot, when he crawled out of the common grave and escaped to the woods where, like a wild beast, he found herbs to heal his wounds.

The fourteen-year-old farm boy had not learned the cost of war, but he knew very well the cost of a kilogram of pork. And here he was, standing in front of me with the bill in his hand, confident of his right to present it to me.

That evening we had pork for dinner. The farmer and his wife went away as usual, very much displeased with us. They avoided our eyes and the woman's face was inflamed from crying. The son remained at home and went about his usual tasks.

The sun went down behind the well-worked fields, its rays pierced by the pointed roofs. The bright glow of sunset quivered in the transparent air outside, but the room was already in shadow.

I heard the gate click and someone with an unfamiliar shuffling gait come in. From where I sat I could see only a corner of the yard. Presently a man entered my field of vision. He looked emaciated and dragged his feet after him, but made his way through the yard with an assurance that made me think he must have been here before. Going over to the pig pen, he stood gazing into its dark depth. He did not see the farmer's son watching him from behind the wood pile. At one moment the boy was about to shout at him, but with a sudden change of expression, as if he had recognised the man, he repressed the impulse.

Now I heard footsteps coming up the porch. The window curtain cut off a view of the upper part of his body; I saw only his legs in mended shoes. Apparently it was painful for him to step on his right foot for he quickly transferred his weight to the left, dragging the right one after him.

For some time I heard his heavy breathing while he fumbled with the handle of the door. Finally the door was opened and he stepped inside. He was an old man in faded clothes of no definite colour and so ill-fitting that they could not have been made for him. The way in which he looked round the room made me feel again that he had been here before.

"How do you do," I said from out of the shadows.

He started and looked at me with an odd expression. It was not fear. When he had taken me in, he returned my greeting, pulled off the round cap issued to prisoners in concentration camps, and asked me something in Polish. I shrugged my shoulders. He made a sweeping gesture and again asked his question in Polish and German. He was looking for the farmer. I said he was living here but had gone away for the night. I was struck by the anxiety with which he awaited my answer.

"*Hier*," he repeated with relief, then thanked me in Polish.

I offered him a heavy oaken chair and when he sat down I was aware of the knobs of his knees sticking out. Now that I had a closer view of him, I saw he was not an old man at all, but one who had endured much suffering. There were hollows at his temples and his face was drawn and bloodless. I had just been given a plate of fried pork and potatoes, hot and savoury, and I could see that he was tantalised by the smell. His eyes kept turning to the plate. Perhaps I was in too much of a hurry to offer it to him, for he recoiled.

"*Nein, nein*," he said, shaking his head vigorously.

"Do have some," I insisted. "They'll bring me some more."

He pushed the plate away with a feeble hand. I no longer insisted, but I did not understand. Somewhat embarrassed, I poured him out a glass of wine. He thanked me with a look and eagerly drank it down, the hollows at his temples inflating and deflating as he swallowed, the hand holding the glass showing almost naked cords at the wrist with bones fanning out to the fingers. It was dreadful to watch his exposed Adam's apple shifting up and down.

Before he finished he was seized by a racking fit of coughing, which left him blue in the face, breathless, with streaming eyes and shaking hands.

"Did you once live here?" I asked, sensing that he was ashamed of being so ill. "Have you been in this house before?"

He shook his head.

"A Pole," he said, explaining his presence here as one who had been forcefully driven out of his native land.

"I wanted to see him." He tapped on the table with his fingers for a moment before he glanced up at me.

"My wife lived here. There." He pointed through the window at the barn. It cost him an effort to lift his hand. "I had a son here, too." Again he looked at me. "When he was born and let out a cry my wife put her hand over his mouth so that no one should hear. But only the dead can be hidden. One day when she was nursing the child the German came in. He didn't say a word, just stood and watched her. She could not explain to me how he watched her, but she trembled all over and cried when she told me about it. What could I do? I was working for a German in the next village. What could I do? I was helpless."

His blue lips moved slowly, as if numb with cold. The faint light coming through the window was reflected glassily in his fixed eyes whose gaze was turned inward.

"Now I know how he watched her. He was feeding her so that she could work for him and the baby was sucking her strength. After that she always hid the child before going out to the fields. She said she could hear him crying when she was away, but I think this cry was always in her ears. Once she was so sure she heard it she came running back. The German was in the yard harnessing his horses to go visiting. The entrance to the pig pen was propped by a board. She rushed to it: she had a premonition. When she pushed the swarming pigs away, there lay our child. She could never see anything else after that. When she went entirely insane the German took her up the hill to the camp. To the crematorium. She did not understand, and that was fortunate."

My scouts were singing softly out in the yard while he told me the story in a mixture of German and Polish. I could hardly make out his face in the twilight—only the deep shadows formed by his sunken cheeks, and the glint of his deep-set eyes.

"I was in the camp for a year and a half, and I lived through it so that I could come back here," he said.

I remembered the look on the German boy's face as he watched him from behind the wood pile. I went to the window and called Margoslin. The song broke off suddenly and I could hear the squeak of an approaching leather jacket. Margoslin stopped and lifted his head: he was a short man.

"Bring the boy here," I said.

25*

For almost ten minutes I heard voices and footsteps in the yard, behind the sheds, and in the neighbourhood of the house. By this time the darkness in the room was relieved only by the grey patches of the windows and a looking-glass hanging in a dark corner. As a matter of precaution I asked the Pole if he knew the village where the farmer and his wife had gone and if he could take us there. Then we sat waiting in silence. At last Margoslin came in. Just as I expected, he said the boy was nowhere to be found.

The four of us—the Pole, Margoslin, Makarushka and I—made our way through the woods. The upper half of the moon rose above the horizon, the lower half apparently caught on the ragged hills. The moon was enormous and copper-coloured and the hills were pitch black. When at last it wrenched free it quickly climbed the sky to the right of us, diminishing as it rose. It had soared high, transforming the world with its white light, when we first saw the village—the bluish walls of the houses, the wet shine of the steep tiled roofs, the coloured glass in the dark windows. We chose a back way. From the barnyards came the warm stagnant smell of mangers and manure; from down below, where a black stream glistened among stones, came the smell of dampness. Stone steps wet with dew led down to the stream.

Two of us kept watch over the house and barn while the other two went softly into the silent yard which, in the moonlight, seemed to have been swept clean. We climbed a wooden ladder into the hay loft. The dog barked until it was hoarse, clanking and pulling at its chain, but no lights appeared in the windows of the house and no doors were opened.

Two white feather mattresses gleamed on the straw in the darkness. They still held the imprint of bodies. We directed our pocket torches into every corner of the loft, the barn, the house, the yard, but we did not find those whom we sought. Nor did we find them the next day. Later we learned they had run away. All three of them. They had taken the road leading West.

The neighbours told us they were a bad lot.

"Why didn't you tell us that before?" we asked.

They shrugged their shoulders.

"We were afraid," they said.

Magda was the only one who said nothing about them, neither good nor bad. In general she said nothing. For several more days she came as usual early in the morning, fed the pigs, swept the yard, milked the cows, performed all the duties that mechanically bound her to life. All the pails and milk cans were filled with milk that gradually went sour.

No doubt the farmer's family shudders at the remembrance of those few May days. The boy was only fourteen years old at the time and his voice was changing. Now his voice has become deep and strong, and in this deep strong voice he and his like are declaring their grievances.

On a May morning soon after the cessation of hostilities a slender lad of fourteen stood in front of me with a bill in his hand. I can see him to this day—his nostrils white, his face blotched with excitement. He did not care what his country had done, he did not want to know; he was interested only in being paid for the pig. And never for a moment did he doubt his right to present his bill.

Translated by Margaret Wettlin

Mikhail Sholokhov
(1905-1984)

In the literary biography of Mikhail Sholokhov, one of the greatest writers of this century and winner of the Nobel Prize, his story, *The Fate of a Man,* published in this edition, is one of its most stirring pages. In July 1941, the author of *Quiet Flows the Don* and *Virgin Soil Upturned* volunteered for the front. During the next four years, war correspondent Sholokhov took part in, and was a witness to many battles. The heroic battle on the Volga unfolded before his eyes. The war did not spare the writer's home. Sholokhov's mother was killed by a Nazi bomb and his house in the Cossack village of Veshenskaya was burnt. The war left an unhealable wound in the writer's heart, which probably explains why readers are so profoundly impressed by his works *Science of Hatred, The Fate of a Man*, and *They Fought for Their Country,* in which the writer describes the terrible sufferings during the Nazi invasion and the unprecedented staunchness of the Soviet people.

The Fate of a Man

For Yevgenia Grigoriyevna Levitskaya,
member of the CPSU since 1903

There was a rare drive and swiftness in the spring that came to the upper reaches of the Don in the first year after the war. At the end of March, warm winds blew from the shores of the Azov Sea and in two days the sandy left bank of the river was bare; in the steppe, the snow-choked gullies and ravines swelled, the streams burst the ice and flooded madly, and the roads became almost completely impassable.

At this unfavourable time of the year it so happened that I had to make a journey to the village of Bukanovskaya. The distance was not great—only about sixty kilometres—but it turned out to be hard going. My friend and I set out before sunrise. The pair of well-fed horses strained at the traces and could scarcely pull the heavy wagon. The wheels sank axle-deep into the damp mush of sand mixed with snow and ice and in an hour creamy-white flecks of foam appeared on the horses' flanks and thighs and under the narrow breech bands, and the fresh morning air was invaded by a sharp, intoxicating smell of sweat and warm harness lavishly smeared with tar.

Where the going was particularly heavy for the horses we got out and walked. It was hard to walk through the slushy snow, which squelched under our boots, but the roadside was still coated with a glittering crust of ice, and there it was even harder. It took us about six hours to do the thirty kilometres as far as the ford over the River Yelanka.

At the village of Mokhovsky the little river, almost dry in summer, had now spread itself over a full kilometre of marshy water meadows, overgrown with alders. We had to make the crossing in a leaky flat-bottomed boat that could not take more than three people at the most. We sent the wagon and horses home. In a collective-farm shed on the other side an old and battered jeep that had been standing there most of the winter was awaiting us. The driver and I, with some misgivings, climbed into the unsteady little craft. My friend stayed behind on the bank with our belongings. We had scarcely pushed off when little fountains of water came spouting up through the rotten planks. We plugged them with anything we could lay hands on and kept bailing until we reached the other side. It took us an hour to reach the far bank of the river. The driver fetched the jeep from the village and went back to the boat.

"If this perishing old tub doesn't fall to bits in the water," he said, picking up an oar, "I'll be back with your friend in a couple of hours. At the earliest."

The village lay a good distance from the river, and down by the water there was the kind of stillness that falls on deserted places only late in autumn or at the very beginning of spring. The air over the water was damp and bitter with the smell of rotting alders, but from the distant steppes bathing in a lilac haze of mist a light breeze brought the eternally young, barely perceptible aroma of earth that has not long been liberated from the snow.

Not far away, on the sand at the water's edge, lay a broken wattle fence. I sat down on it to have a smoke but, when I put my hand in my jacket pocket, I discovered to my dismay that the packet of cigarettes I had been carrying there was soaked. On the way across a wave had slapped over the side of the wallowing boat and splashed me to the waist in muddy water. There had been no time to think of my cigarettes, for I had to drop my oar and start bailing as fast as I could to save us from sinking, but now, vexed at my own carelessness, I drew the sodden packet gingerly out of my pocket, got down on my haunches and began laying out the moist brownish cigarettes one by one on the fence.

It was noon. The sun shone as hot as in May. I hoped the cigarettes would soon dry. It was so hot that I began to regret having put on my quilted army trousers and jacket for the journey. It was the first really warm day of the year. But it was good to sit there alone, abandoning myself completely to the stillness and solitude, to take off my old army cap and let the breeze dry my hair after the heavy work of rowing, and to stare idly at the white big-breasted clouds floating in the faded blue.

Presently I noticed a man come out on the road from behind the end cottages of the village. He was leading a little boy by the hand; about five or six years old he was, I reckoned, not more. They tramped wearily towards the ford, but, on reaching the jeep, turned and came in my direction. The man, tall and rather stooped, came right up to me and said in a deep husky voice:

"Hullo, mate."

"Hullo." I shook the big rough hand he offered me.

The man bent down to the little boy and said: "Say hullo to uncle, son. Looks as if he's another driver like your dad. Only you and I used to drive a lorry, didn't we, and he goes about in that little car over there."

Looking straight at me with eyes that were as bright and clear as the sky, and smiling a little, the boy boldly held out a pink cold hand. I shook it gently and asked: "Feeling chilly, old man? Why's your hand so cold on a hot day like this?"

With a touching childish trustfulness the boy pressed against my knees and lifted his little flaxen eyebrows in surprise.

"But I'm not an old man, uncle. I'm only a boy, and I'm not chilly either. My hands are cold because I've been making snowballs."

Taking the half-empty rucksack off his back, the father sat down heavily beside me and said: "This passenger of mine is a regular young nuisance, he is. He's made me tired as well as himself. If you take a long stride he breaks into a trot; just you try keeping in step with a footslogger like him. Where I could take one pace, I have to take three instead, and so we go on, like a horse and a tortoise. And you need eyes in the back of your head to know what he's doing. As soon as you turn your back, he's off paddling in a puddle or breaking off an icicle and sucking it like a lollipop. No, it's no job for a man to be travelling with someone like him, not on foot anyway." He was silent for a while, then asked: "And what about you, mate? Waiting for your chief?"

I didn't want to tell him I was not a driver. I answered:

"Looks as if I'll have to."

"Is he coming over from the other side?"

"He will be."

"Do you know if the boat will be here soon?"

"In about two hours."

"That's quite a long time. Well, let's take it easy. I'm in no hurry. Just saw you as I was walking past, so I thought to myself there's one of us, drivers, enjoying a spot of sunshine. I'll go over and have a smoke with him, I thought. No fun in smoking alone, any more than in dying alone. You're doing well, I see, smoking cigarettes. Got them wet, eh? Well, mate, wet tobacco's like a doctored horse, neither of them any good. Let's have a go at my old shag instead."

He pulled a worn silk pouch out of the pocket of his thin khaki trousers, and as he unrolled it, I noticed the words embroidered on the corner: "To one of our dear soldiers, from a pupil of Lebedyan-skaya Secondary School."

We smoked the strong home-grown tobacco and for a long time neither of us spoke. I was going to ask him where he was making for with the boy, and what brought him out on such bad roads, but he got his question in first:

"At it all through the war, were you?"

"Nearly all of it."

"Frontline?"

"Yes."

"Well, I had a bellyful of trouble out there too, mate. More than enough of it."

He rested his big dark hands on his knees and let his shoulders droop. When I glanced at him sideways I felt strangely disturbed. Have you ever seen eyes that look as if they have been sprinkled with ash, eyes filled with such unabating pain and sadness that it is hard to look into them? This chance acquaintance of mine had eyes like that.

He broke a dry twisted twig out of the fence and for a minute traced a curious pattern in the sand with it, then he spoke:

"Sometimes I can't sleep at night, I just stare into the darkness and I think: 'What did you do it for, life? Why did you maim me like this? Why did you punish me so?' And I get no answer, either in darkness, or when the sun's shining bright... No, I get no answer, and I'll never get one! "

He checked himself, nudged his little son affectionately and said: "Go on, laddie, go and play down by the water, there's always something for little boys to do by a big river. Only mind you don't get your feet wet."

While we had been smoking together in silence, I had taken a quick look at father and son and one thing about them had struck me as odd. The boy was dressed plainly but in good stout clothes. The way the long-skirted little coat with its soft lining of worn beaver lamb fitted him, the way his tiny boots had been made to fit snugly over the woollen socks, the very neat darn that joined an old tear on the sleeve of the coat, all these things spoke of a woman's hand, the skilful hand of a mother. But the father's appearance was quite different. His quilted jacket was scorched in several places and roughly darned, the patch on his worn khaki trousers was not sewn on properly, but was tacked on with big, mannish stitches; he was wearing an almost new pair of army boots, but his thick woolen socks were full of holes. They had never known the touch of a woman's hand. Either he's a widower, I decided, or there's something wrong between him and his wife.

He watched his son run down to the water, then coughed and again began to speak, and I listened with all my attention.

"To start with, my life was just ordinary. I'm from the Voronezh Province, born there in 1900. During the Civil War I was in the Red Army, in Kikvidze's division. In the famine of 'twenty-two I struck out for the Kuban and worked like an ox for the kulaks, wouldn't be alive today if I hadn't. But my whole family back home, father, mother and sister, starved to death. So I was left all alone. As for relatives anywhere, I hadn't got a single one, not a soul. Well, after a year I came back form the Kuban, sold up my home and went to Voronezh. First I worked as a carpenter, then I went to a factory and learned to be a fitter. And soon I married. My wife had been brought up in a children's home. She was an orphan. Yes, I got a good woman there! Good-tempered, cheerful, always anxious to please. And smart she was, too—no comparison with me. She had known what real trouble was since she was a kid. I dare say that had an effect on her character. Just looking at her from the side, as you might say, she wasn't all that striking, but, you see, I wasn't looking at her from the side. I was looking straight at her. And for me there was no more beautiful woman in the whole world, and there never will be.

"I'd come home from work tired, and bad-tempered as hell sometimes. But no, she'd never fling your rudeness back at you. She'd be so gentle and quiet, couldn't do enough for you, always trying to make you something nice to eat, even when there wasn't enough to go round. It made my heart lighter just to look at her. After a while I'd put my arm round her and say: 'I'm sorry, Irina dear. I was damn rude to you. I had a rotten day at work today.' And again there'd be peace between us, and my mind would be at rest. And you know what that means for your work, mate? In the morning I'd be out of bed like a shot and off to the factory, and any job I laid hands on would go like clockwork. That's what it means to have a real clever girl for a wife.

"Sometimes I'd have a drink with the boys on pay-day. And sometimes, the scissor-legged way I staggered home afterwards, it must have been frightening to watch. The main street wasn't wide enough for me, let alone the side streets. In those days I was tough and strong and I could hold a lot of drink, and I always got home on my own. But sometimes the last stretch would be in bottom gear, you know. I'd finish it on my hands and knees. But again I'd never get a word of reproach, no scolding, no shouting. My Irina, she'd just laugh at me, and she did that careful like, so that even drunk as I was I wouldn't take it wrong. She'd pull my boots off and whisper: 'You'd better lie next to the wall tonight, Andrei, or you might fall out of bed in your sleep.' And I'd just flop down like a sack of oats and everything would go swimming round in front of me. And as I dropped off to sleep, I'd feel her stroking my head softly and whispering kind words, and I knew she felt sorry for me.

"In the morning she'd get me up about two hours before work to give me time to come round. She knew I wouldn't eat anything after being drunk, so she'd get me a pickled cucumber or something like that, and pour me out a good glass of vodka—a hair of the dog, you know. 'Here you are, Andrei, but don't do it any more, dear.' How could a man let someone down who put such trust in him? I'd drink it up, thank her without words, just with a look and a kiss, and go off to work like a lamb. But if she'd said a word to cross me when I was drunk, if she'd started snapping at me, I'd have come home drunk again, believe me. That's what happens in some families, where the wife's a fool. I've seen plenty of it and I know.

"Well, soon the children started arriving. First there was a little boy, then two girls. And that was when I broke away from my mates. I started taking all my pay home to the wife; we had a fair-sized family by then, and I couldn't afford to drink any more. On my day off I'd have just a glass of beer and let it go at that.

"In 'twenty-nine I got interested in motors, I learned the job and started driving a lorry. And when I got into the way of it I didn't want to go back to the factory. Driving seemed to be more fun. And so I lived for ten years without noticing how the time went by. It was like a dream. But what's ten years? Ask any man over forty if he's noticed how the years have been slipping by. You'll find he hasn't noticed a damned thing! The past is like that distant steppe way out there in the haze. This morning I was crossing it and it was clear all round, but now I've covered twenty kilometres there's a haze over it, and you can't tell the trees from the grass, the ploughland from the meadow.

"Those ten years I worked day and night. I earned good money and we lived no worse than other folk. And the children were a joy to us. All three did well at school, and the eldest, Anatoly, turned out to be so bright at mathematics that he even got his name in one of the Moscow papers. Where he inherited this great gift from, I couldn't tell you, mate. But it was certainly flattering, and I was proud of him; mighty proud I was!

"In ten years we saved up a bit of money and before the war we built ourselves a little cottage with two rooms, a storeroom and a covered porch. Irina bought a couple of goats. What more did we want? There was milk for the children's porridge, we had a roof over our heads, clothes on our backs, shoes on our feet, so everything was all right. The only thing was the site, it wasn't a very good place to build. The plot of land I got was not far from an aircraft factory. If my cottage had been somewhere else, my life might have turned out different.

"And then it came—war. The next day I had my call-up papers, and the day after it was 'Report to the station'. All my four saw me off together: Irina, Anatoly, and my daughters, Nastenka and Olyushka. The kids took it well, though the girls couldn't keep back a tear or two. Anatoly just shivered a bit as if he was cold; he was getting on for seventeen by that time. But my Irina... I'd never seen anything like it in all the seventeen years we'd lived together. My shirt and shoulder had stayed wet all night with her tears, and in the morning she was at it again. We got to the station and I felt so sorry for her I couldn't look her in the face. Her lips were all swollen, her hair was poking out from under her shawl, and her eyes were dull and staring, like someone's who's out of his mind. The officers gave the order to get aboard but she flung herself on my chest, and clasped her hands round my neck. She was shaking all over, like a tree that's being chopped down. The children tried to talk her round, and so did I, but nothing helped. Other women chatted to their husbands and sons, but mine clung to me like a leaf to a branch, and just trembled all the time, and couldn't say a word. 'Take a grip on yourself, Irina dear,' I said. 'Say something to me before I go, at least.' And this is what she said, with a sob between every word: 'Andrei ... my darling ... we'll never ... never see each other again ... in this world...'

"There was I with my heart bursting with pity for her, and she says a thing like that to me. She ought to have understood it wasn't easy for me to part with her. I wasn't going off to a party either. And I lost my temper! I pulled her hands apart and gave her a push. It seemed only a gentle push to me, but I was strong as an ox and she staggered back about three paces, then came towards me again with little steps, arms outstretched and I shouted at her: 'Is that the way to say good-bye? Why do you want to bury me before I'm dead?! ' But then I took her in my arms again because I could see she was in a bad way."

He broke off suddenly and in the silence that followed I heard a faint choking sound. His emotion communicated itself to me. I glanced sideways at him but did not see a single tear in those dead, ashy eyes of his. He sat with his head drooping dejectedly. The big hands hanging limply at his sides were shaking slightly; his chin trembled, and so did those firm lips.

"Don't let it get you down, friend, don't think of it," I said quietly, but he seemed not to hear me. Overcoming his emotion with a great effort, he said suddenly in a hoarse, strangely altered voice:

"Till my dying day, till the last hour of my life I'll never forgive myself for pushing her away like that! "

He fell silent again and for a long time. He tried to roll a cigarette, but the strip of newspaper came apart in his fingers and the tobacco spilled on to his knees. In the end he managed to make a clumsy roll of paper and tobacco, took a few hungry pulls at it, then, clearing his throat, went on:

"I tore myself away from Irina, then took her face in my hands and kissed her. Her lips were like ice. I said good-bye to the kids and ran to the carriage, managed to jump on the steps as it was moving. The train started off very slow, and it took me past my family again. I could see my poor little orphaned kids bunched together, waving their hands and trying to smile, but not managing it. And Irina had her hands clasped to her breast; her lips were white as chalk, and she was whispering something, and staring straight at me, and her body was all bent forward as if she was trying to walk against a strong wind... And that's how I'll see her in my memory for the rest of my life—her hands clasped to her breast, those white lips, and her eyes wide open and full of tears. That's mostly how I see her in my dreams too. Why did I push her away like that? Even now, when I remember it, it's like a blunt knife twisting in my heart.

"We were drafted to our units at Belaya Tserkov, in the Ukraine. I was given a three-tonner, and that's what I went to the front in. Well, there's no point in telling you about the war, you saw it yourself and you know what it was like to start with. I got a lot of letters from home, but didn't write much myself. Just now and then I'd write that everything was all right and we were doing a bit of fighting. We may be retreating at present, I'd say, but it won't be long before we gather our strength and give the Fritzes something to think about. And what else could you write? Those were grim times and you didn't feel like writing. And I must say I was never much of a one for harping on a pitiful note. I couldn't stick the sight of those slobbering types that wrote to their wives and girlfriends every day for no reason at all, just to rub their snot over the paper—oh, it's such a hard life, oh, I might get killed! And so he goes on, the son-of-a-bitch, complaining and looking for sympathy, blubbering away, and he can't understand that those poor women and kids are having just as bad a time of it back home as we are. Why, they were carrying the whole country on their shoulders. And what shoulders our women and children must have had not to give in under a weight like that! But they didn't give in, they stuck it out! And then one of those bellyachers writes his pitiful letter and that just knocks a working woman off her feet. After a letter like that, the poor thing won't know what to do with herself or how to face up to her work. No! That's what a man's for, that's what you're a soldier for—to put up with everything, if need be. But if you've got more woman than man in you, then go and put on a frilled skirt to puff out your skinny arse, so you can look like a woman, at least from behind, and go and weed the beet, or milk the cows, because your kind aren't needed at the front. The stink's bad enough there without you!

"But I didn't get even a year's fighting done. I was wounded twice, but only slightly both times, once in the arm, the second time in the leg. The first was a bullet from an aircraft, the second a chunk of shrapnel. The Germans holed my lorry, top and sides, but I was lucky, mate, at first. Yes, I was lucky all the time until I was real unlucky... I got taken prisoner at Lozovenki in the May of 'forty-two. It was an awkward set-up. The Germans were attacking hard and one of our 122 mm howitzer batteries had nearly run out of ammo. We loaded up my lorry chockful of shells. I worked on the job myself till my shirt was sticking to my back. We had to get a move on, because they were closing in on us; on the left we could hear the rumble of tanks, and firing on the right and in front, and things didn't look too healthy.

"'Can you get through, Sokolov?' asks the commander of our company. He need never have asked. Was I going to sit twiddling my thumbs while my mates got killed? 'What are you talking about! ' I told him. 'I've got to get through, and that's that.' 'Get cracking then,' he says, 'and step on it! '

"And step on it I did. Never driven like that before in my life! I knew I wasn't carrying a load of spuds, I knew I had to be careful with the stuff I'd got aboard, but how could I be, when the lads were fighting out there empty-handed, when the whole road was under artillery fire. I did about six kilometres and got pretty near the place. I'd have to turn off the road to get to the hollow where the battery was stationed, and then what did I see? Strike me, if it wasn't our infantry running back across the field on both sides of the road with shells bursting among them. What was I to do? I couldn't turn back, could I? So I gave her all she'd got. There was only about a kilometre to go to the battery. I had already turned off the road, but I never reached them, mate. Must have been a long-range gun landed a heavy one near the lorry. I never heard the bang nor anything, just something burst inside my head, and I don't remember any more. How I stayed alive, and how long I lay there by the ditch, I've got no idea. I opened my eyes, but I couldn't get up; my head kept jerking and I was shaking as if I had a fever. Everything seemed dark, something was scraping and grinding in my left shoulder, and my body ached all over as if somebody had been lamming into me for two days running with anything he could lay hands on. I squirmed about on my belly for a long time, and finally I managed to get up. But still I couldn't tell where I was, nor what had happened to me. My memory was clean gone. But I was scared to lie down. I was scared I'd never get up again, so I just stood there swaying from side to side like a poplar in a gale.

"When I came to and had a look round, my heart felt as if someone had got a pair of pliers round it. The shells I'd been carrying were lying about all round me. Not far away was my lorry, all buckled up, with its wheels in the air. And the fighting? The fighting was going on behind me. Yes, behind me!

"When I realised that, and I'm not ashamed to say it, my legs just caved in under me and I fell as if I'd been pole-axed, because I realised I was cut off behind the enemy lines, or to put it plainly, I was already a prisoner of the Nazis. That's war for you.

"No, it is not an easy thing to take in, mate, it's not easy to understand the fact that you're a prisoner through no fault of your own. And it takes some explaining to a fellow who's never experienced it himself just what that thing means.

"So I lay there and soon I heard the tanks rumbling. Four medium German tanks went by me at full speed in the direction I'd come from. What do you think that felt like? Then came the tractors hauling the guns, and a mobile kitchen, then the infantry, not many of them, not more than a company all told. I'd squint up at them out of the corner of my eye and then I'd press my face into the earth again; it made me sick to look at them, sicker than I can say.

"When I thought they'd all gone past, I lifted my head, and there were six submachine-gunners marching along about a hundred paces away. And as I looked, they turned off the road and came straight towards me, all six of them, without saying a word. Well, I thought, this is it. So I got into a sitting position—I didn't want to die lying down—and then I stood up. One of them stopped a few paces away from me and jerked his gun off his shoulder. And it's funny how a man's made, but at that moment I didn't feel any panic, not even a shiver in my heart. I just looked at him and thought: 'It's going to be a short burst. I wonder where he'll place it? At my head or across my chest?' As if it mattered a damn to me what part of my body he made his holes in.

"Young fellow he was, pretty well built, dark-haired, but his lips were thin as thread, and his eyes had a nasty glint in them. That one won't think twice about shooting me down, I thought. And sure enough, up goes his gun. I looked him straight in the eye and didn't say anything. But another one, a corporal or something, he was older,

almost elderly to look at—shouted something, then pushed the other
fellow aside and came up to me. He babbled something in his own
language and bent my right elbow. Feeling my biceps he was.
'O-o-oh! ' he said, and pointed along the road to where the sun was
setting, as much as to say: 'Off you go, you mule, and work for our
Reich.' Thrifty type he was, the son-of-a-bitch!

"But the dark-haired one had got his eye on my boots and they
looked a good sound pair. He signed to me to take them off. I sat
down on the ground, took off my boots and handed them to him.
Fair snatched them out of my hands, he did. So I unwound my footcloths, and held them out to him, too, looking up at him from the
ground. He shouted and swore, and up went his gun again. But the
others just roared with laughter. Then they marched off. The dark-
haired one looked round at me two or three times before he got to
the road, and his eyes glittered like a wolf-cub's with fury. Anyone
would think I'd taken his boots instead of him taking mine.

"Well, mate, there was nothing for it. I went on to the road, let
out the longest and hottest Voronezh cuss I could think of, and
stepped out westward—a prisoner! But I wasn't much good for
walking by that time—a kilometre an hour was all I could do, not
more. It was like being drunk. You'd try to go straight and something
would just push you from one side of the road to the other. I went on
for a bit and then a column of our chaps, from the same division as I'd
been in, caught up with me. There were about ten German submachine-
gunners guarding them. The one at the front of the column came up
to me and, without saying a word, just bashed me on the head with
his gun. If I'd gone down, he'd have stitched me to the ground with a
burst, but our chaps caught me as I fell and hustled me into the middle of the column and half carried me along for a while. And when
I came to, one of them whispered: 'Don't fall down for God's sake! Keep going while you've got any strength left, or they'll kill
you! ' And though I had pretty little strength left, I managed to
keep going.

"At sunset the Germans strengthened their guard. They brought up
another twenty submachine-gunners in a lorry, and drove us on at a
quicker pace. The badly wounded ones that couldn't keep up with the
rest were shot down in the road. Two tried to make a break for it,
but they forgot that on a moonlit night you can be seen a mile away
out in the open; of course, they got it too. At midnight we came to a
village that was half burned down. They herded us into a church with
a smashed dome. We had to spend the night on the stone floor without a scrap of straw. No one had a greatcoat, so there wasn't anything

to lie on. Some of the boys didn't even have tunics, just cotton undershirts. They were mostly NCOs. They had taken off their tunics so they couldn't be told from the rank-and-file. And the men from the gun crews hadn't got tunics either. They had taken them off while working at the guns.

"That night it poured with rain and we all got wet to the skin. Part of the roof had been smashed by a heavy shell or a bomb and the rest of it was ripped up by shrapnel, there wasn't a dry spot even at the altar. Yes, we stood around the whole night in that church, like sheep in a dark pen. In the middle of the night I felt someone touch my arm and ask: 'Are you wounded, comrade?' 'Why do you ask, mate?' I says. 'I'm a doctor. Perhaps I can help you in some way?' I told him my left shoulder made a creaking noise and was swollen and hurt like hell. And he says firmly: 'Take off your tunic and undershirt.' I took everything off and he started feeling round my shoulder with his thin fingers. And did it hurt! I gritted my teeth and I says to him: 'You must be a vet, not a doctor. Why do you press just where it hurts most, you heartless devil?' But he kept on probing about, and he says to me, angry-like: 'Your job's to keep quiet. I won't have you talking to me like that! Hang on, it's going to hurt you properly now.' And then he gave my arm such a wrench that I saw stars.

"When I got my senses back I asked him: 'What are you doing, you rotten Nazi? My arm's broken to bits and you give it a pull like that.' I heard him chuckle, then he said: 'I thought you'd hit out with your right while I was doing it, but you're a good-tempered chap, it seems. Your arm isn't broken, it was dislocated at the shoulder and I've put it back in its socket. Well, feeling better now?' And sure enough I could feel the pain going out of me. I thanked him so he'd know I meant it, and he went on in the darkness, asking quietly: 'Any wounded?' There was a real doctor for you. Even shut up like that, in pitch darkness, he went on doing his great work.

"It was a restless night. They wouldn't let us out even to relieve ourselves. The guard commander had told us they wouldn't when he drove us into the church in pairs. And as luck would have it, one of the Christians among us wanted to go out bad. He kept on saving it up and at last he burst into tears. 'I can't pollute a holy place!' he says. 'I'm a believer. I'm a Christian. What shall I do, lads?' And you know the kind of chaps we were. Some laughed, others swore, and others started teasing him with all sorts of advice. Cheered us all up, he did, but it turned out bad in the end. He started bashing on the door and asking to be let out. And he got his answer. A Nazi gave a long burst through the door with his submachine-gun. It killed the Christian and three more with him, and another was so badly wounded he died by morning.

"We pulled the dead into a corner, then sat down quiet and thought to ourselves, this isn't a very cheerful start. And presently we started whispering to each other, asking each other where we came from and how we'd got taken prisoner. The chaps who'd been in the same platoon or the same company started calling quietly to each other in the darkness. And next to me I heard two voices talking. One of them says: 'Tomorrow, if they form us up before they take us on farther and call out for the commissars, Communists, and Jews, you needn't try and hide yourself, platoon commander. You won't get away with it. You think just because you've taken off your tunic you'll pass for a ranker? It won't work! I'm not going to suffer because of you. I'll be the first to put the finger on you. I know you're a Communist. I remember how you tried to get me to join the Party. Now you're going to answer for it.' That was the one sitting nearest to me, on the left, and on the other side of him, a young voice answers: 'I always suspected there was a bad streak in you, Kryzhnev. Specially when you refused to join the Party, pretending you were illiterate. But I never thought you'd turn out to be a traitor. You went to school until you were fourteen, didn't you?' And the other one answers in a casual sort of way: 'Yes, I did. So what?' They were quiet for a long time, and then the platoon commander—I could tell him by his voice—says softly: 'Don't give me away, Comrade Kryzhnev.' And the other one laughed quietly. 'You've left your comrades behind on the other side of the line,' he says. 'I'm no comrade of yours, so don't plead with me. I'm going to put the finger on you all the same. My own skin comes first with me.'

"They stopped talking after that, but the vileness of what I'd heard had given me the shivers. 'No,' I thought, 'I won't let you betray your commander, you son-of-a-bitch. You won't walk out of this church on your own two feet, they'll drag you out by the legs! ' Then it began to get light and I could see a fellow with a big fleshy face lying on his back with his hands behind his head, and beside him a little snub-nosed lad, in only an undershirt, sitting with his arms round his knees and looking very pale. 'That kid won't be able to handle this great fat gelding,' I thought. 'I'll have to finish him off myself.'

"I touched the lad's arm and asked him in a whisper: 'You a platoon commander?' He didn't say anything, just nodded. 'That one over there wants to give you away?' I pointed to the fellow lying on his back. He nodded again. 'All right,' I said, 'hold his legs so he won't kick! And be quick about it! ' And I jumped on that fellow and locked my fingers round his throat. He didn't even have time to shout. I·held him under me for a few minutes, then eased off a bit. That was one traitor less, with his tongue hanging out!

"But I felt rotten afterwards and I wanted to wash my hands something terrible, as if it wasn't a man I'd killed but some crawling snake. It was the first time I had killed anyone in my life, and the man I had killed was one of our own. Our own? No, he wasn't. He was worse than the enemy, he was a traitor. I got up and said to the platoon commander: 'Let's get away from here, comrade, the church is a big place.'

"In the morning, just as that Kryzhnev had said, we were all lined up outside the church with a ring of submachine-gunners covering us, and three SS officers started trying to pick out the ones among us they thought were dangerous—Communists, officers, and commissars. But they didn't find any. And they didn't find anybody who was swine enough to give them away either, because nearly half of us were Communists, and there were a lot of officers, too, and commissars. Out of over two hundred men they only picked four. One Jew and three Russians from the rank-and-file. The Russians landed in trouble because they were all dark and had curly hair. The SS men just came up to them and said: 'Jude?' The one they asked said he was a Russian, but they wouldn't even listen. 'Step out! ' and that was that.

"They shot the poor devils and drove us on further. The platoon commander who'd helped me strangle that traitor kept by me right as far as Poznan. The first day of the march he'd edge up to me every now and then and press my hands as we went along. At Poznan we got separated. It happened like this.

"You see, mate, ever since the day I was captured I'd been thinking of escaping. But I wanted it to be a sure thing. All the way to Poznan, where they put us in a proper camp, I never got the right kind of chance. But in the Poznan camp it looked as if I'd got what I wanted. At the end of May they sent us out to a little wood near the camp to dig graves for the prisoners that had died—a lot of our chaps died at that time from dysentery. And while I was digging away at that Poznan clay I had a look round and I noticed that two of our guards had sat down to have a bite; the third was dozing in the sun. So I put down my shovel and went off quietly behind a bush. Then I ran for it, keeping straight towards the sunrise.

"They didn't miss me right away, those guards. Where I found the strength, skinny as I was, to cover nearly forty kilometres in one day, I don't know myself. But nothing came of my effort. On the fourth

day, when I was a long way from that damned camp, they caught me.
There were blood-hounds on my track, and they sniffed me out in a
field of unreaped oats.

"Daybreak had caught me in the open and it was at least three
kilometres to the woods. I was afraid to go on in the daylight, so I lay
low in the oats for the day. I rubbed some grain in my hands, chewed
a little, and was filling my pockets with a supply, when I heard the
barking of dogs and the roar of a motor-bike. My heart sank because
the dogs kept coming nearer. I lay flat and covered my head with my
arms, so they wouldn't bite my face. Well, they came up and it only
took them a minute to tear all my rags off me. I was left in nothing
but what I was born in. They dragged me about in the oats, and then
a big dog got his forepaws on my chest and started making passes at
my throat, but he didn't bite straightaway.

"The Germans came up on two motor-bikes. First they beat me up
good and proper, then they set the dogs on me. And they tore into
me. I was taken back to camp, naked and bloody as I was. They gave
me a month in solitary for trying to escape, but I was still alive. I
kept alive somehow.

"It's pretty grim, mate, to rememeber the things I went through as
a prisoner, let alone tell you about them. When I remember all we had
to suffer out there, in Germany, when I remember all my mates who
were tortured to death in those camps, my heart comes up in my
throat and it's hard to breathe.

"The way they shifted me about in those two years I was a prisoner! I reckon I covered half of Germany. I was in Saxony, at a silicate
plant, in the Ruhr, hauling coal in a mine. I sweated away with a
shovel in Bavaria, I had a spell in Thüringen, and the devil knows what
German soil I didn't have to tread. There's plenty of different scenery
out there, but the way they shot and bashed our lads was the same all
over. And those damned bastards lammed into us like no man here
ever beat an animal. Punching us, kicking us, beating us with rubber
truncheons, or an iron bar if they happened to have one handy, not to
mention their rifle butts and sticks.

"They beat you up just because you were a Russian, because you
were still alive in the world, just because you worked for them. And
they'd beat you for giving them a wrong look, taking a wrong step, for
not turning round the way they wanted. They beat you just so that
one day they'd knock the life out of you, so you'd choke with your
own blood and die of beating. There weren't enough ovens in the
whole of Germany, I reckon, for all of us to be shoved into.

"And everywhere we went they fed us the same—a hundred and

fifty grams of ersatz bread, made half of sawdust, and a thin swill of swedes. Some places they gave us hot water to drink, some places they didn't. But what's the use of talking, judge for yourself. Before the war started I weighed eighty-six kilograms, and by the autumn I couldn't turn more than fifty. Just skin and bones, and hardly enough strength to carry the bones either. But you had to work, and not say a word, and the work we did would have been a lot too much for a carthorse, I reckon.

"At the beginning of September they sent a hundred and forty-two of us Soviet prisoners-of-war from a camp near Küstrin to Camp B-14, not far from Dresden. At that time there were about two thousand in that camp. We were all working in a stone quarry, cutting and crushing their German stone by hand. The stint was four cubic metres a day per man, and for a man, mind you, who could hardly keep body and soul together anyway. And then it really started. After two months, out of the hundred and forty-two men in our group there were only fifty-seven left. How about that, mate? Tough going, eh? We hardly had time to bury our own mates, and then there was a rumour in the camp that the Germans had taken Stalingrad and were pressing on into Siberia. It was one thing on top of another. They held us down so we couldn't lift our eyes from the ground, as if we were asking to be put there, into that German earth. And every day the camp guards were drinking and bawling their songs, rejoicing for all they were worth.

"One evening we came back to our hut from work. It had been raining all day and our rags were soaking: we were all shivering from the cold wind and couldn't stop our teeth chattering. There wasn't anywhere to get dry or warm, and we were as hungry as death itself, or even worse. But we were never given any food in the evenings.

"Well, I took off my wet rags, threw them on to my bunk and said: 'They want you to do four cubic metres a day, but one cubic metre would be plenty to bury one of us.' That was all I said, but, would you believe it, among our own fellows there was one dirty dog who went and reported my bitter words to the camp commandant.

"The camp commandant, or Lagerführer, as they called him, was a German called Müller. Not very tall, thick-set, hair like a bunch of tow; sort of bleached all over. The hair on his head, his eyelashes, even his eyes were a kind of faded colour, and he was pop-eyed besides. Spoke Russian like you and me, even had a bit of a Volga accent, as if he'd been born and bred in those parts. And could he swear! He was a terror for it. I sometimes wonder where the bastard ever learned that trade. He'd line us up in front of the block—that's what they called the hut—and walk down the line surrounded by his bunch of SS men with his right hand drawn back. He wore a leather glove and under the leather there was a strip of lead to protect his fingers. He'd walk down the line and bloody every other man's nose for him. 'Inoculation against flu', he used to call it. And so it went on every day. Altogether there were four blocks in the camp, and one day he'd give the first block their 'inoculation', next day it'd be the second, and so on. That bastard worked regular, never took a day off. There was only one thing he didn't understand, the fool; before he started on his round he'd stand out in front there, and to get himself real worked up for it, he'd start cursing. He'd stand there cursing away for all he was worth, and, do you know, he'd make us feel a bit better. You see, the words sounded like our own, it was like a breath of air from over there. If he'd known his cursing and swearing gave us pleasure, he wouldn't have done it in Russian, he'd have stuck to his own language. Only one of our fellows, a pal of mine from Moscow, used to get wild with him. 'When he curses like that,' he says, 'I shut my eyes and think I'm in Moscow, having one at the local, and it just makes me dizzy for a glass of beer.'

"Well, the day after I said that about the cubic metres, that commandant had me up on the mat. In the evening an interpreter and two guards came to our hut. 'Sokolov Andrei?' I answered up. 'Outside! Quick march! Herr Lagerführer wants to see you.' I guessed what he wanted me for. It was curtains. So I said good-bye to my pals—they all knew I was going to my death. Then I took a deep breath and followed the guards. As I went across the camp yard, I looked up at the stars and said good-bye to them too, and I thought to myself: 'Well, you've had your full dose of torture, Andrei Sokolov, Number 331.' I felt somehow sorry for Irina and the kids, then I got over it and began screwing up my courage to face the barrel of that pistol without flinching, like a soldier should, so the enemy wouldn't see how hard it'd be for me at the last minute to part with this life, bad though it was.

"In the commandant's room there were flowers on the window-sill. It was a nice clean place, like one of our clubs. At the table there were all the camp's officers. Five of 'em, sitting there, downing schnapps and chewing bacon fat. On the table there was a big bottle, already open, plenty of bread, bacon fat, soused apples, all kinds of open tins. I took one glance at all that grub, and you wouldn't believe it, but I felt so sick I nearly vomited. I was hungry as a wolf, you see, and I'd forgotten what the sight of human food was like, and now there was all this stuff in front of me. Somehow I kept my sickness down, but it cost me a great effort to tear my eyes away from that table.

"Right in front of me sat Müller, half-drunk, flicking his pistol from one hand to the other, playing with it. He had his eye fixed on me, like a snake. Well, I stood to attention, snapped my broken-down heels together, and reported in a loud voice like this: 'Prisoner-of-war Andrei Sokolov at your service, Herr Kommandant.' And he says to me: 'So, you Russian Ivan, four cubic metres of quarrying is too much for you, is it?' 'Yes, Herr Kommandant,' I said, 'it is.' 'And is one cubic metre enough to make a grave for you?' 'Yes, Herr Kommandant, quite enough and to spare.'

"He gets up and says: 'I shall do you a great honour. I shall now shoot you in person for those words. It will make a mess here, so we'll go into the yard. You can sign off out there.' 'As you like,' I told him. He stood thinking for a minute, then tossed his pistol on the table and poured out a full glass of schnapps, took a piece of bread, put a slice of fat on it, held the lot out to me and said: 'Before you die, Russian Ivan, drink to the triumph of German arms.'

"I had taken the glass and the bread out of his hand, but when I heard those words, something seemed to scald me inside. Me, a Russian soldier, I thought, drink to the victory of German arms? What'll you want next, Herr Kommandant? It's all up with me anyway. You can go to hell with your schnapps!

"I put the glass down on the table, and the bread with it, and I said: 'Thank you for your hospitality, but I don't drink.' He smiles. 'So you don't want to drink to our victory? In that case, drink to your own death.' What had I got to lose? 'To my death and relief from torment then,' I said. And with that, I took the glass and poured it down my throat in two gulps. But I didn't touch the bread. I just wiped my lips politely with my hand and said: 'Thank you for your hospitality. I am ready, Herr Kommandant, you can sign me off now.'

"But he was looking at me sharply: 'Have a bite to eat before you die,' he said. But I said to him: 'I never eat after the first glass.' Then he poured out a second and handed it to me. I drank the second and again I didn't touch the food. I was staking everything on courage, you see. Anyway, I thought, I'll get drunk before I go out into that yard to die. And the commandant's fair eyebrows shot up in the air. 'Why don't you eat, Russian Ivan? Don't be shy! ' But I stuck to my guns: 'Excuse me, Herr Kommandant, but I don't eat after the second glass either.' He puffed up his cheeks and snorted, and then he gave such a roar of laughter, and while he laughed he said something quickly in German, must have been translating my words to his friends. The others laughed, too, pushed their chairs back, turned their big mugs round to look at me, and I noticed something different in their looks, something a bit softer-like.

"The commandant poured me out a third glass and his hands were shaking with laughter. I drank that glass slowly, bit off a little bit of bread and put the rest down on the table. I wanted to show the bastards that even though I was half dead with hunger I wasn't going to gobble the scraps they flung me, that I had my own, Russian dignity and pride, and that they hadn't turned me into an animal as they had wanted to.

"After that the commandant got a serious look on his face, straightened the two iron crosses on his chest, came out from behind the table unarmed and said: 'Look here, Sokolov, you're a real Russian soldier. You're a fine soldier. I am a soldier, too, and I respect a worthy enemy, I shall not shoot you. What is more, today our gallant armies have reached the Volga and taken complete possession of Stalingrad. That is a great joy for us, and therefore I graciously grant you your life. Go to your block and take this with you for your courage.' And he handed me a small loaf of bread from the table, and a lump of bacon fat.

"I clutched that bread to my chest, tight as I could, and picked up the fat in my other hand. I was so taken aback at this unexpected turn of events that I didn't even say thank you, just did a left about-turn, and went to the door. And all the while I was thinking, now he'll blast daylight through my shoulder-blades and I'll never get this grub back to the lads. But no, nothing happened. Again death passed me by and I only felt the cold breath of it.

"I got out of the commandant's room without a stagger, but outside I went reeling all over the place. I lurched into the hut and pitched flat down on the cement floor, unconscious. The lads woke me up next morning, when it was still dark. 'Tell us what happened! ' Then I remembered what had happened at the commandant's and told them. 'How are we going to share out the grub?' the man in the bunk next to me asked, and his voice was trembling. 'Equal shares all round,' I told him. We waited till it got light. We cut up the bread and fat with a bit of thread. Each of us got a piece of bread about the size of a matchbox, not a crumb was wasted. And as for the fat—well, of course, there was only enough to grease your lips with. But we parcelled it out, fair shares all round.

"Soon they put about three hundred of the strongest of us on draining a marsh, then off we went to the Ruhr to work in the mines. And there I stayed until 'forty-four. By that time our lads had knocked some of the stuffing out of Germany and the Nazis had stopped

looking down on us, prisoners. One day they lined us up, the whole
day-shift, and some visiting Oberleutnant said through an interpreter:
'Anyone who served in the army or worked before the war as a driver—
one pace forward.' About seven of us who'd been drivers before
stepped out. They gave us some old overalls and took us under guard
to Potsdam. When we got there, we were split up. I was detailed to
work in 'Todt'. That was what the Germans called the set-up they had
for building roads and defence works.

"I drove a German major of the engineers about in an Opel-Admi-
ral. Now that was a real Nazi hog for you! Short fellow with a pot-
belly, as broad as he was tall, and a back-side on him as big as any
wench's. He had three chins hanging down over his collar in front, and
three whopping folds round his neck at the back. Must have carried a
good hundredweight of pure fat on him, I should think. When he
walked, he puffed like a steam-engine, and when he sat down to eat—
hold tight! He'd go on all day, chewing and taking swigs from his flask
of brandy. Now and then I came in for a bit too. He'd stop on the
road, cut up some sausage and cheese, and have a drink; and when he
was in a good mood he'd toss me a scrap like to a dog. Never handed
it to me. Oh, no, he considered that beneath him. But, be that as it
may, there was no comparing it to the camp, and little by little I
began to look like a man again. I even began to put on weight.

"For about two weeks I drove the major to and fro between Potsdam
and Berlin, then he was sent to the front-line area to build defences
against our troops. And then I gave up sleep. All night long I'd be
thinking how to escape to my own side, my own country.

"We arrived in the town of Polotsk. At dawn, for the first time in
two years I heard the boom of our artillery, and you can guess how my
heart thumped at the sound. Why, mate, even when I first started court-
ing Irina, it never beat like that! The fighting was going on east of Polotsk, about eighteen kilometres away. The Germans in the town were
sore as hell, and jumpy, and my old pot-belly started drinking more and
more. During the daytime we would drive round and he'd give instructions on how to build the fortifications, and at night he'd sit by himself
drinking. He got all puffy, and there were great bags under his eyes.

"Well, I thought, no need to wait any longer, this is my chance.
And I'm not going to escape alone, I've got to take old pot-belly with
me, he'll come in useful over there!

"In a heap of rubble I found a heavy iron weight and wrapped a
rag round it, so that if I had to hit him there wouldn't be any blood. I
picked up a length of telephone wire in the road, got everything I
needed ready, and hid it all under the front seat. One evening, two

days before I said goodbye to the Germans, I was on my way back from the filling station and I saw a German Unter staggering along blind drunk, grabbing at the wall. I pulled up, led him into a damaged building, shook him out of his uniform, and took his cap off his head. Then I hid the whole lot under the seat and I was ready.

"On the morning of June 29th, my major told me to take him out of town in the direction of Trosnitsa. He was in charge of some defences that were being built there. We drove off. The major was sitting on the back seat, taking a quiet doze, and I sat in front with my heart trying to jump out of my mouth. I drove fast, but outside the town I slowed down, then stopped and got out and had a look round; a long way behind there were two lorries coming on slowly. I got out my iron weight and opened the door wide. Old pot-belly was lying back on the seat, snoring as if he'd got his wife beside him. Well, I gave him a bang on the left temple with my iron. His head flopped on to his chest. I gave him another one, just to make sure, but I didn't want to kill him. I wanted to take him over alive. He was going to be able to tell our lads a lot of things. So I pulled the pistol out of his holster and shoved it in my pocket. Then I pushed a bracket down behind the back seat, tied the telephone wire round the major's neck and fastened it to the bracket. That was so he wouldn't tumble over on his side when I drove fast. I pulled on the German uniform and cap, and drove the car straight for the place where the earth was rumbling, where the fighting was.

"I ripped across the German front-line between two pillboxes. A bunch of submachine-gunners popped up out of a dugout and I slowed down purposely so they would see I had a major with me. They started shouting and waving their arms to show me I mustn't go on, but I pretended not to understand and roared off at about eighty. Before they realised what was happening and opened fire I was on no man's land, weaving round the shell-holes no worse than a hare.

"There were the Germans firing from behind, and then our own chaps got fierce and had a smack at me from the front. Put four bullets through the wind-screen and riddled the radiator. But not far away I spotted a little wood near a lake, and some of our chaps running towards the car, so I drove into the wood and got out. Then I fell on the ground and kissed it. I could hardly breathe.

"A young fellow, with khaki shoulder-straps on his tunic I'd never seen before, reached me first and says with a grin: 'Aha, you lousy Fritz, lost your way, eh?' I tore off my German tunic, threw the German cap down at my feet, and I says to him: 'You lovely young kid. Sonny boy! Me a Fritz when I was born and bred in Voronezh! I was prisoner-of-war, see? And now unhitch that fat hog sitting in the car, take his briefcase and escort him to your commander.' I handed over my pistol and was passed from one person to the next until evening when I had to report to the colonel in command of the division. By that time I had been fed and taken to the bath-house and questioned, and given a new uniform, so I went to the colonel's dugout in proper order, clean in body and soul, and properly dressed. The colonel got up from his table, and came over to me, and in front of all the officers there, he kissed me and said: 'Thank you, soldier, for the fine gift you brought us. Your major and his briefcase have told us more than any twenty Germans we might capture on the front-line. I shall recommend you for a decoration.' His words and the affection he showed moved me so much I couldn't keep my lips from trembling, and all I could say was: 'Comrade Colonel, I request to be enrolled in an infantry unit.'

"But the colonel laughed and slapped me on the shoulder. 'What kind of a fighter do you think you'd make when you can hardly stand on your feet? I'm sending you off to hospital straightaway. They'll patch you up there and put some food inside you, and after that you'll go home to your family for a month's leave, and when you come back to us, we'll think where to put you.'

"The colonel and all the officers that were in the dugout with him shook hands and said good-bye to me, and I went out with my head spinning because in the two years I'd been away I'd forgotten what it was like to be treated like a human being. And mind you, mate, it was a long time before I got out of the habit of pulling my head down into my shoulders when I had to talk to the high-ups, as if I was still scared of being hit. That was the training we got in those Nazi camps.

"As soon as I got into hospital I wrote Irina a letter. I told her in a few words all about how I was taken prisoner and how I escaped with the German major. Just what made me boast like a kid, I couldn't tell you. Why, I couldn't even hold back from saying the colonel had promised to recommend me for a medal...

"For a couple of weeks I just slept and ate. They fed me a little at a time, but often; if they'd given me all the food I wanted, so the doctor said, I might have gone under. But after the two weeks were up, I wouldn't look at food. There was no reply from home and, I must admit, I began to get mopy. Couldn't think of eating, sleep wouldn't come to me, and all kinds of bad thoughts kept creeping into my head. In the third week I got a letter from Voronezh. But it wasn't from Irina, it was from a neighbour of mine, a joiner. I wouldn't wish anyone to get a letter like that. He wrote that the Germans had bombed the aircraft factory, and my cottage had got a direct hit with a heavy bomb. Irina and the girls were at home when it dropped. There was nothing left, he wrote, only a deep hole where the house had been... At first I couldn't finish reading that letter. Everything went dark before my eyes and my heart squeezed into a tight little ball so that I thought it would never open up again. I lay back on my bed and when I got a bit of strength back I read the letter to the end. My neighbour wrote that Anatoly was away in town during the bombing. He returned in the evening, took one look at the hole where his home had been, and went back to town the same night. All he told my neighbour, before he went, was that he was going to volunteer for the front.

"When my heart eased up and I heard the blood rushing in my ears, I remembered how Irina had clung to me when we parted at the station. That woman's heart of hers must have known all along we were not to see each other again in this world. And I had pushed her away... Once I had a family, a home of my own, it had all taken years to build, and it was all destroyed in a flash, and I was left all alone. It must be a dream, I thought, this messed-up life of mine. Why, when I had been a prisoner, nearly every night, in my mind, of course, I had talked to Irina and the kids, tried to cheer them up by promising them I'd come home and they mustn't cry. I'm tough, I said, I can stand it, we'll all be together again one day. For two years I had been talking to the dead! "

The big man was silent for a minute. When he spoke again, his voice faltered. "Let's have a smoke, mate, I feel as if I was choking."

We lighted up. The tapping of a wood-pecker sounded very loud in the flooded woodland. The warm breeze still rustled the dry leaves of the alders, the clouds were still floating past in the towering blue, as though under taut white sails, but in those minutes of solemn silence the boundless world preparing for the great fulfilment of spring, for that eternal affirmation of the living in life, seemed quite different to me.

It was too distressing to keep silent and I asked:

"What happened then?"

"What happened then?" the story-teller responded reluctantly. "Then I got a month's leave from the colonel, and a week later I was in Voronezh. I went on foot to the place where I had once lived with my family. There was a deep hole full of rusty water. The weeds all round came up to your waist. It was empty and still as a graveyard. I felt it bad then, mate, I can tell you! I stood there in sorrow, then I went back to the station. I wasn't there more than an hour altogether.

I went back to the division the same day.

"But about three months later I did get a flash of joy, like a gleam of sunlight through the clouds. I got news of Anatoly. He sent me a letter from another front. He had got my address from that neighbour of mine. It seems he'd been to an artillery school to start with; his gift for mathematics stood him in good stead there. After a year he graduated with honours and went to the front, and now he wrote he had been promoted to captain, was commanding a battery of 'forty-fives', and had been decorated six times. In a word, he'd left his old man far behind. And again I felt real proud of him. Say what you like, but my own son was a captain, and in command of a battery. That was something! And all those decorations too. It didn't matter that his dad was just carting shells and other stuff about in a Studebaker. His dad's time was past, but he, a captain, had everything ahead of him.

"At nights now I began weaving an old man's dreams. When the war was over I'd get my son married and live with them. I'd do a bit of carpentry and look after the kiddies. I'd do all the kind of things an old man does. But that all went bust too. In the winter we went on advancing without a break and there wasn't time to write to each other very often, but towards the end of the war, right up near Berlin, I sent Anatoly a letter one morning and got an answer the very next day. It turned out that he and I had come up to the German capital by different routes and were now very close to each other. I could hardly wait for the moment when we'd meet. Well, the moment came... Right on the 9th of May, on the morning of Victory Day, my Anatoly was killed by a German sniper.

"The company commander sent for me in the afternoon. I saw there was a strange artillery officer sitting with him. I went into the room and he stood up as if he was meeting a senior. My C.O. said: 'The Colonel has come to see you, Sokolov,' and turned away to the window. Something went through me like an electric shock. I knew there was trouble coming. The lieutenant-colonel came up to me and said: 'Bear up, father. Your son, Captain Sokolov, was killed today at his battery. Come with me.'

"I swayed, but I kept my feet. Even now it seems unreal the way that lieutenant-colonel and I drove in that big car along those streets strewn with rubble. I've only a foggy memory of the soldiers drawn up in line and the coffin covered with red velvet. But my Anatoly I saw as plain as I can see you now, mate. I went up to the coffin. Yes, it was my son lying there, and yet it wasn't. My son had been a lad, always smiling, with narrow shoulders and a sharp little Adam's apple sticking out of his thin neck, but here was a young broad-shouldered, full-grown man, and good-looking too. His eyes were half-closed as if he was looking past me into the far distance. Only the corners of his lips still had a bit of the smile my son used to have. The Anatoly I knew once. I kissed him and stepped aside. The lieutenant-colonel made a speech. My Anatoly's friends were wiping their tears, but I couldn't cry. I reckon the tears dried up in my heart. Perhaps that's why it still hurts so much.

"I buried my last joy and hope in that foreign German soil, the battery fired a volley to send off their commander on his long journey, and something seemed to snap inside me. When I got back to my unit I was a different man. Soon after that I was demobbed. Where was I to go? To Voronezh? Not for anything! I remembered I had a friend who had been invalided out of the army back in the winter and was living in Uryupinsk; he had asked me to come and live with him. So I went.

"My friend and his wife had no children. They lived in a cottage of their own on the edge of the town. He had a disability pension, but he worked as a driver in a lorry depot and I got a job there too. I settled with my friend and they gave me a home. We used to drive various loads about the suburbs and in the autumn we switched over to grain delivery work. It was then I got to know my new son, the one that's playing down there in the sand.

"First thing you'd do when you got back from a long trip would be to go to a café for a bite of something, and, of course, you'd put away a glass of vodka to get rid of your tiredness. It's a bad habit, but I had quite a liking for it by that time, I must admit. Well, one day I noticed this lad near the café, and the next day I noticed him again. What a little ragamuffin he was! His face all smeared with watermelon juice and dust, dirty as anything, hair all over the place, but he'd got a pair of eyes like stars in the night sky, after it's been raining! And I grew so fond of him that, funny though it may seem, I started missing him, and I'd hurry to finish my run so I could get back to the café and see him sooner. That's where he got his food—he ate what people gave him.

"The fourth day I came in straight from the state farm with my lorry loaded with grain and pulled in at the café. There was my little fellow sitting on the steps, kicking his legs, and pretty hungry by the look of him. I poked my head out of the window and shouted to him: 'Hi, Vanya! Come on, jump aboard, I'll give you a ride to the elevator, and then we'll come back here and have some dinner.' My shout made him start, then he jumped down from the steps, scrambled on to the running board and pulled himself up to the window. 'How do you know my name's Vanya?' he says quietly, and he opens those lovely eyes of his wide, waiting for my answer. Well, I told him I was just one of those chaps who know everything.

"He came round to the right side. I opened the door and let him in beside me, and off we went. Lively little fellow he was, but suddenly he got quiet, and started looking at me from under those long curly eyelashes of his, and sighing. Such a little fellow and he'd already learned to sigh. Was that the thing for him to be doing? 'Where's your father, Vanya?' I asked. 'He was killed at the front,' he whispered. 'And Mummy?' 'Mummy was killed by a bomb when we were in the train.' 'Where were you coming from in the train?' 'I don't know, I don't remember...' 'And haven't you got any family at all?' 'No, nobody.' 'But where do you sleep at night?' 'Anywhere I can find.'

'I felt the hot tears welling up inside me and I made up my mind at once. Why should we suffer alone and separate like this! I'd take him in as my own son. And straightaway I felt easier in my mind and there was a sort of brightness there. I leaned over to him and asked, very quiet-like: 'Vanya, do you know who I am?' And he just breathed it out: 'Who?' And still as quiet, I says to him: 'I'm your father.'

"Lord alive, what happened then! He threw his arms round my neck, he kissed my cheeks, my lips, my forehead, and started hollering away like a little bird. Deafening it was. 'Daddy dear! I knew it! I knew you'd find me! I knew you'd find me whatever happened! I've been waiting so long for you to find me! ' He pressed himself to me and he was trembling all over, like a blade of grass in the wind. My eyes were misty and I was trembling, too, and my hands were shaking... How I managed to keep hold of the wheel I don't know. Even so I put her in the ditch and stopped the engine. While my eyes were so misty I was afraid to go, in case I knocked someone down. We sat there for about five minutes and my little son was still clinging to me for all he was worth, and not saying anything, just trembling all over. I put my right arm round him, hugged him gently, and turned the lorry round with my left hand and drove back to the cottage where I lived. I just couldn't go to the elevator after that.

"I left the lorry at the gate, took my new son in my arms and carried him into the house. And he got his little arms round my neck and hung on tight. He pressed his cheek to my unshaven chin and stuck there. And that's how I carried him in. My friend and his wife were both at home. I came in and winked at them with both eyes. Then, bold and cheerful, I said: 'Well, I've found my little Vanya at last. Here we are, good people.' They hadn't got any children themselves and they both wanted a kid, so they guessed what was up straightaway and started bustling around. And the kid just wouldn't let me put him down. But I managed it somehow. I washed his hands with soap and sat him down at the table. My friend's wife ladled him out a plate of soup, and when she saw how he gulped it down, she just burst into tears. She stood at the stove, crying into her apron. And my Vanya, he saw she was crying, and he ran up to her, tugged at her skirt and said: 'Why are you crying, Auntie? Daddy found me near the café. Everyone ought to be happy, and you are crying.' But she only cried all the harder.

"After dinner I took him to the barber's to have his hair cut, and at home I gave him a bath myself in a tub and wrapped him up in a clean sheet. He hugged me tight and went to sleep in my arms. I laid him gently in bed, drove off to the elevator, unloaded the grain and took the lorry back to the depot. Then I went to the shops. I bought him a pair of serge trousers, a shirt, a pair of sandals and a straw cap. Of course, it all turned out to be the wrong size and no good for quality. My friend's wife gave me a ticking-off over the trousers: 'Are you crazy,' she says, 'dressing a boy in serge trousers in heat like this! ' And the next minute she had the sewing-machine on the table and was rummaging in the chest, and in an hour she had a pair of cotton shorts and a white shirt ready for my Vanya. I took him to bed with me and for the first time for many a night fell asleep peacefully. I woke up about four times in the night though. And there he was, nestling in the crook of my arm, like a sparrow under the eaves, breathing away softly. I can't find words to tell you what joy I felt. I'd try not to move, so as not to disturb him, but then I'd get up very quiet, light a match and just stand there, admiring him...

"Just before daybreak I woke. I couldn't make out why it seemed so stuffy. It was my young son. He'd climbed out of his sheet and was lying right across my chest, with his little foot on my throat. He's a rare young fidget to sleep with, he is; but I've got used to him. I miss him when he's not there. At night, I can stroke him while he's sleeping. I can smell his curls. It takes some of the pain out of my heart, makes it a bit softer. It had just about turned to stone, you know.

"At first he used to ride with me in the lorry, then I realised that that wouldn't do. After all, what do I need when I'm on my own? A hunk of bread and an onion with a pinch of salt will last a soldier the whole day. But with him it's different. Now you've got to boil an egg for him, and he can't get along without something hot. But I had my work to do. So I plucked up my courage and left him in the care of my friend's wife. Well, he just cried all day, and in the evening ran away to the elevator to meet me. Waited there till late at night.

"I had a hard time with him at first. After one very tiring day we went to bed when it was still light. He used to be always chirruping like a sparrow, but this time he was very quiet. 'What are you thinking about, son?' I asked. He just looked up at the ceiling. 'What did you do with your leather coat, Daddy?' And I'd never had a leather coat in my life! I had to get round it somehow. 'Left it in Voronezh,' I told him. 'And why were you so long looking for me?' So I said: 'I looked for you, sonny, in Germany, in Poland, and all over Byelorussia, and you turned up in Uryupinsk.' 'Is Uryupinsk nearer than Germany? Is it far from our house to Poland?' We went on talking like that till we dropped off to sleep.

"But do you think there wasn't a reason for his asking about that leather coat, mate? No, there was a reason behind it all right. It meant at some time or other his real father had worn a coat like that, and he had just remembered it. A kid's memory is like summer lightning, you know; it flashes and lights things up for a bit, then dies away. And that was how his memory worked, like the flashes of summer lightning.

"We might have gone on living another year in Uryupinsk together, but in November I had an accident. I was driving along a muddy road through a village and I went into a skid. There happened to be a cow in the way and I knocked it over. Well, you know how it is—the women raised a hullabaloo, a crowd gathered, and soon there was a traffic inspector on the spot. The cow got up, stuck its tail in the air and went galloping away down the street, but I lost my licence. I went through the winter as a joiner, and then got in touch with an old army friend—he works as a driver in your district—and he invited me to come and stay with him. You can do joinery work for half a year, he says, then you can get a new licence in our region. So now my son and I, we're on the march to Kashary.

"But even if I hadn't had that accident with the cow, you know, I'd have left Uryupinsk just the same. I can't stay in one place for long. When my Vanya gets older and he's got to go to school, I expect I'll knuckle under and settle down. But for the time being we're tramping the Russian land together."

"Does he get tired?" I asked.

"Well, he doesn't go far on his own feet; most of the time he rides on me. I hoist him on to my shoulder and carry him. When he wants to stretch his legs, he jumps down and runs about at the side of the road, prancing around like a little goat. No, it's not that, mate, we'd get along all right. The trouble is my heart's got a knock in it somewhere, ought to have a piston changed. Sometimes it gives me such a stab I nearly get a black-out. I'm afraid one day I may die in my sleep and frighten my little son. And that's not the only thing. Nearly every night I see the dear ones I've lost in my dreams. And mostly it's as if I was behind barbed wire and they were on the other side, at liberty. I talk about everything to Irina and the children, but as soon as I try to pull the barbed wire apart, they go away, seem to melt before my eyes. And there's another funny thing about it. In the daytime I always keep a firm grip on myself, you'll never get a sigh out of me. But sometimes I wake up at night and my pillow's wet through."

From the river came the sound of my friend's voice and the splash of oars in the water.

This stranger, who now seemed a close friend of mine, held out his big hand, firm as a block of wood.

"Good-bye, mate, good luck to you! "

"Good luck and a good journey to Kashary! "

'Thanks. Hey, sonny, let's go to the boat.''

The boy ran to his side, took hold of the corner of his jacket and started off with tiny steps beside his striding father.

Two orphans, two grains of sand swept into strange parts by the tremendous hurricane of war... What did the future hold for them? I wanted to believe that this Russian, this man of unbreakable will, would stick it out, and that the boy would grow at his father's side into a man who could endure anything, overcome any obstacle if his country called upon him to do so.

I felt sad as I watched them go. Perhaps all would have been well at our parting if Vanya, after going a few paces, had not twisted round on his stumpy legs and waved to me with his little rosy hand. And suddenly a soft but taloned paw seemed to grip my heart, and I turned hastily away. No, not only in their sleep do they weep, these elderly men whose hair turned grey in the years of war. They weep in their waking hours, too. The thing is to be able to turn away in time. The main thing is not to wound a child's heart, not to let him see the unwilling tear that burns the cheek of a man.

Translated by Robert Daglish

SHOLOKHOV M. *Collected Works.* Vol. 1. *Short
Stories*

The volume contains short stories written in the
1920s and 1930s, some of which have never before
appeared in English. In these early narratives the
author writes of the momentous events that befell
him and his people—the Civil War on the Don and
elsewhere in Russia and the reshaping of life in the
countryside. They show that the young writer's
heart never lacked love of humanity or hatred of
the evils that distort and corrupt human life.

SHOLOKHOV M. *Collected Works.* Vols. 2, 3, 4, 5.
Quiet Flows the Don. A novel

The translation presented in these volumes is an
entirely new rendering of the whole text of the novel.
In depicting the life of the Don Cossacks at various
social levels, the writer introduces us to many unique
personalities, caught up in the whirlwind of events in
the First World War, the Revolution in Russia, and
the Civil War, and shows the complex struggle between
the new and the old in public life and people's minds.

For *Quiet Flows the Don* Sholokhov received the
Nobel Prize.

Robert Daglish's translation is the first unabridged
English translation of the novel.

SHOLOKHOV M. *Collected Works.* Vols. 6 and 7.
Virgin Soil Upturned. A novel.
In two books

The novel is about collectivisation in the 1930s when individual peasant farmers voluntarily joined the collective farm movement to raise stock and work the land in common. The breakup of the long-established order triggered sharp contradictions between the new life and out-moded traditions. The focal point of the novel, the little village of Gremyachi Log, mirrors the enormous historical changes taking place in men's minds.

SHOLOKHOV M. *Collected Works.* Vol. 8. *They Fought for Their Country. The Fate of a Man*

This volume contains Sholokhov's prose writings about the Second World War.

The chapters from the novel *They Fought for Their Country* appeared originally as serials in the Soviet press. They cover one of the most tragic stages of the war, the battles of the summer 1942 in the Don steppes.

The short story *The Fate of a Man* (1957) is also about the war years. Sholokhov shows us a man of great courage and human dignity, an ordinary Soviet soldier who in the struggle against fascism went through some of the worst things war can do to anyone.

REQUEST TO READERS

Raduga Publishers would be glad to have your opinion of this book, its translation and design and any suggestions you may have for future publications.

Please send all your comments to 17, Zubovsky Boulevard, Moscow, USSR.

Пароль: Победа! (Рассказы и очерки о
Великой Отечественной войне).
В 2-х тт. Т. 2.
Составитель В. Н. Севрук.
На английском языке.
Редактор русского текста А. А. Кудряшова.